THE STIRLING SINGLES OF
THE GREAT NORTHERN RAILWAY

David & Charles Locomotive Monographs

General Editor
O. S. NOCK, B.Sc., M.I.C.E., M.I.Mech.E., M.I.Loco.E.

The Midland Compounds, by O. S. Nock

The Stirling Singles of the Great Northern Railway, by Kenneth H. Leech and Maurice G. Boddy

In preparation

The Great Western Railway 4-Cylinder 4—6—os, by A. F. Cook

The Joy Valve Express Passenger Engines of the L.N.W.R., by O. S. Nock

No. 1004, one of the last six 8–footers, as running 1909–1914

REPRINTS OF ECONOMIC CLASSICS

AUGUSTUS M. KELLEY • PUBLISHERS

NEW YORK • 1968

DAVID & CHARLES LOCOMOTIVE MONOGRAPHS

THE
STIRLING SINGLES

OF THE

GREAT NORTHERN RAILWAY

KENNETH H. LEECH, B.Sc., M.I.C.E., M.I.Loco.E.

AND

MAURICE G. BODDY

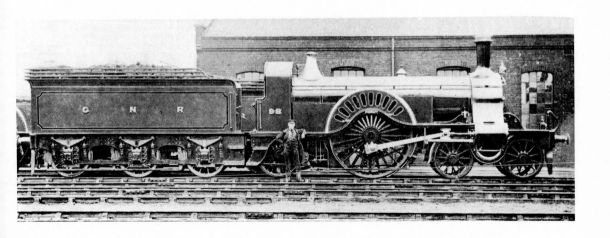

DAVID & CHARLES : DAWLISH . . . . MACDONALD : LONDON

IN MEMORY OF
C.E.L., W.J.R. and J.F.V.

Published in the U. S. A. by
AUGUSTUS M. KELLEY, PUBLISHERS
New York, New York

©

KENNETH H. LEECH & MAURICE G. BODDY
1965

First Published in 1965 by
David & Charles (Publishers) Ltd.
Strand, Dawlish, Devon

Made and Printed in Great Britain by
W. J. Holman Ltd., Dawlish, Devon

CONTENTS

		PAGE
PREFACE		9
CHAPTER 1.	Preliminary Survey	11
2.	The Engines in General and Their Work ...	19
3.	The Stirling Straightback Boilers	28
4.	Early 2—2—2s: 7 ft. and 7 ft. 6 in.	38
5.	The First Eight-footer—No. 1	50
6.	The Eight-foot 4—2—2s: December 1870 to 1893	64
7.	The Later 7 ft. 6 in. 2—2—2s	87
8.	Performance: Speed: Coal Consumption ...	100
9.	Performance: The 1888 and 1895 Races ...	108
10.	The Last Eight-footers	113
11.	Rebuilds of Sturrock Engines	121
12.	The Eight-footer Rebuilds	129
13.	Some Personal Reminiscences	138
14.	Miscellany	144
ACKNOWLEDGEMENTS		156
STIRLING SINGLES CHRONOLOGY		157
INDEX		159

PREFACE

No one writing today about the Stirling era on the Great Northern Railway can use his own experience or the memory of any living person as a basis for his work. That age has passed into history; and the only direct sources of information which remain are the references in contemporary writings and the official records of the railway company. Quite a lot was, indeed, published in the columns chiefly of *Engineering* and *The Engineer,* and other technical journals; and, in the years immediately succeeding the Stirling period, also in *The Railway Magazine* and other shorter-lived periodicals. These sources have necessarily been used by the present writers, and grateful acknowledgement is made.

But the only prime sources of accurate information must be the official records of the railway company itself. Here the subject matter divides into two categories: the political aspect and the technical. The official archives have fortunately been preserved, and are accessible. From these the changing and developing policies of the railway can be observed and studied; yet it still needs a good deal of intuition and even guesswork to form a detailed and consistent picture of how things actually happened, and the underlying motives and human reactions.

The technical side, dealing with the locomotives themselves and with the cold facts concerning them, ought to be easier. But in the case of the Great Northern Railway's records at Doncaster works this is far from being so. During the 1939-45 war, Edward Thompson, then Chief Mechanical Engineer of the London & Northern Eastern Railway, ordered the destruction of all old records and drawings. This most regrettable order was fairly thoroughly carried out, and almost all the irreplaceable archives dealing with Stirling and Sturrock engines went up in flame and smoke. Fortunately there were, here and there, odd notebooks; and, especially, three large volumes of records of dates of construction, repair and scrapping of locomotives still on the running list in 1900. These volumes also gave brief particulars of some of the major repairs carried out, and the date of each general repair. But since only one page was allotted to each engine,

no full and detailed particulars were given. The twelve books containing these were all destroyed. We must be grateful for the three remaining volumes. Their continued existence is due to the zeal and judgement of the late Mr. E. Windle, then Chief Draughtsman at Doncaster, who secreted these volumes in his office safe during the danger period.

But, unknown to Edward Thompson, his predecessor, Sir Nigel Gresley, on the outbreak of war in 1939, had given instructions for the preservation of as many as possible of the old general arrangement drawings of Great Northern engines against possible enemy action. These drawings had been sealed in canisters and stored in an old boiler barrel, which was then buried in the ground in the works. And, luckily, not only buried, but forgotten until long after the war was over. To these two happy chances we owe such other records as remain. They are invaluable, but alas! incomplete. The gaps in the information they afford are considerable, and there is no bridging them except by —yes, by intuition and guesswork.

The following pages, therefore, make use of all known facts, and from these seek to solve quite a number of puzzling happenings. The authors can only claim that they have done their best in the way of explanation and have not suppressed or distorted any facts.

One of the authors has had a lifelong and passionate devotion to all Stirling engines: the other has acquired a wide and intimate knowledge of all Doncaster locomotive affairs. Both are railwaymen of some experience.

No book about early Great Northern engines can omit reference to G. F. Bird's classic *The Locomotives of the Great Northern Railway,* originally published in serial form in *The Locomotive Magazine* in 1898-99. Bird, of course, covered a much wider field than do the present authors, and his account of each class is necessarily brief. When he compiled his book there was scanty encouragement from official sources for anyone seeking precise information upon points of locomotive history —rather the reverse. Bird apparently had no access to actual drawings and records, and consequently some of the information in his book needs amendment in the light of recently discovered evidence.

To the C.M. & E.E., Eastern Region British Railways, for permission to examine the records at Doncaster Works; to the Archivist, British Railways Board; to John H. Scholes, Curator of Historical Relics; to the York Railway Museum team; to the Railway Correspondence and Travel Society; to the Stephenson Locomotive Society; and to E. Craven, for help with points relating to the Sturrock engines, the authors wish to express their most grateful thanks for invaluable help.

K. H. LEECH
M. G. BODDY

January 1965

CHAPTER 1

PRELIMINARY SURVEY

PATRICK Stirling built both inside-cylinder and outside-cylinder, single-wheel express engines for the Great Northern Railway. The first of these engines was completed at Doncaster works, where all of them were built, nearly a hundred years ago; and the last survivor disappeared from service almost fifty years ago. The work they did, and the conditions under which they did it, differed widely from those of the present day. Loads which taxed their powers to the limit would now be regarded as rather light; the average speeds at which they were required to run, then the highest in the world, are now well below present-day average railway speeds. The maximum speeds they attained have become everyday commonplaces of railway travel and of course have long since been completely eclipsed by the speeds of motor cars and aeroplanes.

The general appearance of the Stirling locomotives is uncompromisingly Victorian and antiquated. There is nothing of the modern 'Christmas tree' design, with all working parts strung outside and only too visible, even though the accessibility of some of the excrescences may sometimes be hindered by the presence of others. Stirling, on the contrary, concealed everything which might mar the neat and workmanlike external appearance of his engines, between the frames or behind splashers and sandboxes.

So what is the special appeal of these outmoded machines which, apart from a solitary museum specimen, can never have been seen in steam at all, let alone in actual service, except by really elderly railway enthusiasts of today? It can be said on behalf of the inside-cylinder classes that they were the very neatest and simplest engines ever to be on top-link passenger express duties. On them everything which could be tucked away out of sight was indeed so tucked away. The outstanding impression they conveyed to the observer was of horizontal and parallel straight lines: the curves were there, but they were subordinated, from the aesthetic point of view, to the 'straight-line' aspect. In running, the only objects to give any sense of motion, apart from the exhaust puffs from the chimney, were the spokes of the wheels and the balance weight on the driving wheel rim as it appeared and disappeared into its splasher.

But the outside-cylinder engines were in their day THE most celebrated of express locomotives. They were intended, according to their designer, to work trains of 150 tons behind the tender at average speeds of 51 miles an hour between stops. They were able to do this work with ease and certainty and with ability to make up a great deal of lost time. Before they were outclassed they were coping successfully with trains of 200 tons at 54 miles an hour; and for twenty full years they had been the standard express passenger locomotives of the Great Northern Railway.

That is the railway operating side of the picture. They were also thoroughly economical for coal consumption and maintenance. Even as late as 1909, almost forty years after the first '8-footer' —as they were always called—had been built, No. 776 stationed at Peterborough was consistently one of the lightest engines on coal, being second only to the Ivatt small 'Atlantic' No. 988, then the only engine on the Great Northern fitted with a super-heater and, as such, setting new high standards of economy. After a few teething troubles in their very early days had been put right the design of the 8-footers was not altered, except in detail, for 24 years. As an engineering job they were everything they should be—for their period—except that perhaps they cost a little more to build than most engines of their day.

But their supreme excellence, especially in their later days when detail design had been tidied up and the pursuit of neatness and simplicity could go no further, was their outstanding beauty of appearance, never before achieved—and so universally acknowledged—on a railway engine and, in the opinion of the authors, never reached since; even though one or two classes of single-wheeled express locomotives of generally similar dimensions on other railways, over 20 years after the 8-footers had been introduced, perhaps ran them close in symmetry and beauty of external appearance.

It was the combination of the exceptionally large driving wheel with outside cylinders which formed the central feature of their artistic excellence; and all the larger items of the design and every detail, from the chimney down to the piston-rod crosshead and the proportions of the connecting-rod and its big end, were wholly harmonious and balanced. One fault, indeed, was found in this respect by some critics: the side elevation of the cab, they said, was too severe. Perhaps there may have been a little sting in this. At any rate the last six 8-footers had extra curves put into the cab sides, and when the first surprise at their original appearance was over, most people seem to have regarded the change as an improvement.

It is well known that Uruguay used an engraving of one of the 8-footers—well over life size, judging by the astonished human who also figured in the design—on an issue of stamps. Furthermore, when *The Railway Magazine* was launched, in July 1897, the design on the paper cover incorporated a drawing of one of these engines in a typical Great Northern Railway setting; and it was used in the cover of the first six bound volumes of the magazine.

Stirling was proud of the engines, as well he might be. The original design had been gradually perfected, he felt, and his care in choosing the curves and the proportions of the engines was well repaid. The curves were most carefully thought out: the radius, for instance, of the front elevation of the smokebox, joining the semi-circular upper half of the smokebox to the cylinders, was 2 ft. 5¼ in. Who nowadays would not have let it go at 2 ft. 6 in.? And all the radii of frame plate edges, and the compound radii which made up the curves of the chimney, and the tiny detail of the bits and pieces—all these show the imprint of a strong, individual personality who took thought and care, who knew what he wanted and made sure that he got it.

Moreover, it was not only the 8-footers which had been gradually perfected. Throughout Stirling's reign at Doncaster there was a steady and consistent development and change in detail design. It is true that the total number of types of engine which he built was not great. Besides the 8-footers, there were 7 ft. and 7 ft. 6 in. inside-cylinder singles, 6 ft. 6 in. four-coupled, 5 ft. 6 in. front-coupled,

and six-coupled—all tender engines; and four-coupled side and well tank engines, and six-coupled saddle-tanks. In every one of these classes there was the same year-by-year, batch-by-batch, gradual development of an originally sound design, fined down little by little by an engineer perfectionist to the almost perfect machine for the job, at any rate in the light of engineering knowledge and experience at the time. Cheapness of first cost, reliability, economy, cheapness of maintenance—all of these; but by the time this near-perfection had been attained, the forward-looking vision had been lost, with the onset of old age and an accelerating tempo of changing circumstances.

From this introduction we can look at the Stirling singles and their designer in a little more detail.

Patrick Stirling was born on June 29, 1820 at Kilmarnock, the elder son of the Reverend Robert Stirling. Engineering ran in the family, for not only had Patrick's father invented a 'regenerative' hot air engine, which made possible a much higher thermal efficiency than ever before, but his uncle was the Engineer-proprietor of the Dundee Foundry. Patrick was apprenticed to his uncle, and

Patrick Stirling, about 1890, aged 70. It was in celebration of his seventieth birthday that a drinking fountain was erected in Doncaster by the Great Northern enginemen

was thus brought into early contact with railway engines, the firm then being engaged in the construction of locomotives for the Arbroath & Forfar Railway.

His first important position in the railway world was his appointment as Locomotive Engineer of the Glasgow & South Western Railway, dating from May 3, 1853. In the thirteen years before he resigned on March 1, 1866 to take up a similar post on the Great Northern Railway he was responsible for a variety of locomotive designs, which became more 'modern' in appearance and detail as class succeeded class, until his G. & S.W.R. goods and mixed traffic engines of 1860-66 became in most particulars the prototypes of his first equivalent engines for the Great Northern. But, for his G. & S.W.R. express engines, Stirling had produced outside-cylinder 2—2—2s, whereas his first Great Northern express designs were for several very good reasons provided with inside cylinders.

Stirling became Locomotive Engineer of the Great Northern Railway as successor to Archibald Sturrock, who had held the position since 1850. It has been generally accepted that Sturrock's retirement just before he reached the age of 50 was

due to his coming into possession, through inheritance and marriage, of ample private means. No doubt this fact influenced his action, but it is fair to point out that between 1863 and 1866 he had cost the G.N.R. a great deal of money in the design and construction of 50 steam tenders and the ordering of 70 large goods engines intended to be fitted with steam tenders. In practice these tenders proved to be almost a complete failure and this, together with the high cost of his engines, may well have led to trouble with the directors, even if it was not the cause of his resignation. At any rate, even as late as 1878, reference was made at a board meeting to the 'very considerable sum' which had thus been 'lost to the company'.

To what extent Sturrock had forfeited the confidence of the board must remain purely a matter of conjecture. But his complete independence of them financially was undoubtedly a principal factor in certain events that took place in the year 1866. The archives of British Railways show that on January 23, 1866 Stirling had given notice of his resignation from the Glasgow & South Western Railway, to take effect from March 1; and, although Stirling's appointment at Doncaster was not ratified

No. 63 at Peterborough, about 1895.   Still fitted with the old vacuum brake ejector on the righthand side of the smokebox—only the brakepipe connection is visible in this view—the engine has been 'modernised' by the addition of sidechains and a flanged smokebox front plate, as well as a cast-iron chimney and Ramsbottom safety valve

13

until October 1, his hand is clearly shown in the details of a drawing dated July 11, 1866. Sturrock was retained as Consulting Engineer until the end of December, 1866, but in the circumstances one can well imagine that his attention to detail would be rapidly lessening by mid-summer.

At any rate, it was Stirling who, towards the end of 1866, was authorised to disconnect the steam gear on these tenders as a preliminary to its complete removal at the next repairs at Doncaster. It

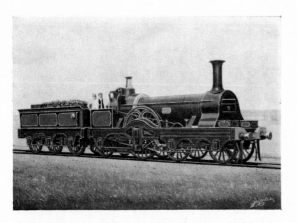

No. 215, Sturrock's 7ft. 6in. single, from an old photograph. Originally built, like the Broad Gauge Great Western 4-2-2's, as a rigid wheelbase engine, she was soon altered, so that her four leading wheels became a bogie

must be remembered that in addition to these steam tenders having mechanical troubles the enginemen were also protesting against having to work them. Sturrock, like Stirling, was a nephew* of the Stirling of the Dundee Foundry and also had served his apprenticeship there, their periods of apprenticeship overlapping, so that it is at least possible that Sturrock may have given his cousin the tip that the job was falling vacant and may have recommended him as his successor.

Naturally, after the apparent extravagance of Sturrock, the Great Northern board were out for his successor to show the utmost economy in carrying on his job. Stirling seems to have taken this as a reasonable challenge to his skill as a locomotive engineer.

---

* The Sturrocks and Stirlings of Dundee appear to have been closely associated for several generations. The relationship between Patrick Stirling and Archibald Sturrock seems to have been first noticed by Mr C. Hamilton Ellis in his *Twenty Locomotive Men.*

His early designs were almost complete copies of Sturrock's equivalent engines, but with the original design modified so as to be as cheap as possible to build. The 0—4—2 well-tanks of 1868, for instance, had single frames except for the trailing wheels instead of the much more expensive double frames, and a cheaper and more simple type of boiler than the elaborate boiler and firebox design of the Sturrock engines. The same criteria apply also to the Stirling 0—6—0 goods engines of 1867 and to the 2—2—2 express passenger engines of 1868.

The development of the Doncaster works to enable the G.N.R. to build its own locomotives without having to pay the profits of contractors is a further instance of aiming at ultimate overall economy. Moreover, in Stirling's reports to the directors, especially in the early years of his appointment, attention is frequently drawn to the cheap first cost and economical maintenance of the engines of his own design, compared with those of Sturrock's. When Stirling went to the Great Northern in 1866 there were about four hundred engines at work and they earned about £4,600 per engine per annum. Seven years later with identical train-mile receipts his engines earned £5,600 per annum each, with a cost of a fraction over threepence per train-mile for maintenance and renewals. It seems clear that Stirling, perhaps as a result of this 'plugging' of his own designs, was given a very free hand to replace any of the older engines which could be regarded as worn out, subject of course to the financial control of the board.

That the importance of economy in providing locomotive power was an ever-present consideration, though varying in intensity with the financial position of the railway, is shown by the fact that an economy drive from 1879 onwards was the cause of the handsome built-up chimney being abandoned and replaced by the single-piece cast-iron chimney, neat enough, but costing less and lasting longer. It seems probable that the majority of railway boards of directors used the example of Sir Richard Moon of the L.N.W.R., that most cheeseparing of economists, and his limitation of Ramsbottom's and Webb's designs to very small, cheap engines only, as a yardstick to measure the cost of their own locomotives. Forty years later, Churchward was to suffer under the G.W.R. General Manager's direct comparison of the costs of G.W.R. and L.N.W.R. 4—6—0 engines.

There is a further similarity between the circumstances of Churchward and Stirling, in that both seem to have been averse to any decoration of their engines. Stirling started off with black splasher beadings but went over to polished brass after the first few engines. Churchward was compelled by his Locomotive Committee to stick to the traditional G.W.R. copper-capped chimney and brass beadings and it took a war to enable him to revert to cast-iron chimneys and remove splasher beadings.

The question of how the relatively expensive 8 ft. singles come to fit into the general picture of enforced economy will be answered in the chapters dealing with this class; but it may be said here that the building of the 2—2—2 singles of 1885-94, when 23 of this type were constructed as against eight 8-footers in the same period, was another result of the special economy drive of the 1880s, combined with the need to replace worn-out Sturrock main-line engines.

There was never any encouragement from the board for Stirling to look forward and design engines against possible future requirements. After his death the one thing which was universally recognised about him was that his designs were just right for the jobs they had to do, but that their margin of available power was of the minimum which would ensure satisfactory and reliable operation. His obituary notice in *The Engineer* shows the degree to which this was recognised at the time

—'His originality of design and his keen sense of mechanical fitness have rendered his locomotives celebrated all over the world. Probably there is not a railway in existence on which the road, the locomotives and the work to be done are in such complete harmony.'

In the nineteenth century there was no such thing as a fixed retiring age. Patrick Stirling was devoted to his job and the board had appreciated it. Nevertheless, at a board meeting on November 1, 1895 it was resolved to appoint H. A. Ivatt as Locomotive Engineer, though Stirling's death did not occur until November 11.* The negotiations with Ivatt had been going on in the strictest confidence for over two months. There was no one in the Great Northern organisation at Doncaster who was considered big enough for the job, so the board cast their net wider, and H. A. Ivatt, who was then

---

*John Shotton, Stirling's Works Manager at Doncaster for nearly 29 years, had died in May 1895, and in notifying this to the board Stirling had suggested that the directors might 'consider it an advantageous opportunity at my time of life of appointing a person who would be able to take my place at any time'. Stirling's death was due to heart failure consequent upon bronchopneumonia.

No. 92, the 7ft. 6in. single which 'used up' the driving wheels of Sturrock's No. 215.
The photograph was taken in about 1878, since she is equipped with non-automatic vacuum brake: otherwise she appears as built with the original open slots in the driving splasher

THE STIRLING SINGLES

Locomotive Engineer of the Great Southern & Western Railway of Ireland, was approached. It was realised that the Stirling engines were not proving equal to the heaviest loads which the introduction of corridor stock and restaurant cars had imposed upon them. This was true enough, but it was the continual pressure for economies and the habitual cutting down of Stirling's submissions of locomotive requirements to the board which had been the prime cause of the developing inadequacy of the Stirling express engines under rapidly increasing demands of traffic.

As far back as 1879 Stirling had proposed to increase the diameters of the boilers on coupled engines from 4 ft. 0½ in. to 4 ft. 5 in., but the economy drive which was then just starting caused this idea to be dropped, except for the well-tanks (Stirling and Sturrock 0—4—2WT and Stirling 0—4—4WT classes) which badly needed the extra adhesion weight of the larger boilers for the in-creasing suburban traffic. Stirling had already fitted such large diameter boilers to the six mineral 0—6—0 engines built specially in 1871-74 for hauling heavy loads of up to nearly 700 tons between Doncaster and Peterborough by way of Lincoln and Boston, but the general proposal to fit 4 ft. 5 in. diameter boilers to main-line engines was not revived again until the early part of 1895, when drawings for such boilers were made. A batch of six-coupled goods engines with 4 ft. 7½ in. diameter wheels received these larger diameter domeless boilers.

The engines, however, were not completed until 1896, after Stirling's death. None of his 2—4—0 or 7 ft. 2—2—2 tender engines received any of these domeless 4 ft. 5 in. diameter boilers, though quite a number of the six-coupled goods tender engines did.

Ivatt took over the general dimensions of these boilers for his own first engine designs, increasing

No. 53 at Belle Isle, 1897, just backing down into Kings Cross to head a down express.
The headlamps will be repositioned before leaving the terminus: one
at the foot of the chimney, the other over the left-hand buffer

No. 221 leaving Boston, 1892. She has been rebuilt with new deep frames, but has not yet had the brake pipe carried forward to a hose connection on the front bufferbeam

the grate area by reducing the firebox water legs from 3 in. to $1\frac{3}{4}$ in., and later adding a dome and using two plates instead of three for the barrel. These modified boilers were also used as replacements on a wide variety of Stirling engines which had hitherto carried 4 ft. $2\frac{1}{2}$ in. diameter boilers. The reduction in width of the water legs of the firebox was not wholly satisfactory and after a few years the old Stirling dimension of 3 in. was again standardised by Ivatt for the several classes of engines of his design which originally were fitted with these quasi-Stirling boilers.

Stirling's designs of single-wheeled express passenger locomotives fell broadly into two classes, 2—2—2s with inside cylinders and 4—2—2s with outside cylinders. There were wide variations of dimensions within each of these types of wheel arrangement, the earlier and smaller engines being developed in both types into larger and more powerful ones. It will be made clear in later chapters how there was throughout each class a steady change and improvement in detail from engine to engine, as experience showed changes to be desirable. In most respects older engines were brought into line with the later practice when they came into Doncaster works for subsequent heavy general repairs.

In addition to building engines of his own design Stirling rebuilt a number of his predecessor's 2—2—2 singles, of several classes, and also rebuilt six large Sturrock 2—4—0s as 2—2—2s. Unfortunately, it is not absolutely certain how many engines of the earlier classes were actually rebuilt. In the early years there was no immediate need to increase to any great extent the total number of locomotives on the books, and yet the older locomotives were becoming worn out and inadequate for the work they had to do. Thus when a new Stirling engine was built it frequently took the running number, regardless of class, of one of the older engines either just scrapped or down for withdrawal shortly. From time to time it was found that one or other of these when brought into Doncaster was worth keeping in service for a while longer. No doubt in some cases there was some particular service for which they had been earmarked and for which no equally suitable alternative engine was available at the time. At any rate, such retained engines were returned to service with the letter 'A' suffixed to their running numbers.

At first there were only one or two such numbers. The first two which appear in the records are Nos. 121A and 396A, transferred to the duplicate list in March 1870; and there were only eight duplicate list engines by the end of 1872. After this the numbers gradually rose until there were 21 lettered 'A' in the first half of 1881 and 26 by the end of that year; and year by year there was a tendency for the numbers to increase, although there were fluctuations when more old engines were scrapped than transferred to the duplicate list. At the end of 1887 there were 37 and by the end of

No. 236, about 1898, looking generally as in Stirling's day, but with auxiliary oil boxes on front sandboxes for the driving axleboxes. Her smokebox front plate appears to have been reinforced inside the smokebox by some form of stiffening plate, no doubt due to its having wasted thin

B

1888 this number had increased to 42. At this point the records are broken and do not start again until 1896, in which year Ivatt had taken charge; there were then 39 duplicate list engines in service.

This practice of transferring old locomotives to a duplicate list combined with the absence of records at Doncaster makes it impossible to state with certainty how many early engines actually survived to be rebuilt. There were in all five classes of single-wheelers of Sturrock or pre-Sturrock vintage which did come in for rebuilding in addition to the 2—4—0s mentioned above. These rebuilt engines will be dealt with separately in more detail, as far as available information permits, since they clearly come into the overall picture of the Stirling single-wheelers.

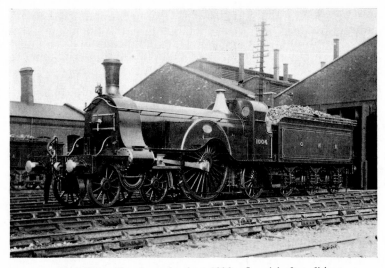

No. 1004 at Peterborough, about 1896. In original condition, except for new cylinders, and with original tender

CHAPTER 2

THE ENGINES IN GENERAL AND THEIR WORK

DURING the years of his superintendency at Doncaster, that is from the middle of 1866 to the end of 1895, Stirling had 851 engines built to his designs, of which nine were not new, but rebuilds of engines he had inherited from Sturrock, which were so radically reconstructed as to justify new Doncaster works numbers. These engines were Nos. 10, 20, 42 and 43, rebuilt from the old 'Little Sharp' 2—2—2 tender engines of 1847-50 into o—4—2 well-tanks in 1873-74; and Nos. 470 and 471, Manning Wardle o—6—o side-tanks of 1863, which were rebuilt into o—6—o saddle-tanks in 1872 using—according to the Doncaster repairs book—only the original wheels.

The other three engines, the saddle-tanks Nos. 124, 162 and 392, had been rebuilt as such in 1867 (in that order) from o—6—o tender engines, retaining their old domed boilers and weatherboards but receiving Stirling frames and motion and an angular version of his rounded saddle-tank. In 1868 they were fitted with new Stirling straightback boilers and cabs. As a combined result of the 1867 and 1868 rebuildings little of the original engines can have remained, and they were accordingly allotted Doncaster works numbers.

After Stirling's death a further 67 engines were built to his design in 1896 and 1897, though on ten of these engines, the 2—4—os Nos. 1061-70, domed boilers were fitted; and cabs, splashers and sand-gear, as well as other details, were changed to Ivatt standards.

Of these 918 engines only 89 were single-wheelers, less than one in ten of the locomotive stock. The singles were of three main classes, and in addition, three engines which did not fall strictly into any of the main classes, but were intermediate

No. 8 in 1877-8, with non-automatic vacuum brake fitted, and with feed-water delivery into boiler barrel. As first built, the feed-water delivery was on the side of the firebox

in size between the smaller and the larger engines. And even of these three engines, two were of one type and the third, built 15 years before the other two, differed from them, and from all other Stirling engines, in many of the leading dimensions.

The earliest, and smallest, engines were built between March 1868 and June 1870. The class numbered twelve engines; they were 2—2—2s with 7 ft. 1 in. driving wheels. The shape of the cab of the first six engines was different from that of the last six. On the earlier engines its design was taken unchanged from Stirling's last engines for the G. & S.W.R. It had circular sidewindows, but nowhere for the enginemen to lean on in looking out of the cabside. These cabs were unpopular with the footplate crews, and all engines originally fitted with them, whether single-wheelers or coupled engines, were later provided with the standard Stirling cabs.

This earliest class was a single-wheeler version of the first design of Stirling 2—4—0. The coupled engines must have given every satisfaction, for the original design was continued with only minor changes throughout the Stirling period. The boilers,

cylinders, leading wheels and all details which did not have to be different, were the same on the two classes, the 2—2—2 and the 2—4—0. Stirling conducted some comparative trials between them and was confirmed in his predilection for single-wheelers by the 2—2—2s having the best of it, especially on the long climb from Kings Cross to Potters Bar.

The 8-footers were the next class to appear, No. 1 being turned out from Doncaster works on April 20, 1870. She was not entirely satisfactory as originally built, and all subsequent engines were provided with larger fireboxes, involving a longer trailing wheelbase, and with many of the details, major as well as minor, altered. After No. 1, the 8-footers were built in pairs. It might indeed be said that the two engines of each pair were 'identical twins', but that the other engines of the class were only brother —or sister—engines, since in many cases changes were made between each successive pair of engines.

Seeing that the construction of the 8-footers was spread over a period of 25 years—all but a fortnight!—it would indeed have been miraculous if no change had been desirable; but the laying down of the engines two at a time, rather than in batches of

No. 39, the last 7ft. single to be built, taken in about 1898. The driving wheel splasher slots are no longer lined out, but painted the same light green as the rest of the splasher

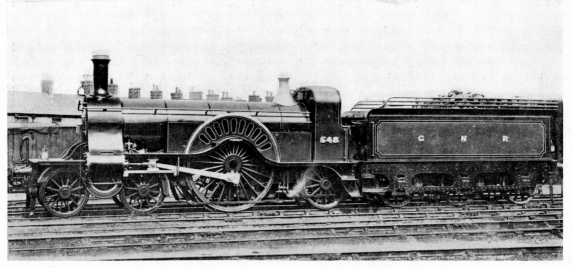

No. 548 at Peterborough, about 1895. One of the few engines which retained her original shallow frames throughout her life, and was never provided with the curved footplate angle ahead of the cylinders

ten or more, certainly added to the individuality of the 8 ft. singles, and up to the last six engines, which were of substantially increased dimensions, there was no point at which it could be said that the class had crystallised out into standardisation throughout. It is true that the last six engines, Nos. 1003-08, were laid down as a batch, but even here, and although constructed at so late a date as between November 1894 and April 1895, there were minor differences between most of these six engines, by which an expert could recognise the identity of the engine without the aid of its running number or Doncaster works plate.

In all there were eventually 53 8-footers, 47 of the original design, the earlier engines more or less brought up to date by rebuilding between December 1880 and October 1889, and the six larger engines of 1894-95.

The first of the three 'odd' engines was No. 92, completed in June 1870, a 7 ft. 7 in. single of slightly larger dimensions than the 7 ft. 1 in. engines of the No. 6 class. The reason for her existence and why she remained unique will be related in the chapter dealing with this engine. The other two 'odd' engines were Nos. 238 and 232, completed in June and August 1885 respectively. These seem to have been at first intended as an up-to-date version of No. 92, but nothing except the boiler tubes and bearing springs remained common to all three of these intermediate-sized engines.

The last type of Stirling single-wheeler was the 7 ft. $7\frac{1}{2}$ in. 2—2—2 class numbering 21 engines in all, on which the main dimensions were increased to be comparable with the 8 ft. engines, though there was nothing but the boiler tubes actually interchangeable with the 8-footers. The first engine of this larger class, No. 234, was completed in June 1886, ten months after No. 232 had been put into service. Ten of these engines were built, in pairs, between June 1886 and January 1889. Then there was a gap until the next five were turned out, as a batch, during the first half of 1892; and the final six, again as a batch, made their appearance between April and July 1894.

It was only the 7 ft. singles which possessed any degree of interchangeability of boilers and motion with Stirling's coupled engines of any classes. No. 92 had standard cylinders, but her boiler and motion were special. The 8-footers had no parts of any importance in common with any other classes. Smokebox doors, buffers, injectors, lubricators, of course; but these were merely Great Northern standard ancillary equipment. The large 7 ft. $7\frac{1}{2}$ in. singles seemed at first glance to have boilers interchangeable with the 8-footers, but this was not so, quite apart from the different shapes of the smokebox tubeplates: the main frames of the 8-footers were 4 ft. $0\frac{1}{2}$ in. apart, those of the 7 ft. $7\frac{1}{2}$ in. engines 4 ft. $1\frac{1}{2}$ in., so that, though an 8-footer box would pass between the frames of the 7 ft. $7\frac{1}{2}$ in. class, the reverse was not the case, the widths over firebox being 3 ft. $11\frac{1}{2}$ in. and 4 ft. $0\frac{1}{2}$ in. respectively.

Leading and trailing wheels and their axles and axleboxes on the 7 ft. $7\frac{1}{2}$ in. engines were, however, interchangeable with the leading wheels assembly on the 2—4—0s built at the same time.

No. 48 on up Leeds express, period about 1888 (the cast-iron chimney and the corridor coach preclude an earlier date). The very short rail lengths and the depth of the ballast are characteristic of the Great Northern permanent way of those days

The general picture is that all the single-wheelers were regarded as special engines for their own particular and more arduous work, and that while any odd standard parts were conveniently used, there was no attempt to cramp the proportions of the design merely for the sake of standardisation. In Stirling's days the singles were always regarded as the *élite*, the aristocrats of the Great Northern locomotive department.

The frameplates of all classes of the single-wheelers were $1\frac{1}{4}$ in. thick; Stirling's coupled engines had $1\frac{1}{4}$ in., 1 3/16 in. or $1\frac{1}{8}$ in. frameplates according to the class. There is, it is true, one general arrangement drawing, of the 1880 8-footers, which shows 1 3/16 in. thickness, but this is certainly a draughtsman's error, and No. 1's frames, to this drawing, are $1\frac{1}{4}$ in. All frames earlier and later were shown as $1\frac{1}{4}$ in. That even Doncaster draughtsmen in the nineteenth century could make errors is shown by one tracing—not the original drawing—where the left side frame is given as $1\frac{1}{4}$ in., the right side as 1 3/16 in.! The original drawing shows both $1\frac{1}{4}$ in. thick. And the guard irons on the front bufferbeam are shown incorrectly on two of the

general arrangement drawings. There is perhaps some excuse for a tracing not being perfect, but the original ink drawings on backed paper, and tinted, have quite a number of dimensional and other errors, some quite serious.

Up to 1894 doubleheading on the expresses was forbidden, and none of the single-wheelers until then had been fitted with a brakepipe connection at the front bufferbeam. The introduction of corridor stock, dining cars and sleeping cars had by this time put up the weights of trains so that the single-wheelers on the heaviest and fastest trains were apt to lose time in bad weather conditions, and very reluctantly Stirling was forced to agree to a certain amount of doubleheading. Here again, the present writer, in looking back over his own experience when dry-sanding seemed invariably to be far more effective and reliable than steam-sanding, cannot help wondering if the introduction of steam-sand in 1886 on the then latest single-wheelers, which were naturally rostered for the heaviest expresses, may not have helped to seal their early doom.

Steam-sanding, or compressed-air-sanding, when all is well, is an excellent method of putting the sand just where it is needed and will do most good, but its functioning is far less reliable than any other feature on a steam locomotive. The merest trace of moisture in the sand, or a difference in grain size, can produce erratic sanding or even a total failure of the sand to flow. And it is fatally easy to leave the steam valve just open, when sanding is going well, and thus empty the sandboxes before anything amiss is noticed.

With dry sand, a fairly continuous manual operation of the sandgear is necessary. The flow will normally stop unless this is done—and in any case a sanding lever out of place is a larger object to attract attention than a small steam-cock handle or handwheel.

Of course, sanding or no sanding, the limits of practicable loading for even the most powerful single-wheeler were inevitably very soon to be well and truly exceeded. Nevertheless, it would have been pleasant to have been able to record that while Stirling was alive, it was never necessary to double-head one of his singles.

Within a year or two of his taking over at Doncaster, the engines of his predecessor, Sturrock, began to require new boilers and cylinders. Stirling took in hand those engines which measured up to the secondary work of the Great Northern at the time, and rebuilt a number of them with cylinders of his own design and new domeless boilers. About 40 to 45 such engines were rebuilt as single-wheelers—the exact number is not known for certain—and they also come into the picture of the 'Stirling singles'.

The programme of new engine building, and the rebuilding of older engines as carried out by Stirling, is summarised in the following tables:

or aeroplanes, let alone rockets, to give rise to comparisons. Moreover, the next fastest object on the earth in the service of man was a galloping horse at less than half the speed of a railway train.

And it must not be forgotten that during the

LEADING PARTICULARS OF STIRLING SINGLE-WHEELERS

Date	Running No. of first engine	Wheel arrgt.	No. built	Cylinders Diam. Stroke	Leading wl. diam.	Driving wl. diam.	Trailing wl. diam.	Grate area sq. ft.	Chap. ref.
1868–70	No. 6	2-2-2	12	17″ × 24″	4′ 1″	7′ 1″	4′ 1″	16·25	4
1870	92	2-2-2	1	17½″ × 24″	,,	7′ 7″	,,	,,	4
1870	No. 1	4-2-2	1	18″ × 28″	3′ 11″	8′ 1″	,,	15·8	5
1870–71	No. 8	4-2-2	2	,,	,,	,,	,,	17·75	6
1871–76	No. 2	4-2-2	10	,,	,,	,,	,,	,,	6
1876–80	221	4-2-2	14	,,	,,	,,	4′ 7″	,,	6
1880–83	662	4-2-2	10	,,	,,	,,	,,	,,	6
1884–85	771	4-2-2	4	,,	,,	,,	,,	,,	6
1885	238	2-2-2	2	18½″ × 26″	4′ 1½″	7′ 7½″	4′ 1½″	17·3	7
1886	234	2-2-2	10	,,	,,	,,	,,	18·4	7
1887	775	4-2-2	4	18″ × 28″	3′ 11½″	8′ 1½″	4′ 7½″	17·75	6
1892	871	2-2-2	5	18½″ × 26″	4′ 1½″	7′ 7½″	4′ 1½″	18·4	7
1893	1001	4-2-2	2	18″ × 28″	3′ 11½″	8′ 1½″	4′ 7½″	17·75	6
1894	876	2-2-2	6	18½″ × 26″	4′ 1½″	7′ 7½″	4′ 1½″	18·4	7
1894–95	1003	4-2-2	5	19½″ × 28″	3′ 11½″	8′ 1½″	4′ 7½″	20·0	10
1895	1008	4-2-2	1	19″ × 28″	,,	,,	,,	,,	10

LEADING PARTICULARS OF EARLIER ENGINES REBUILT BY STIRLING AS 2-2-2s
(See Chapter 11)

Class	Date built	Date first rebuilt	Cylinders Diam. Stroke	Leading wl. diam.	Driving wl. diam.	Trailing wl. diam.	Grate area sq. ft.
51	1848–50	1867	16″ × 21″	3′ 10″	6′ 1″	3′ 10″	14
91	1851–52	1867	16½″ × 21″	4′ 1″	6′ 7″	4′ 1″	14
201	1851	1866	16″ × 22″	3′ 6″	6′ 1″	3′ 6″	14
203	1852–53	1867	16″ × 22″	4′ 1″	6′ 7″	4′ 1″	14
229	1860–61	1868	17″ × 22″	4′ 3″	7′ 0″	4′ 3″	16
264	1866–67*	1873	17″ × 24″	4′ 3½″	7′ 0″	4′ 3½″	16·25

*Nos. 264–69 were originally built as 2-4-0s.

In this preliminary survey something must also be said of the running conditions under which the Stirling singles had to work. In studying their performances and assessing their merit in ordinary service on passenger trains there are several points which need to be especially borne in mind.

The first and most fundamental difference between the outlook of today and that of 65 to 95 years ago is that in those days the only high speeds attained anywhere were those of the steam locomotive hauling trains. There were no motor-cars, Stirling era the Great Northern was not only the railway with the fastest running times in Britain; it was the fastest in the world. So that any Stirling single on an express to Leeds or the North would normally be covering more miles in the hour than could be attained anywhere else by human invention or effort.

There was, therefore, little incentive for enginemen to do more than keep their booked running times, and there were some fairly severe discouragements against setting up higher speed performances than necessary—though this is a state of affairs which seems here and there to have persisted to the end of the steam locomotive period of railways. Only a few years ago, a locomotive inspector bewailed to the writer that the result of his having helped a keen and willing crew to make a really exceptional run after a late start—a well publicised performance too—was a dressing-down from his superiors for setting a standard which could not be maintained day in, day out, and which would only lead to trouble with the operating department, if any future performance fell short.

There is no doubt that this restrictive point of view was very much in evidence in Stirling's day. In 1910 a driver recalled how in the 1895 Race to the North when he was firing on one of the runs on a 7 ft. 6 in. single, his mate had eased the engine down considerably, saying they were going plenty

fast enough, and if they didn't look out they might get let in for it as a regular thing. And Driver Falkinder, who in the 1895 Race drove No. 668 on the night when the fastest time to Grantham was made, assured Rous-Marten that 'he was restrained by positive instructions from putting his engine to her fullest speed, either up or down hill'.

There were two other factors which tended to prevent an individual driver from indulging in extra fast running, or making up more time than could be done without extending the engine to any degree. The first was the coal bonus. The present writer does not know how this operated on the Great Northern in Stirling's day, but a common method used to be to provide a monthly cash bonus to the driver in each link who burned the least coal per mile. The work was spread as evenly as possible through the link, and of course in those days every

No. 663 at Peterborough about 1899. Showing the cleaners' patterning of the tallow with which the paintwork had been wiped, a style of finish more pleasing to the cleaners than to the photographer. The chimney has been fitted with a liner, an unusual provision

top link express driver had his one regular engine; in most cases so did the enginemen in other passenger links. And this itself was a second factor. A driver who could rely on having the same engine every day, except when she was being washed out or was under repair, almost invariably took the greatest trouble and care to bring his engine into first-class condition and preserve her in this condition as long as possible. The first thing he would think of in deciding whether to try to recover time or not was whether he could do it without shortening the life or comfort of the engine before her next general repairs. In those days connecting rod big ends and the fit of driving axleboxes in their guides could be and were adjusted so that no knocks, such as any modern steam locomotive usually develops within a month or two after being repaired, were ever heard. It was boiler condition, cylinder and tyre wear and sideplay in axle bearings which led to an engine's being shopped for repairs; and these latter defects repercussed only faintly on the footplate at the time under discussion.

There was in fact a completely different climate conditioning the reactions of enginemen then, and such drivers as the Kings Cross men Sam Watson, No. 774, and Harry Tappenden, No. 53, who had these engines in their prime and who were noted for running downhill faster than most other drivers, were exceptional. But they were meticulous in looking after their engines. According to W. J. Reynolds, Watson, in particular, used to spend the days on which No. 774 was washed out in prowling round her in the shed, to ensure that nobody dared to tamper with her, and to see that the work he might have booked was done, and all put back just as it should be.

There was also the state of the permanent way to be taken into account, and its higher resistance to motion than the much heavier and more solid track of today, to say nothing of the rough riding of the six-wheeled carriages which formed the great bulk of the Great Northern main-line stock. Even now, guards occasionally get complaints from passengers about rough riding and rough handling of

No. 878, as built, about 1898. The last batch of 7ft. 6in. singles was provided with front brake pipe connections and front buffer beam side chains when built. They also had the flanged front plate to the smokebox instead of the flat plate fixed to the wrapper by means of angle irons, which was at first fitted to the earlier engines of the class

coaches in braking. As one who travelled regularly during several years in those very hard riding G.N.R. six-wheelers, the present writer can state confidently that passengers of those days really could have grounds for complaint, especially in the end compartments; the middle compartments were, by contrast, not at all bad; that is, until one had been spoilt by a ride in a bogie carriage.

The last point to be mentioned is the actual ability of the engines to run fast, even downhill. During the first 15 years of the Stirling period, none of his locomotives on the Great Northern Railway worked at a higher boiler pressure than 140 lb. per sq. in. In the next few years engines with new boilers might be worked at 150 lb. per sq. in. and during the last eight or nine years new boilers might be pressed to 160 lb. per sq. in. But the bulk of the older engines still worked at 140 lb. Try out a modern steam engine, with superheater and long travel piston valves and all the latest improvements, at 140 lb. per sq. in. and you would find a very feeble and lack-lustre specimen, unrecognisable compared with its full-pressure self. And this quite apart from any question of cylinder proportions and much higher tractive effort.

The large driving wheels of the singles undoubtedly helped to offset the twin handicaps of low pressure and flat slide-valves with minimum travel and (sometimes) strangled steam ports. Short travel was a practical necessity with unbalanced flat slide-valves. Even with the travel cut to a minimum quite a large amount of the engine horsepower was absorbed in driving them, especially with the regulator wide open and full boiler pressure on the back of them, depending of course on the effectiveness of their lubrication.

Without being too dogmatic, it seems pretty certain that up to 30 or even 40 h.p. might be absorbed in driving the valve-gear on an engine running fast and working fairly hard. No wonder most engines with flat slide-valves tended to be driven with only partially opened regulators, thereby reducing appreciably the steam chest pressure and with it the friction of the slide-valves.

In confirmation of this point, the present writer's cousin Cecil Laundy reported in 1911 that No. 1003's driver had told him that it was necessary to work her with the regulator partially closed, or she tended to run her eccentric straps warm, a clear indication of heavy loading on the straps.

The internal friction of the locomotives of those days was undoubtedly high, and any attempt to get the utmost out of an engine increased it appreciably.

A writer of today has expressed the view that the steam locomotive is out of date because of the skill needed to handle it by the driver and fireman.

No. 666, Driver William Edis, her regular engineman, at Kings Cross, 11 September, 1891

certainly a diesel or electric locomotive does not need the skill or the comradely co-operation between the enginemen. When the present writer quoted to an engineman of today the remark of a retiring top link driver about driving diesels, that he 'used to wish his missus knew the road; she

o. 773, about 1890, probably at Grantham. The first engine to be built new with the cast-iron chimney

would come along and drive, and get on with her knitting as well', the reply was 'Well, we still have the responsibility', a fair comment. But in the days of the single-wheeler a driver's skill in handling his engine, especially in starting and up the banks, made all the difference to the performance. Sir William Stanier once remarked, at a meeting of the Institution of Locomotive Engineers, that in his young days the drivers of the old Great Western singles used to start out of Paddington with eight bogie coaches without a slip; and yet the modern six-coupled engine never seemed to start her train without slipping at least once.

There is no doubt that the old drivers used sand far more freely in getting away from stations and in tunnels than their counterparts of yesterday, or even of 20 years ago, did.

How else could the driver of No. 22 during the 1895 racing, with a load of 134 tons, get through

Holloway from Kings Cross in 3 min. 31 sec.? The distance is over 1½ miles and there is a continuous ascent from the start, of 1 in 105. Moreover, the line passes through two tunnels, the first of which was always wet due to leakage from the Regent's Canal just overhead. Ivatt 'Atlantics' and even Gresley 'Pacifics' have been known to stall here. One is inevitably led to the conclusion that No. 22's sand-gear was in good condition and was certainly used. Probably even better times to Holloway were made in the last week of the 1895 racing, but unfortunately they were not noted.

There was a practice at one period that some main-line expresses leaving Kings Cross were helped in their starts by the engine which had brought in the empty stock acting as a 'banker' as far as the end of the platform, or perhaps on occasions even further. Whether this applied to all or any of the cases quoted in these pages is not known, but there was never any specific mention of it in the original descriptions and logs, and there is evidence to indicate that it was discontinued at some time in the 'eighties.

No. 1006, as originally built, 1895. Note that the cylinder cover has only 14 studs. These cylinders were replaced at an early date by new cylinders with 18 studs in the covers

CHAPTER 3

THE STIRLING STRAIGHTBACK BOILERS

THERE are always technical puzzles in the why and wherefore of design in the work of any engineer, and quite a number of these are apparent when the general picture of Stirling's boilers and their many changes in detail are studied. For example, the barrels of Stirling's boilers were always constructed of three pieces, or rings, with the smallest diameter at the smokebox end. Each section of barrel was overlapped by the next one nearer to the firebox; the firebox itself overlapped the largest diameter barrel ring. Up to 1880 the standard diameter outside the smallest ring was 3 ft. 10½ in.; the plates were ½ in. thick, so that the largest barrel ring had an outside diameter of 4 ft. 0½ in.

In 1866 the three-ring barrel was almost certainly a necessity due to the difficulty then of obtaining boiler plates large enough to make a two-ring barrel

feasible, yet after 1885 at the latest it seems certai that steel plates large enough for a two-ring barre could have been obtained. Ivatt in 1896 almost a once fixed upon a two-ring domed version of th three-ring 4 ft. 5 in. boiler designed by Stirling i 1895 as his future standard.

From 1880 onwards Stirling increased th diameter of his boiler barrels. On all classes excep the 8 ft. and 7 ft. 6 in. single-wheelers it went u to 4 ft. 2½ in. maximum outside diameter; on thes large single-wheelers clearance between the drivin wheel flanges seems to have necessitated a maximun diameter of 4 ft. 2 in. Stirling would not quit forgo the boiler lagging at the point of minimun clearance, though it was inevitably reduced i thickness here. Nevertheless, the standard 4 ft. 2½ in boilers were fitted on the 7 ft. singles just as on th

No. 222, 7ft. single, at Peterborough about 1896. The small diameter of the top of the Ramsbottom safety valve casing shows that the engine was reboilered prior to 1884. Actually the date of the first reboilering was 1879

ngines with smaller diameter wheels, even though the top of the flange of the driving wheel to all intents was level with the centre line of the boiler. Perhaps the relatively small area of lagging cutaway needed, together, of course, with the existence of such a large number of interchangeable boilers, may have tipped the balance in favour of the ft. 2½ in. diameter.

A 4 ft. 5 in. diameter boiler intended for the —4—os was drawn out in August 1879, but this was never built. It is just barely possible that the increased weight might not have been acceptable on all branch lines to the civil engineers; but by far the most probable reason for its not being carried into practice was the extra cost. Stirling was always balancing delicately on the narrow margin between his engines being up to their work and their costing a penny too much. What he gained from the care and success with which he sustained this balance was a remarkably free hand in the way he ran his department. One of the advantages of this free hand was undoubtedly his being able to get away with a much greater adhesion loading on the driving axles of his single-wheelers than his permitted figure. A recent description of the change when Ivatt took the directors around the Doncaster works, compared with Stirling's habit of leading the way and only letting the directors see just what he wanted them to, shows how thoroughly Stirling was master in his own domain.

Although the general outlines of the characteristic Stirling straightback boiler were settled with his first design for the Great Northern, the No. 280 class of 2—4—os, yet changes were frequent in the internal details, at least during the first 20 years of his superintendency. The height of the crown of the inside copper firebox above the boiler centre line started, in 1866, at 8¼ in., measured to the underside of the plate. In 1870 it had risen to 10 in. on No. 1 the first 8-footer, No. 92 the first 7 ft. 6 in. single, and No. 395 the first of four 0—6—0 saddle-tank engines with 5 ft. 1 in. diameter driving wheels, built 1871-73 but whose design had been drawn out in 1870 also. By the end of 1870 it had been lowered to 9½ inches for No. 8, the second 8-footer, and for other boilers; but for these other boilers the dimension was further reduced in 1872 to 8½ in. and probably for the 1872-73 8-footers also—though the earliest surviving drawing showing this dimension for the 8-footers is dated 1874.

One engine, No. 5, had the height reduced to 7½ inches in 1877. This was probably due to the realisation of the effect of the more rapid deceleration with the continuous brakes then being fitted on all passenger stock; this deceleration caused the water in the boiler to surge forward to a much greater degree than had previously been the case, frequently leaving the firebox crown uncovered for an appreciable time. This, of course, led to the

Nos. 53 and 7 on down 'Flying Scotsman' at Hadley Wood, about 1899. This weight of train, about 255 tons tare, was just outside the limit for consistent timekeeping in all weather conditions for one engine only, but was a light job for a pair of 8-footers

dropping of fusible plugs and even to burning of the plate. A lower firebox crown thus became more or less a practical necessity, and it is quite possible that all the high-crown engines were altered similarly to No. 5, though there is nothing in the remaining records to confirm this.

There was no further change then until 1884, when the height was again reduced, this time to $6\frac{1}{2}$ in. for the 8-footers and the 7 ft. 6 in. singles; on other classes of engines the crown remained $\frac{1}{4}$ in. higher, at $6\frac{3}{4}$ in. No doubt this was due to these boilers being $\frac{1}{2}$ in. larger in diameter, at 4 ft. $2\frac{1}{2}$ in., than the boilers on the singles. In 1892, when the copper plate was increased in thickness from $\frac{1}{2}$ in. to 9/16 in., the height became 6 11/16 in. for the 4 ft. $2\frac{1}{2}$ in. diameter boilers, while on the No. 1003 class of 8-footers in 1894 it remained at $6\frac{1}{2}$ in., as in the previous batches of single-wheelers. On the 1895 boiler design, 4 ft. 5 in. diameter, it came down even lower, to 5 15/16 in.

The type of roofstays used also varied, not quite year by year, but certainly class by class. Starting off in 1866 with the longitudinal girder stays which had been Sturrock's previous practice, by 1870 Stirling had abandoned their use and had adopted direct staying throughout, using no girder stays at all, quite a bold departure from generally accepted practice. He continued to use direct stays throughout until 1880 when, on the new 4 ft. 2 in. and 4 ft. $2\frac{1}{2}$ in. diameter boilers built that year, the front rows of direct stays were replaced by transverse girder stays; two rows of girders for the normal 5 ft. 6 in. long fireboxes and three rows for the longer 6 ft. 2 in. fireboxes of the 8-footers. Yet the 1888 drawing of the No. 775 batch of 8-footers shows again all direct stays, whilst the equivalent fireboxes of the large 7 ft. 6 in. singles of only two years earlier show two rows only of girder stays.

The general impression produced by all this chopping and changing, and confirmed by the present writer's personal experience with hard water in steam locomotives, is that the longitudinal girder stays inherited from Sturrock gave rise to trouble because of the difficulty of removing scale, in washing out and rodding, from the firebox crowns and that the rigid direct stays overcame this trouble, but themselves caused a different form of trouble at the front two or three rows to develop; probably grooving or cracking of the copper plate close up against the tube plate flange. The provision of girder stays

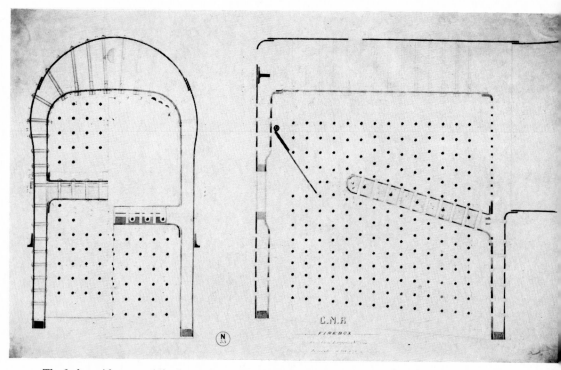

The firebox with water midfeather used on No. 8, the second 8-footer. The boiler feedwater entered at the tip of the midfeather. The original of this drawing no longer exists, and unfortunately the photostat copy is not a good one. The tube arrangement on the L.H. view has had a piece of paper pasted over it

at this end of the firebox, permitting the breathing of the copper firebox over an area sufficient to prevent trouble with the plate, must have proved the satisfactory happy mean, for the practice was continued by Ivatt after Stirling's death.

The number and diameter of fire-tubes were also matters upon which no general decision seems to have been reached until after 1886 when all new 4 ft. $2\frac{1}{2}$ in. diameter boilers were provided with 174 tubes $1\frac{1}{4}$ in. in diameter; this remained the standard thereafter until Stirling's death. But his earliest boilers, only 4 ft. $0\frac{1}{2}$ in. in diameter, originally had no fewer than 206 tubes, $1\frac{1}{4}$ in. in diameter, though after a year or two this was reduced to 192. Then came the series of experiments starting with the 1 9/16 in. diameter tubes on the 7 ft. single No. 222 and the $1\frac{5}{8}$ in. and 1 9/16 in. diameter tubes on No. 1 and on No. 8, the 8-footers. After that, $1\frac{1}{4}$ in. appears to have been standardised for at least ten years, though the number of tubes varied.

It is difficult indeed to see why there should have been such variants, in the same nominal size of boiler barrel, as 162, 163, 169, 170, 172, 173, 174, 175, 183, 184, 187 and 194 tubes, in all cases $1\frac{3}{4}$ in.

in diameter; but so in fact it was. Then in 1884-85 two classes were built new with boilers having $1\frac{5}{8}$ in. diameter tubes, 186 in number in both cases. These were the 0—4—4 suburban tank engines with 4 ft. $2\frac{1}{2}$ in. diameter barrels and the two intermediate 7 ft. 6 in. engines, Nos. 238 and 232, with 4 ft. 2 in. diameter barrels. But when a further batch of 7 ft. 6 in. singles was built from 1886 onwards, though their boilers were also provided with 186 tubes, these were of $1\frac{1}{4}$ in. diameter. Yet the 1892 and 1894 batches of these engines, and the 8-footers from 1888 on, all had 174 tubes $1\frac{3}{4}$ in. diameter.

Among the several gaps in our detailed knowledge of the Stirling era is the lack of certainty regarding working pressures standardised for new boilers at any particular period. No official records are in existence and other sources of evidence are sometimes contradictory. Sturrock had settled for the then extremely high pressure of 150 lb. per sq. in. right from the start of his superintendency in 1850. Stirling seems to have lowered this pressure on his own early designs to 130 lb. per sq. in., but it is possible that some of the smaller engines were

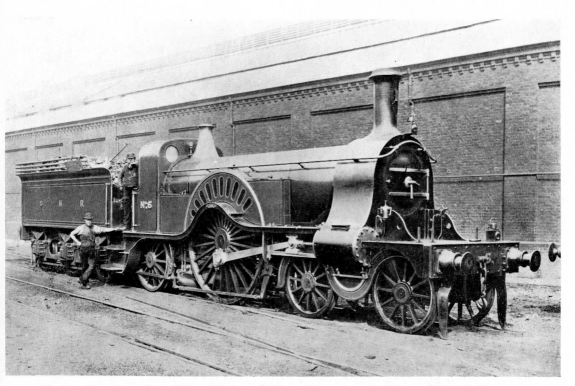

No. 5 at Kings Cross about 1889. Rebuilt by Stirling with new frames and larger diameter boiler—note the flattening of the lagging at the sandbox—yet still carrying her original buffers, as, in fact, she continued to do throughout her life

worked at only 120 lb. per sq. in. No. 1 is stated in Bird's account to have had a working pressure of 140 lb. per sq. in., but according to another authority this was only 130 lb. per sq. in., the same as the other tender engines of that period.

Apparently after a few years there was a general increase to 140 lb. per sq. in., and in 1884 Bird quotes 160 lb. per sq. in. as the working pressure for the No. 771 batch of 8-footers. Yet *The Engineer* in 1888 gives 140 lb. as the official figure for this batch; and Rous-Marten in 1892 also gives 140 lb. as the working pressure of an 8-footer being tried out for speed.

In 1885, the intermediate 7 ft. 6 in. singles, Nos. 238 and 232, are quoted as having a boiler pressure of 150 lb. per sq. in. In 1886 the succeeding batch of 7 ft. 6 in. single-wheelers, starting with No. 234, was stated in *The Engineer* and elsewhere to have had a working pressure of 160 lb. per sq. in. and, from 1887 on, most of the standard classes are said to have been worked at this pressure. Finally, the last six 8-footers, Nos. 1003 to 1008 in 1894-95, are quoted by Bird and Rous-Marten as working at 170 lb. per sq. in. The engine diagrams of the early Ivatt period show the working pressure of these last

engines as 160 lb. per sq. in.; and certainly when the present writer last saw No. 1003, in July 1914, her boiler was working at 160 lb. Unfortunately it cannot now be remembered whether the pressure indication was a red line on the pressure gauge or the tablet on the boiler back plate. There are indications from the Ivatt engine diagrams that all the surviving 8-footers were regarded as being in one category and it is by far the most likely surmise that Nos. 1003 to 1008 had had their 170 lb. reduced to 160 under the Ivatt classification.

The general picture over the almost thirty years of Stirling's superintendency is that the working pressure for new boilers was gradually raised from 130 lb. per sq. in. to 160 lb. and possibly 170 lb. per sq. in. However, there were boilers in service on the older engines, especially the 8-footers, set to blow off at lower pressures than that of new boilers. Probably it was not until 1892 at the earliest that all the single-wheelers had received boilers working at 160 lb.

A rough guide might be to regard 130 lb. per sq. in. as the standard pressure from 1866 to 1874, 140 lb. thenceforward to 1880, 150 lb. from 1880 to 1885, and 160 lb. from 1886 onwards, with the

No. 47, about 1900. Her original crosshead has been replaced by a new one of the later (1881) design

last six 8-footers forming the beginning of the next step forward, at 170 lb.

Although there were a few instances of copper tubes being specified, in his boilers Stirling nearly always used solid drawn brass tubes, ferruled at the firebox end and expanded into the smokebox tube plate, and his inner fireboxes were all copper, with tube plates, from 1870 on, $\frac{3}{4}$ in. thick all over and wrapper plates $\frac{1}{2}$ in. thick. His first three designs, including the 7 ft. singles, had the tube plates $\frac{7}{8}$ in. thick over the tube area, swaged down to $\frac{1}{2}$ in. over the stayed area. From about 1890 on, copper side and crown plates were made 9/16 in. thick instead of $\frac{1}{2}$ in.

At first, the firehole plate of the inner firebox was dished outwards to enable a thinner firehole ring to be used, though at the expense of a local reduction in the water leg at this point. In this Stirling followed Sturrock's practice, but it was not long before he standardised on 3 in. water legs with flat firehole plates in both inner and outer fireboxes; adhering to this design of maximum simplicity ever afterwards.

His standard design of firehole door swung open horizontally on a vertical hinge on its right (except on his earliest engines, where the hinge was on the left) and carried a flap, or 'throttle valve' as it was described in specifications, controllable by a notched sector and latch, forming an additional deflector plate. This design remained standard right through to the end of the Great Northern as a separate railway, and even after that.

His regulator was of the pull-out type with a horizontal handle which was extended past its fulcrum across the boiler back plate to the fireman's side. If it was stiff to operate, then the fireman could 'give a pound', pushing to assist in opening the regulator and pulling to close it, the reverse of the driver's action. On the driver's side of the handle there was a bolt with thumb-nut which slid in a curved slot on a small bracket attached to the back plate pad. This could be used as a clamp to secure the regulator in any desired position, an idea which would strike any modern 'backroom boy' with horror; quite the opposite idea to the deadman's handle, or pedal, which seems to be the present-day ideal, even when there are two men in the cab.

The regulator was a simple slide-valve, with no pilot valve to make it easier to operate. With the low working pressure and the large leverage available, to say nothing of the convenient and powerful push and pull method of operation, graduation of the regulator opening was normally as fine as could be wished. The regulator valve itself was located in the smokebox and, in a Stirling boiler, steam was always collected through a large number of $\frac{5}{8}$ in. diameter holes in the upper surface of a pipe— 4 in. to $5\frac{1}{2}$ in. inside diameter, depending upon the class of boiler—extending from the firebox back plate to the smokebox tubeplate; through this pipe the rod operating the regulator valve passed. In Sturrock's apparently domeless boilers the method

No. 94 on Lord Salisbury's daily special train to Hatfield, passing Oakleigh Park, 1900

of steam collection had been to provide a shallow dome over the firebox below the safety valves and six small, vertical, open-ended pipes led up into this from the large longitudinal pipe, through which the regulator rod passed to the regulator valve in the smokebox; almost a dome, but without the appearance of one.

Most of Stirling's grates—and all those on the single-wheelers—sloped gently forward to the front and the ashpans were provided with a front damper only.

The middle ring of the boiler barrel was always provided at its lower side with a mud-drum or mud-collector—an inverted dome—closed at its base, with a manhole cover for inspection and for removing mud and loose scale. In the early 1880s, when Stirling's already neat external designs were still further cleaned up, the delivery from the injectors, which had previously been piped to external clackboxes on the horizontal centreline of the front ring of the boiler barrel, was instead piped into the sides of this drum. After about seven years in this position the clackboxes were removed to the boiler back plate in the cab and the feed water was conducted to the front end of the boiler barrel through pipes inside the barrel. This layout applied only to the 8-footers and the 7 ft. 6 in. singles and not, in Stirling's day, to the 7 ft. singles; although, roughly speaking, most of Stirling's new boilers subsequent to about 1887 had the clacks on the boiler back plate and not on the barrel. The principal exceptions were boilers for engines fitted with condensing apparatus and crosshead-driven pumps; these were provided with special clackboxes on the sides of the barrel, incorporating petcocks to persuade the pumps to start delivery by the preventing of air-locks.

A small yet ingenious detail was that the whistle base, screwed into the firebox wrapper plate, not only supplied steam to the whistle but also provided the connection to the boiler pressure gauge.

All Stirling's smokeboxes were provided with liners, separated by about an inch of air from the wrapper plates, and preserving these from corrosion by the smokebox gases. The liner was far more readily renewable than the riveted-up smokebox plates—in those days, at any rate. More recently it has been an easy and often an unsightly matter to weld in a new section of plate. The smokeboxes of the 8-footers were somewhat elaborate in construction, with the wrapper plate giving the appearance of being continuous and enveloping both cylinders, although actually there were butt joints on the boiler centreline. When removing the boiler for repairs it was easier to leave the whole smokebox *in situ* on the frames, cutting out the rivets in the angle-iron that attached the front tube plate to the smokebox.

Originally Stirling used the two spring balance safety valves standardised earlier by Sturrock. The valves themselves were large, but could easily be tampered with by foolhardy enginemen. In 1875 he began to change to Ramsbottom duplex safety valves, and these were so satisfactory that they were continued throughout the Stirling and Ivatt periods into the early days of the Gresley *régime*. Both types of safety valve were housed in similar polished brass casings, but the Ramsbottom valve needed a large casing, and the single 'cowtail' was curved, whereas the levers of the spring balance

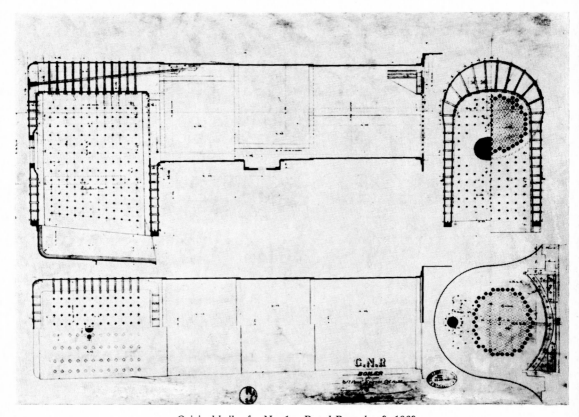

Original boiler for No. 1. Dated December 9, 1869

valves were straight and horizontal, diverging slightly right and left towards the rear, with the whistle mounted between them. When Ramsbottom valves were adopted the whistle was moved a few inches to the right, the driver's side.

The smokebox door design remained almost unchanged throughout, though its diameter varied with different boilers from 3 ft. 4 in. to 3 ft. 9 in. It fitted flush with the smokebox front plate and was bedded on an angle-iron ring inside the smokebox, this ring being of slightly smaller diameter than the door and the door opening in the smokebox plate. The outside diameter of the door was turned on a 45° bevel, this fitting into a similar chamfered recess in the smokebox front plate. There was sufficient spring due to the relatively small dishing of the door to permit it to bed satisfactorily in its recess and on the angle-iron of the smokebox opening, even if heat had warped the latter slightly. In fact, red hot smokebox doors were rare on Stirling engines; less frequent certainly than with the Ivatt single-dished door which superseded the Stirling

design. This does not necessarily mean that the later door was of a poorer design. In Stirling days there were no spark arresters and the smokeboxes were more or less 'self cleaning', practically all the cinders passing through the tubes into the smokebox being ejected—while still incandescent—through the chimney. In Ivatt days, spark arresters were fitted and smokeboxes quickly became partially filled with half-burned cinders which needed only the smallest ingress of air to start burning afresh, so almost inevitably leading to the warping of the smokebox front plate. Even the mere presence of warm cinders up against a flat plate, stiffened at its edges as the smokebox front plate is, can give rise, temporarily at any rate, to some distortion of the plate.

The design and dimensions of the Stirling smokebox door hinges were again settled once and for all, but for the first few years the straps on the hinges were carried across to the far edge of the smokebox door; the neater design with the ends of the strap radiused, and terminating some three inches short

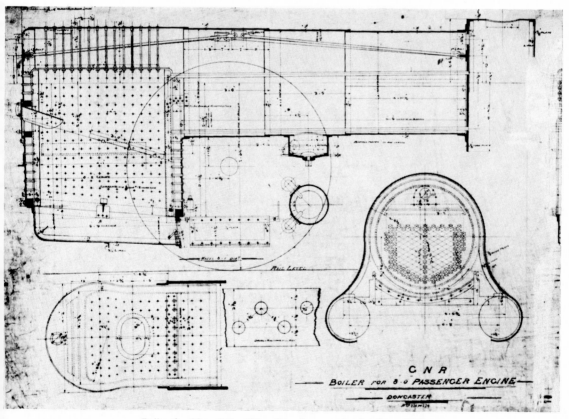

Boiler for Nos. 771—774. Drawing not dated: about 1884

of the edge of the door, did not appear until about 1872.

A further example of the degree to which neatness of external surfaces was carried was the use of the handrails along the side of the boiler to carry the blower pipe from the cab to the smokebox. On the early engines this was on the right; then in the 1880s the adoption of combination ejectors for the automatic vacuum brake, located on the boiler back plate on the driver's side, made it rather more convenient to pipe the blower connection through the left handrail. Finally, when a lubricator was put in the cab on the fireman's side to feed oil to slide valves and pistons, the blower reverted to the right handrail and the oil feed-pipe occupied the inside of the left handrail.

Two last points remain to be noticed. For his earliest boilers Stirling had followed Sturrock in staying the front tube plate to the boiler barrel by plate gusset stays, and using short tie-rods at an angle to stay the firebox back plate to the rear of the barrel. No. 1's original boiler was stayed in this way.

But after a few years he adopted the method of staying both the smokebox tube plate and the firebox back plate by long tie-rods, or longitudinal stays, approximately half the length overall of the boiler, passing through the steam space and pin-jointed to tee-section brackets riveted to the water-side of the smokebox tube plate, firebox back plate and boiler barrel. The horizontal tee-bracket on the

No. 662 at Boston, 1899. Her original wrought iron driving wheels have been replaced by cast steel

inside of the barrel served as the anchorage for both the front and rear stays. This method of tying the end plates of the boiler to the middle remained standard Doncaster practice to the end of boiler construction at the works; only such details differed as the actual number of stays employed and the number and position of the middle brackets. (See the drawings on pages 34 and 35.)

Finally, in addition to the usual hydraulic and steam tests of boilers there was a further, very

No. 874 in original condition, about 1893. The brakepipe has not yet been carried forward to the front buffer beam

36

unusual but practical, test. The plates near all the riveted joints were clouted violently with sledge hammers. If no seam or rivet started to weep under this 'shock treatment' then the boiler would remain tight in service under the normal strains and vibrations of its life on a locomotive.

To sum up, everything in Stirling's practice and career shows him to have been an intensely practical man, empirical in his outlook, but with a strong sense of the fitness of things, and the common sense and wide experience to prevent his ideas and notions from leading him astray.

No. 1004 near Werrington, on Boston train 1911. With Ivatt cast-iron chimney, moulded to simulate the built-up type, and with a smaller Stirling tender than originally provided. The chimney was almost exactly the same length and diameter as the plain cast iron chimney originally drawn out for Nos. 1003—1008, but never fitted

CHAPTER 4

EARLY 2-2-2s:
7 ft. AND 7 ft. 6 in.

THE earliest evidence still in existence that Stirling was taking a hand in Great Northern locomotive design seems to be a drawing dated July 11, 1866, showing the general arrangement of a rebuilding of the two 'Jenny Lind' 2—2—2 engines Nos. 201 and 202, built in 1851 by Messrs. E. B. Wilson. This drawing shows the standard Stirling built-up chimney and hood cab brought unchanged from Kilmarnock, together with a domed boiler with raised firebox of Sturrock-period design. Sketched over this drawing is a later version of the engine with a straightback boiler of slightly larger proportions and the cab altered to the later standard Stirling design. The 1866 cab had no step in the side elevation to provide a support for the driver when leaning out of the side of the cab. Contrary to Stirling's usual practice at the time, probably because the cab was rather shorter than usual, no side windows were provided. In their final 'straight-back' form, the two engines looked like miniature

No. 14, 7 ft. single, as built. Photograph probably taken August 24, 1868, the day she was 'out of works, new'. With no brakes and with side-window cab

versions of the 7 ft. singles which were Stirling's first design of express passenger engine for the Great Northern. These two rebuilds are dealt with in detail in a later chapter.

But it would be wrong to regard the rebuilt 'Jenny Linds' as true prototypes of the 7 ft. singles. In his early days on the Great Northern, Stirling, as has been pointed out, was clearly concerned with building engines equivalent to the best existing Sturrock engines in general design and proportions but less costly than their Sturrock equivalents, due to the simplicity and consequent cheapness of their boilers and chassis. (The Stirling 0—4—2 well-tanks, the 0—6—0 goods engines and the 2—4—0s are all examples of this.)

So it was that the No. 6 class of Stirling 7 ft. singles had as its basis the Sturrock No. 229 class of 7 ft. singles. But their very expensive boiler with its elaborate raised firebox with water midfeather was replaced by a boiler of the most straightforward design and simplest construction. A two-bearing crank axle was substituted for the Sturrock four-bearing one which had always been costly to machine and fit. Stirling needed the outside bearings for his carrying wheels to ensure a steady-riding engine on the inferior Great Northern track. These outside bearings also solved other problems in connection with placing the leading wheels well forward—again improving the riding of the locomotive as a vehicle—and the springing of the trailing wheels. So that the Stirling 7 ft. singles of 1868, though looking rather like much enlarged 'Jenny Linds', had in fact a different line of descent.

The same cylinders, boilers and motion were used as on the No. 280 class 2—4—0s. These were also used on the No. 474 class 0—6—0s and No. 18 class 0—4—2s with, however, slightly altered smokebox connections on the cylinders and 2 in. shorter boiler barrels, so that already an appreciable

No. 6, the first 7 ft. single, photograph taken about 1877. Fitted with non-automatic vacuum brake and duplex ejector. Still carrying her original side-window cab

degree of standardisation had been set up for new Great Northern engines.

The first engine of the class, No. 6, was completed at Doncaster on March 26, 1868, being the fourth new engine built there—the first three, o—4—2 mixed traffic engines, having been turned out on January 3, February 12 and 17, 1868 respectively.

In all, twelve engines of the class were built between March 1868 and June 1870, each one taking the number of an old engine as this was withdrawn; so that the few Doncaster records still remaining today show them as 'Rebuilt: boiler new', whereas, in fact, they were all completely new engines using nothing whatever of their predecessors. But they were charged to current account and not to capital, a standard subterfuge in Stirling

days. The first six engines originally had the side-window cab of Stirling's earliest design, but the seventh engine, No. 55, which was turned out in May 1869, had the later standard cab when new; and as the older engines came in for general repairs their cabs were brought into line with the later ones. The first six engines were built as a single batch, but the remaining six were built in pairs, a system which had become standard practice at Doncaster and was to persist for over 20 years.

As built, all had 4 ft. $0\frac{1}{2}$ in. diameter boilers, two spring balance safety valves and chimneys built up in three pieces; Stirling's Great Northern standard features of those days. Their driving-wheel splashers were slotted with seven openings in fan shape. They were fitted with Alex. Friedmann's injectors, which were later replaced by Gresham and Craven's.

No. 4, 7 ft. single at Peterborough about 1896. 'Modernised' by Stirling, but still carrying the external brake ejector originally provided for the non-automatic vacuum brake

The boilers on the earlier 7 ft. singles were originally provided with 206 tubes of $1\frac{3}{4}$ in. diameter, but on the later engines the number was reduced to 192 of the same diameter. On one engine only the experiment was made of reducing the diameter of the 192 tubes to 1 9/16 in. Stirling stated that he had found this boiler 'quite as efficient' as the others, and that he was now—in October 1868—making a number of boilers with 1 9/16 in. diameter tubes. He further emphasised the financial saving to be achieved: that a set of 192 brass tubes $1\frac{3}{4}$ in. outside diameter cost £127 14s. 8d., but that the set of 1 9/16 in. tubes cost only £92 3s. 8d., the smaller tubes being, moreover, one wire-gauge thinner than the larger ones. Finally, that the smaller tubes did not pass so much unconsumed fuel as those of large diameter, and smokeboxes did not have to be emptied so often.

Stirling certainly pursued this small-tube notion quite persistently, for in February 1871 he was quoted as using $1\frac{3}{8}$ in. outside diameter for tubes up to 10 ft. 6 in. length, but that he was retaining 1 9/16 in. diameter on longer tubes. It was even said that line-side fires started by sparks had been much reduced! This was indeed going a bit too far, since only a very small proportion of boilers in service was equipped with the small tubes.

It is at any rate certain that the blast pipe nozzles of the locomotives fitted with the small tubes were reduced from the standard $4\frac{3}{8}$ in. diameter to $4\frac{1}{4}$ in., and, though Stirling expressed the view that the engines would maintain a sufficient supply of steam with the $4\frac{3}{8}$ in. nozzle, yet the $4\frac{1}{4}$ in. nozzles were retained. The consequent increase in back pressure when working hard, or at high speeds, must have affected the free running of the engines, and it may even have provided the basis of a reported remark of Stirling's in 1871 that he had given the 8 ft. singles larger cylinders because the 7 ft. singles had been found somewhat deficient in cylinder power. This experiment with small diameter tubes had

No. 21, 7 ft. single, rebuilt with domed boiler by Ivatt, at Kings Cross about 1898. An engine which, perhaps because of its 'perky' appearance, always seemed to be going well. No photographs are known of Nos. 21, 41 and 61 before rebuilding with domed boilers

further unfortunate side effects outside the class for it led to No. 1, the first 8-footer, being provided with only 175 tubes of $1\frac{5}{8}$ in. diameter and on No. 8, the second 8-footer, the diameter was further reduced to 1 9/16 in., though the number of tubes was increased to 217. But, after a few years, $1\frac{3}{4}$ in. became the standard tube diameter, except in one or two cases, and the number of tubes levelled out finally at 174.

The following table shows the brief history of these engines and their boilers.

No. 37, 7 ft. single, about 1894-5

Engine No.	Doncaster Works No.	First Boiler		Second Boiler		Third Boiler		Broken up	Remarks
		New	Mileage	New	Mileage	New	Mileage		
No. 4	8	24- 6-68	485,512	20- 3-82	418,707	15-10-94	—	19- 6-06	
No. 6	4	26- 3-68	358,840	27- 5-80	420,160	10- 5-94	—	10- 5-04	
14	11	24- 8-68	478,573	5- 4-82	486,831	18-12-99	—	27- 7-04	(a)
21	9	6- 7-68	539,114	8- 6-83	495,094	14-10-97	—	9-11-06	
37	48	8- 6-70	585,607	18- 4-88	—	—	—	10- 7-05	
39	51	30- 6-70	422,162	13-12-84	374,451	27- 5-97	—	19- 6-06	
41	6	27- 5-68	472,763	4- 9-82	383,376	23- 3-98	—	3- 4-07	
55	26	17- 5-69	—	27-12-83	—	17-10-98	—	3- 7-06	(b)
61	27	22- 6-69	—	6- 3-83	—	21- 4-98	—	22-11-07	
63	32	17- 8-69	—	30- 6-84	—	13- 4-97	—	15-10-07	
215	34	7-10-69	—	13- 2-84	—	5- 2-96	—	15-10-07	(c)
222	5	30- 4-68	—	4- 8-79	—	25- 5-93	—	9- 1-06	

Notes: The second boilers were 4ft. $2\frac{1}{2}$in. diameter except that on No. 222 which was 4ft. $0\frac{1}{2}$in. The third boilers were also 4ft. $2\frac{1}{2}$in. diameter except those on Nos. 21, 41 and 61 which were domed 4ft. 5in. diameter.
  (a) A fourth boiler, 4ft. $2\frac{1}{2}$in. diameter ex No. 55, was fitted 17-10-03 to No. 14.
  (b) A fourth boiler, domed 4ft. 5in. diameter, was fitted 1-8-03 to No. 55.
  (c) A fourth boiler, 4ft. $2\frac{1}{2}$in. diameter ex 2-4-0 No. 88, was fitted 30-10-03 to No. 215.

Unfortunately, Doncaster records only show mileage figures for seven out of the twelve original boilers on the class, though no doubt the mileages achieved by the boilers on the other five engines were proportional to their length of life. It was said that No. 222 was the first engine fitted with the 1 9/16 in. diameter tubes, though this cannot now be verified. But this engine was involved in an accident at the beginning of November 1869, and was damaged sufficiently seriously for a general repair to prove necessary. Possibly the shorter life of this particular boiler was in some measure attributable to this accident. With this exception the boilers of the class certainly show an excellent life. There is no doubt that this was a triumphant proof of Stirling's contention that his boilers were not only cheap to construct but were long lived.

These engines had no brakes at all when new. This practice was quite normal at the time, the tender handbrake being regarded as all that was necessary. But during the 1870s the importance of continuous braking throughout passenger trains was beginning to be generally realised. In 1875 a series of trials was held at Newark, under the auspices of the Board of Trade, to investigate the several systems of continuous braking then being developed. In this year the Great Northern Railway fitted one of the 7 ft. singles, No. 55, with the ejector and other equipment of the Smith's vacuum brake. No. 55 took part in the Newark trials and as a result the Smith's simple vacuum brake became the Great Northern standard. This brake suffered from the fatal defect that, although it was continuous throughout the train, the 'vacuum'—the difference in pressure between the atmosphere and the inside of the train pipe and cylinders which actually applied the brakes—had to be generated afresh for every application. A relatively small leak from the atmosphere into the train pipe, perhaps at one of the flexible couplings between coaches, or a fall in steam pressure on the engine, could result in an adequate degree of vacuum not being obtained and thus cause a partial failure of the brake. In addition, a breakaway between two coaches would cause both halves of the train to be unbraked—except for the handbrakes on the tender and in the guard's van.

EXPRESS PASSENGER LOCOMOTIVE; GREAT NORTHERN RAILWAY

CONSTRUCTED FROM THE DESIGNS OF MR. PATRICK STIRLING, LOCOMOTIVE SUPERINTENDENT.

(*For Description, see the opposite Page.*)

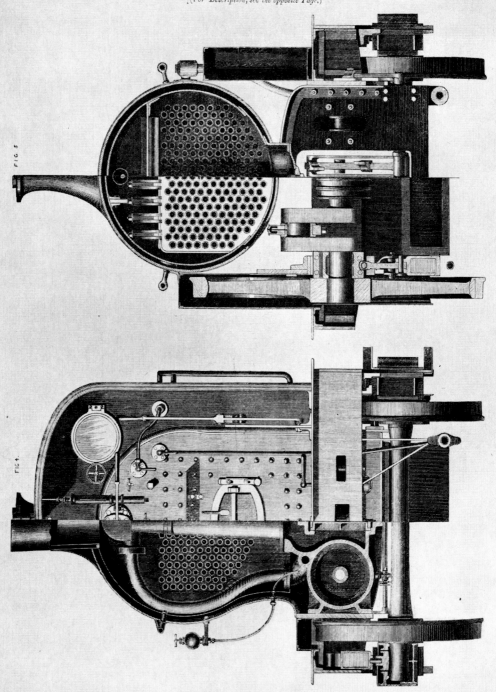

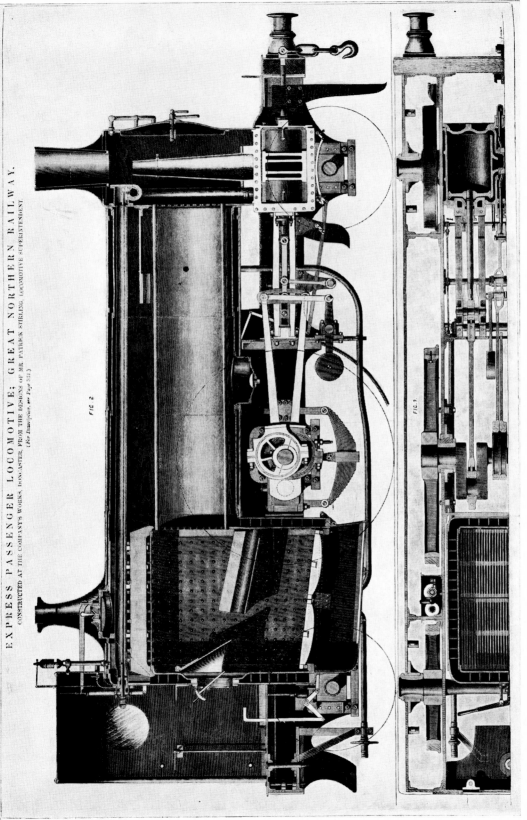

EXPRESS PASSENGER LOCOMOTIVE; GREAT NORTHERN RAILWAY.

CONSTRUCTED AT THE COMPANY'S WORKS, DONCASTER, FROM THE DESIGNS OF MR PATRICK STIRLING, LOCOMOTIVE SUPERINTENDENT

(For Description see Page 355.)

FIG 2

FIG 3

General arrangement sectional drawings of the 7 ft. singles as built in 1868. All the standard Stirling details are embodied: the intermediate slide valve spindle supported by a link, the first type of connecting rod big end, the cotter adjustable small end, the firehole deflector-plate slung completely inside the firebox, the girder roof stays, the gusset type of longitudinal boiler stays and the very high blast pipe

Yet, in spite of this glaring potential danger, all Great Northern passenger stock, carriages and locomotives, was equipped with the simple vacuum brake between 1876 and 1881. But it was not long after this that a series of accidents on other railways and the mounting pressure of public opinion forced the Great Northern to take the next step forward into safety, and equip all passenger locomotives and carriages with the automatic vacuum brake between 1884 and 1889. In most cases the old large ejectors remained *in situ* on the engines.

To come back to the 7 ft. singles, they, like all the engines built before 1881, were brought into line as nearly as possible with the current practice in the early 1880s. Splasher slots were closed by backing plates, painted and lined out, the newer and slightly larger boilers with higher working pressure were fitted, and towards the end of the decade cast-iron chimneys began to supersede the built-up type. Automatic vacuum brakes were fitted on all engines of this class but the ugly external ejectors used for the simple vacuum brakes of the 1870s were retained. This was a practice which remained true until the end of Stirling's superintendency on most of the engines built before 1884.

On engines with small leading wheels the ejectors were left in the same position above the running plate, at the right-hand side of the smokebox. On six-coupled and front-coupled engines the ejectors were placed out of sight below the running plate ahead of the smokebox; the copper steam pipe and the brass exhaust-pipe bend at the front of the smokebox being the only excrescences visible. Some of the early ejectors were duplex, that is, there were two similar ejectors side by side, with the object of obtaining a braking vacuum more rapidly on the non-automatic brake than could be achieved by one

ejector. The duplex ejectors, with their heavy steam consumption, disappeared when the automatic brake superseded the simple type, between 1884 and 1889.

Ivatt must have thought that there was still work which these engines could tackle efficiently, for four of the class were rebuilt by him with his standard 4 ft. 5 in. diameter domed boilers and given new cabs and plain driving splashers. The front sand-boxes were removed from above the running plate ahead of the splashers to below the running plate, as on all Stirling inside-cylinder engines with single leading wheels in Ivatt's day. The leading and trailing springs were brought above the running plate and longer springs than Stirling's were provided for both. The pitch of the boiler had to be raised to 7 ft. 11 in. to clear the large driving wheels and this gave a very compact, almost dumpy, appearance to these relatively short engines. The first three engines so rebuilt were Nos. 21, 41 and 61, in October 1897, March 1898 and April 1898 respectively. No. 55, the last to be fitted, received her domed boiler in August 1903, although actually 'to traffic' in the following month. A chimney of the type provided for Ivatt's eight-coupled goods engines was fitted, above which the dome positively towered.

It is an interesting commentary on the continuing usefulness of these elderly 7 ft. singles on secondary lines that no fewer than 25 of the 53 8-footers had been broken up before any of the 7 ft. singles were condemned. No. 6, the first to be built, was also the first to go; in May 1904, after a life of just over 36 years.

No. 215 received a second-hand straightback boiler in October 1903, but is then said to have been stowed away at the back of Colwick shed and to have hardly turned a wheel until she was withdrawn in October 1907. In the meantime she had been stripped of everything which could be used on other engines and eventually had to be towed to Doncaster for scrapping, no longer possessing the parts to enable her to move herself. Nos. 63 and 215 were withdrawn for breaking up under the same circular notice, dated October 15, 1907. No. 61, the last survivor of the class, followed them a month later. They had certainly well earned their cost and maintenance.

Some examples of the day-to-day running of these engines were fortunately logged by Messrs E. L. Ahrons and J. F. Vickery and the first tabulated here concerns engine No. 55, while still in 'Stirling' condition, hauling a heavy load of 180 tons. It is true that the road is favourable from Peascliffe Tunnel down to Newark and level across the Trent

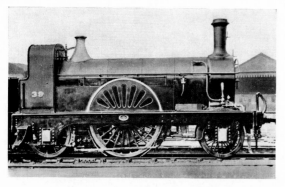

No. 39, 7 ft. single, about 1892. 'Modernised' by Stirling, but still retaining her original buffers

No. 41, 7 ft. single rebuilt by Ivatt. Photograph dated about 1902. Note that new driving splashers without slots have been provided

Valley; but the little engine climbed the bank from Crow Park up to Markham Box in excellent style:

G.N.R. GRANTHAM—RETFORD

Load: 180 tons tare, approx. 200 tons full
Engine: Stirling 7ft. 2-2-2 No. 55

Dist. Miles		Actual m. s.	Av. Speed m.p.h.
0·0	GRANTHAM .	0 00	—
1·5	*Milepost* 107	4 00	—
4·2	Barkston . .	7 29	46·5
6·0	Hougham . .	9 18	59·3
9·9	Claypole . .	12 59	63·5*
14·6	NEWARK .	17 26	63·3
17·5	*Milepost* 123	20 22	59·5
21·9	Crow Park .	24 57	57·6
26·4	Tuxford . .	30 40	47·3
28·2	Markham Box .	33 08	43·8†
31·5	*Milepost* 137 .	36 58	51·7‡
		sigs.	
33·1	RETFORD . .	40 32	—

* max. speed before Claypole 64·3 m.p.h.
† min. speed 41·5 m.p.h.
‡ max. speed before Retford 58 m.p.h.
Schedule time 42 min.
Net time 39 min.

Ahrons logged the passing times at every milepost on this run, and his figures show that the engine dropped speed from 62 m.p.h. through Newark station to no lower than a steady 58 m.p.h. on the level across the Trent Valley. The bank from Crow Park northward includes a mile at 1 in 300, and then 2½ miles continuously at 1 in 200 almost to Tuxford station, with easier gradients up to the summit at Markham Box. For an engine with 17½ in. by 24 in. cylinders, and a boiler pressure of 140 lb. per sq. in., this was an extraordinarily fine performance.

In the year 1905 J. F. Vickery logged a run with No. 21 of the same class, but after the engine had been rebuilt by Ivatt with a domed boiler carrying 170 lb. pressure. Nevertheless, as the accompanying log shows, a load of more than 300 tons was a tremendous proposition, especially on the uphill section to Potters Bar. The train was booked to clear Potters Bar in 9 min. from Hatfield, 5 miles; and as it had to draw up, on account of its length, it was not surprising that a little time was lost there. But the driver was evidently determined not to lose anything in overall time, and a very fast descent was made to Finsbury Park. Vickery did not record the milepost times, but the maximum speed must have been at least 75 m.p.h. between Wood Green and Hornsey. What a picture the train must have made flying through Wood Green station with its assortment of 17 coaches!

G.N.R. HATFIELD—FINSBURY PARK

Load: 17 vehicles (4 eight-wheeled, 11 six-wheeled, 2 four-wheeled). 282 tons tare, 312 tons full
Engine: 2-2-2 No. 21 (rebuilt with Ivatt domed boiler).

Dist. Miles		Actual m. s.	Av. Speeds m.p.h.
0·0	HATFIELD .	0 00	—
5·0	POTTERS BAR .	10 10	—
2·1	Hadley Wood .	4 02	31·9
3·5	New Barnet .	5 34	55·7
6·2	New Southgate .	8 02	66·2
8·6	Hornsey . .	10 01	71·8
9·2	Harringay . .	10 36	66·8
10·1	FINSBURY PARK	12 04	—

Overall time Hatfield—Finsbury Park 24 min. 34 sec.
Schedule time   ,,   ,,   25 min.

No. 55. The last 7 ft. single rebuilt by Ivatt; about 1904. The chimney top is well below the level of the top of the dome. Apparently a similar chimney to that used on the Ivatt 0-8-0's (Long Toms) has been fitted. The defective paint work on the front ring of the boiler barrel gives the impression that an outside clackbox for the feedwater delivery was located here but, so far as can be traced, this was not the case

THE 7 ft. 6 in. SINGLE—No. 92

The method of building-up a wrought-iron locomotive wheel in the days before steel castings were available was an elaborate one. First, each spoke was forged, tapering in thickness from one end to the other. The thicker end was set-up and then forged into the shape of an arrow-head. The thinner end was sometimes drawn out into a T-shape, the top of the T being curved to form a segment of the rim of the wheel. When all the spokes were assembled there was a complete rim, requiring to be welded between each spoke. Sometimes a bar was bent round to form a complete rim, welded to form a ring, and the thinner end of each spoke was welded to this rim.

The thicker, arrow-head ends fitted together to form the boss. A circular plate below and above—with the wheel lying horizontally—gave the boss the extra thickness usually called for on the drawing and reinforced any slightly unsound welds. The whole boss assembly was raised to welding heat on a smith's hearth, and forge welded under the hammer; in earlier days a drop-hammer, but in later years at Doncaster a steam-hammer, was used. The rim welds were dealt with individually.

To produce such wheels was indeed highly skilled work and each wheel occupied many man-hours of labour. Wheels were therefore expensive items on the earlier locomotives. Carrying wheels lasted well, but frequently driving wheels did not last the life of the engine. With cast-steel wheels it is rare indeed for a locomotive to have needed new wheels:

the reverse process, for a condemned locomotive to bequeath its wheels to a successor, has not been uncommon in recent years, and this was also the case in regard to Sturrock's famous 7 ft. 6 in. single No. 215. When, in the autumn of 1869, No. 215 was condemned, her driving wheels were considered too good to scrap. But No. 215 was the only engine in existence on the Great Northern Railway with 7 ft. 6 in. diameter wheels, so that there was no direct inheritor for them.

It must be admitted that it was an odd step for Stirling to take, to design and build a new locomotive purely and simply to use up those wheels. It would not have been out of place to have used them in one of the last two engines of the batch of twelve single-wheelers which constituted his first express passenger engine design, although the first ten engines, already built, had 7 ft. wheels. At any rate, it would have been possible to utilise almost everything already in preparation for one of the remaining two 7 ft. engines, except the wheels.

But Stirling decided otherwise, and prepared drawings of an engine to take No. 215's wheels, which differed in all main dimensions from the twelve 7 ft. singles. The number 92 was allotted to the engine before completion—but what a pity that she could not have been allowed to carry the number 215 as a direct memento of the Sturrock engine!

No. 92, as built, had special frames and motion, and a special boiler all to herself. The barrel was 4 in. longer and the inner firebox 6 in. deeper from crown to foundation ring than on the 7 ft. engines. The wheelbase was increased by 6 in., 3 in. more between leading and driving, and 3 in. more between driving and trailing wheels, so that connecting rods and eccentric rods were also non-standard.

No. 61, 7-ft. single, rebuilt by Ivatt, at Peterborough about 1900. The last engine of the class to survive

Stirling 7ft. single No. 215, taken at Doncaster at the end of March, 1884,
after the engine had been fitted with the 4ft. 2½in. diameter
boiler and the splasher slots filled in

But in Stirling's day there was little attempt to standardise on lengths of connecting rods, although such items as crank axles, axle boxes, big-ends and brasses were kept to the minimum. There were, in fact, connecting rods of eight different lengths in use on his inside-cylinder engines.

No. 92's big-ends were the same as those on the 7 ft. singles, the early design with the open-ended strap forged in one piece with the rod, generally similar in appearance to the 8-footer big ends, except for the cotter being ahead of the crank pin. This design was dropped in favour of the conventional strap type, in which the strap is a separate piece bolted to the solid large end of the connecting rod. This latter design has the great advantage of projecting rearward the minimum distance behind the crank pin, the bolts and the cotter for 'taking-up' the big-end brasses all being ahead of the crank pin, thus enabling the longest possible firebox to be used for any given distance between axles. Stirling began to use it when he increased the stroke of his inside cylinders from 24 in. to 26 in., and was able to retain approximately the previous distance between the firebox throat plate and the centre of the crank axle—though this dimension varied slightly from class to class.

The cylinders of No. 92 were bored out new to 17½ in. diameter, whilst the No. 6 class had 17 in. cylinders; but the distances between centres of cylinders and between port faces remained the same, so that the only apparent alterations needed were a slight change in the steam and exhaust ports and possibly different cylinder covers. Both these are surmises only; the general arrangement drawings seem to show exactly the same design of cylinder, merely bored out larger for No. 92.

Still, it is not in character to think of Stirling sacrificing several years of cylinder life for the want of a relatively small amount of corebox making.

Moreover, when any of the 7 ft. engines required new cylinders, these were made 17½ in. diameter. We shall see that, 20 years later, on his enlarged 7 ft. 6 in. singles Stirling started off with larger cylinders, 18½ in. diameter, but replaced them, when worn out, with 18 in. cylinders.

No. 92 was completed in June 1870, only a couple of months after No. 1, although No. 92 carried a Doncaster works number, 49, one lower than the 8-footer.

It is an interesting cross reference to the 'teething troubles' of No. 1 that, just a month after she had been put into service, the drawings of No. 92, her construction not yet completed, were altered to show a much lower blast pipe orifice level, in accordance with the alterations carried out on No. 1's blast pipe and noted on that engine's general arrangement drawing. Evidently the 8-footer had been in trouble due to bad steaming from the very outset.

There can be no doubt that No. 92 was a thoroughly successful engine. Thirty years after her construction, she was still being referred to as 'the swiftest engine that ever ran on Great Northern metals'—and this was only two years before she was broken up, and 14 years after another and more powerful class of 7 ft. 6 in. singles had been constructed.

The steam and exhaust ports in her cylinders were fairly generously proportioned in relation to the cylinder volume; and the large driving wheel, with its slow rate of revolution even at high speeds, provided just the right conditions for free running, at any rate with the light trains of the '70s and '80s of the last century.

It is interesting to note, in regard to No. 92's free running characteristics, that theoretically also she might have been expected to be very good. Apart from the 7 ft. engines with their original 17 in. cylinders which were then working at only 130 lb. per sq. in. steam pressure the ratio of port size to cylinder volume on No. 92 was equalled only by those engines of the enlarged 7 ft. 6 in. class which happened to be fitted with the 18 in. x 26 in. cylinders with the larger ports designed for the $18\frac{1}{2}$ in. x 26 in. cylinders. The 8-footers come off very unfavourably in comparison, even taking into account the larger diameter of the driving wheels; and the last batch of 8-footers, Nos. 1003 to 1008, was the worst of all in this respect, though their higher working pressure undoubtedly in practice improved the flow of steam *into* the cylinders.

It is all the more regrettable that there does not appear to be any record of a run behind No. 92, let alone any information about the maximum speed she achieved.

The working pressure of her original boiler is given as 130 lb. per sq. in. There is no existing record of any reboilering of No. 92 before 1894; but 24 years is an unheard-of length of life for a Stirling express passenger engine boiler. No. 92 was a Peterborough engine, and engines stationed there and at Kings Cross in the Stirling period did not always go to Doncaster for their general repairs.

No. 92, 7 ft. 6 in. single at Kings Cross about 1898. She has been fitted with the larger diameter Stirling boiler, necessarily higher pitched to clear the connecting rod big ends on top centres, so that the cab windows, still in their original position, lie very close to the boiler barrel

These were frequently undertaken in the workshops attached to the running shed, and there are instances on record of cylinders and even boilers being fitted new at one or other of these two sheds. Perhaps the fact that they were the sheds at the greatest distances from Doncaster may have had an influence on the quite considerable degree of autonomy they enjoyed, until Ivatt terminated it in 1901.

It is practically certain that No. 92 had a new boiler some time between 1880 and 1884, probably in early 1883. This would have been a 4 ft. 2 in. diameter boiler: the working pressure would have depended on the exact year in which it was fitted. The most likely figure would be 150 lb. per sq. in. for the boiler fitted in the '80s. The 1894 boiler would have been almost certainly pressed to 160 lb. per sq. in. This last boiler long outlived the engine and was in use for many years subsequently as a stationary boiler at Essex Street, Bradford.

As first built, the slots in the driving splashers were open, but they were closed in by backing plates soon after 1880. The closed-in slots were painted the dark shade of green used for tender panel surrounds, and lined out with a black edging and a fine white line. In the early '90s the lining-out of the slots was discontinued and the whole splasher painted the standard light green.

No. 92's cab footsteps were, originally, graceful but meagre, and, as was done on nearly all engines with similar steps, they were filled in after a few years by a plate between the step and the trailing wheel hornplates. No doubt this was done to obviate any risk of an engineman's foot slipping from the step and getting trapped in the trailing wheel spokes.

A curious additional link between Sturrock's No. 215 and Stirling's No. 92 is that No. 215's regular fireman became No. 92's regular driver in later years. The only known photograph of No. 215 was in the possession of this man, Driver Peary, who lived to over 90 years of age. The fresh air on No. 215's footplate, protected only by the sketchiest of weather-boards, evidently did him no permanent harm.

No. 215's driving wheels did not in fact last throughout No. 92's lifetime. A drawing, for a new pair of driving wheels for No. 92, was made in December 1882, and the new wheels to this drawing were the ones by which she was propelled during the last 20 years or so of her existence. An interesting point arising out of this comparatively early scrapping of No. 215's wheels is that an engine built solely in order to use up these costly wheels remained in existence after those wheels were scrapped and a second pair of costly wheels had had to be made for her. It raises also a query of whether the building, two years later, of the 7 ft. 6 in. singles Nos. 238 and 232 may not have been suggested to Stirling's mind by the desirability of keeping No. 92 in service, and the necessity of drawing and manufacturing her new wheels. There were, however, other factors to be taken into account concerning the genesis of the 1885 engines, which will be discussed in the chapter dealing with them.

CHAPTER 5

THE FIRST EIGHT-FOOTER—No. 1

By the autumn of 1869 Sturrock's large 4—2—2, No. 215, built in November 1853, had been withdrawn from service and in the October her number had been allotted to a Stirling 7 ft. single. The Sturrock engine had been built in anticipation of a new, fast service to York and the North, which did not materialise; and she remained the solitary specimen of her class, probably the best of the two or three standard gauge locomotives of the period which measured up in dimensions and power with the Broad Gauge 8 ft. singles. The life of the average express locomotive boiler of those days was about 14 years, and cylinders seem to have lasted about the same time, perhaps a little less in some cases, so that fairly evidently No. 215 would have required a very extensive renewal had she not been condemned. As first built, she had the reputation of being a troublesome engine and though no doubt her early defects had been overcome, yet there can have been no incentive to spend a lot of money on a worn-out singleton. More than 55 years later, on the Great Western Railway, *The Great Bear* afforded an almost exact parallel, except that there were enough standard parts in her to justify a drastic conversion and not a condemnation.

But when No. 215 had been scrapped—except for her driving wheels, which were used again in Stirling's No. 92—the G.N.R. was left with a stud of recent express passenger engines of only moderate boiler power and tractive effort and a few engines, somewhat older, with rather more boiler power but no greater tractive effort. These engines were well enough for immediate requirements, but had no margin for the future expected steady increase in traffic. The time was evidently ripe for a new design of express passenger locomotive of increased power. The existing Stirling designs of 7 ft. singles and 6 ft. 6 in. coupled engines, cheap to build and maintain, would take the main share of all except the fastest and heaviest passenger expresses; and four years had now

elapsed since the costly and unsuccessful attempt of Sturrock to get one engine crew to operate two engines, in his No. 400 class goods engines with steam tenders.

In 1868 Stirling had borrowed from the Great Eastern Railway the Sinclair 2—2—2 outside-cylinder 7 ft. single engine, No. 293, and it had run in service in comparison with the Stirling and Sturrock 7 ft. singles. No official reason has ever been given for these trial runs, but it would seem that the riding qualities of a short wheelbase, outside-cylinder engine as compared with inside-cylinder engines of similar size, though of rather longer wheelbase, must have been an important issue. Moreover, Stirling himself had built 2—2—2 outside-cylinder singles (of rather smaller dimensions) for the Glasgow & South Western Railway and no doubt was familiar with any defects of the type in riding qualities; in particular, lateral oscillation due to the fore and aft thrusts of the widely spaced pistons: but the speeds required on the Great Northern line were far above those called for in the 1850s and 1860s on the Glasgow & South Western.

It seems likely that Stirling had had a new and larger design of single-wheeler in his mind as far back as 1868 and that this new design was committed to the use of outside-cylinders; as a result of the 1868 trials the use of a bogie became essential, if the highest speeds were to be attained with safety in regard to the locomotive as a carriage. At any rate, the design of the famous Stirling 8-footer was prepared and the first engine of the class completed in April 1870, with specially selected running and works numbers; the works number, 50, was a couple of months ahead of its due date, Nos. 49 and 51 appearing at the end of June 1870, and 'No. 1' obviously was not a true replacement of the tiny general purpose locomotive, the original 'Sharpie' No. 1 of 1847.

Why did Stirling base his design on such a large

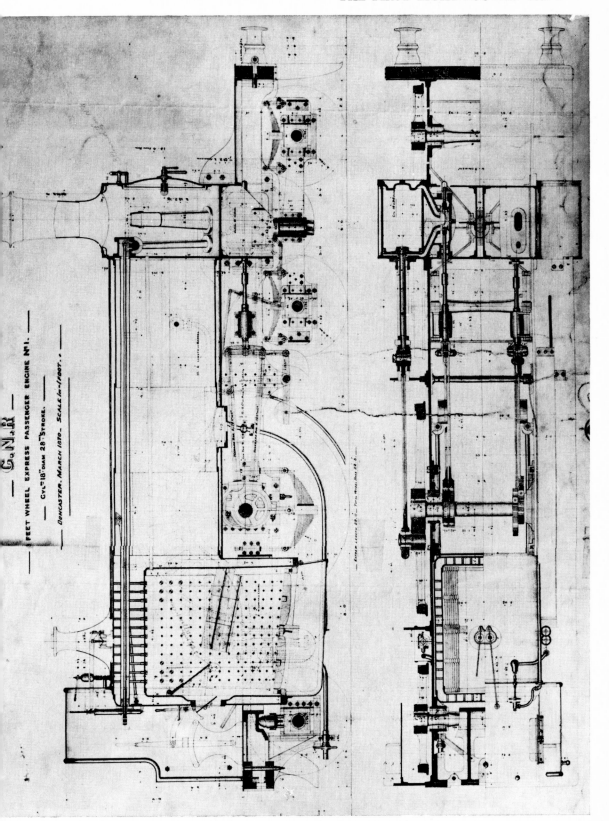

The 1870 General Arrangement drawing of No. 1

diameter of wheel as eight feet? His own reason, that the larger the wheel the better the adhesion to the rail, is a perfectly valid one; even solid friction does increase with the area of contact between surfaces, especially under the intensive loadings which are created by the weight on a curved tyre

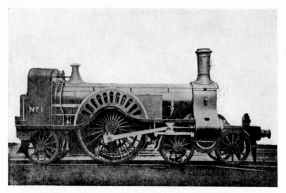

Photo of No. 1 as built in 1870. The original photograph purchased in that year by K.H.L.'s father, is faded almost to nothing, and is extremely dilapidated. This print has been built up by a succession of copy-negatives

surface supported by a flat rail head. But apart from this, the bad effect of high local stress intensity on the rail due to a heavy load on a small diameter wheel has to be taken into account even nowadays; on British Railways the larger the wheel the greater is the axle loading permitted—the P/D rule, where P is the axle loading permitted and D the wheel diameter. Stirling undoubtedly wished to obtain permission for the greatest possible axle loading and the use of a large wheel probably helped him in this. Also, there is evidence that the official and permitted axle loadings of the Stirling single-wheelers were always appreciably less than the actual loadings. Furthermore, after Stirling's death and the two cases of broken rails in 1895-96, Ivatt was compelled to reduce the weights on the driving axles of the last six 8-footers and to bring the actual loadings of all engines into line with the official figures; with the result that Great Northern engine-men everywhere complained that the engines had been altered and spoiled, so that they could no longer do their work properly.

Once the 8 ft. wheel had been decided upon, inside cylinders could no longer be considered, partly on account of the great leverage which side pressure on the flange of such a large wheel could exert to flex the crank axle, especially one with such a long throw as the contemplated 14 in. But

the fact that the boiler centre line would have had to be raised from the proposed 7 ft. 1 in. to 7 ft. 10½ in., an unheard of figure at that time on the 4 ft. 8½ in. gauge, to clear the cranks at top centres, was an overruling reason for outside cylinders.

No. 1, as built, was far from being a satisfactory engine. The firebox casing was made only 5 ft. 6 in. long, the same as on all Stirling's previous tender engines, though the boiler had to fill 18 in. x 28 in. cylinders, albeit driving larger wheels, instead of the 17 in. x 24 in. of the earlier engines. The firebox crown was exceptionally high, but the tubes were relatively few in number—175, only 1⅝ in. diameter—and the total heating surface was only 968 sq. ft., of which the tubes provided 875½ sq. ft. and the firebox 92½ sq. ft. The blast pipe was high; too high, for the height was reduced almost at once by 5½ in. and the lower position became standard throughout the class. The slide-valves were of the balanced type, though not exhausting through the back, as on two of the engines rebuilt by Ivatt in 1897 and 1899. These original valves must have been troublesome, for no other Stirling engine was ever fitted with balanced slide-valves during his lifetime.

The main outlines of the engine as built were very similar to the appearance of No. 1 today, but in accordance with the practice of those days there were no brakes at all on the engine.

The footplate angle ahead of the cylinders was shallower than at present and ran between cylinder cover and buffer beam without the curved front section, which now follows the line of the bogie wheel tyres. The bogie splashers themselves were carried rather further round the leading wheels at the front than they are now; the curves at the rear bogie wheels which finish off the trailing ends of these splashers remain as originally and are of a rather more splayed-out character than they were

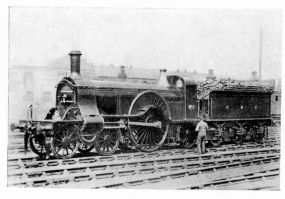

No. 1 as running in 1898

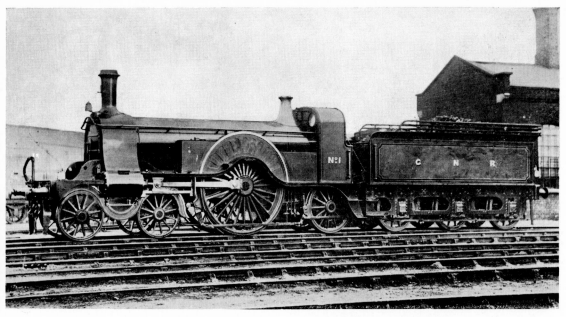

No. 1 at Peterborough about 1900. The chimney, the remains of which she now carries, gives the engine a dignity and artistic proportion now lacking

on any other engines of the class. The driving-wheel splashers carried eleven ornamental slots, again special to No. 1. All other 8-footers with slotted splashers had only ten slots, the small slot at the leading end having been omitted, almost certainly because of the risk while the engine was in motion of a driver's foot slipping into it and getting injured by the spokes whirling past.

The bogie wheel tyres were made only 5 in. wide from the outside face of the tread to the back of the flange, as compared with the $5\frac{1}{4}$ in. of the driving and trailing wheels, in order to give just that little bit of extra clearance behind the crosshead and also on the cylinder cover, when the bogie turned on a curve. No wonder the class was a terror for model makers, and no wonder so many of them reduced the bogie wheel diameter, increased the bogie wheelbase or spread the centres of the cylinders—or all three!—in any case spoiling the grace and symmetry of the original.

It was the cylinder itself, measured from the back of the casting over to the front cover joint, which was disposed centrally between the bogie wheels. The front flange of the cylinder projected ahead of the smokebox, so that the smokebox itself was slightly to the rear of the bogie centre line, the chimney being set forward on the smokebox so as to come on the centre distance between the bogie

wheels again. These points applied to every engine of the class and not to No. 1 only.

It will be noted that the expression 'bogie centre line' has been used in the previous paragraph. The bogie pivot on No. 1 and all her successors was placed 3 in. behind this transverse 'centre line', that is, 3 ft. 6 in. behind the leading bogie wheels and 3 ft. ahead of the rear bogie wheels. This again eased the problem of crosshead and frame clearance at the rear bogie wheels on curves; and also had a good effect, which Stirling did not fail to point out, of loading the leading bogie wheels more lightly than the trailing bogie wheels, thereby, as he put it, 'laying down the road for the driving wheels'. On No. 1, as originally built, no side play seems to have been provided for the trailing wheels under the cab, but it was soon apparent that this was highly desirable, and $\frac{3}{8}$ in. side play was shown on all later engines, 3/16 in. each side; a very meagre allowance and one perhaps that applied only on the drawing board. Still, frames are mildly flexible under a side load and wear does sometimes take place on side bearing faces, so that the 8-footers, like many other later engines with nominally rigid wheelbases, got round their curves without undue trouble.

The slide bars were of the fish-bellied type, yet again special to No. 1, all subsequent engines having parallel slide bars $2\frac{5}{8}$ in. thick throughout their length. The crosshead was the same as on all other engines of the class built up to 1880, a neat design but not so neat as the modified design introduced in 1880 when the two small notches, above and below the piston-rod socket, were suppressed. The unusual method of lubricating the small end of the connecting rod remained unchanged throughout the class. A lubricator reservoir was fixed to the side of the crosshead adjacent to the main frames, which fed oil by a short pipe into a cup-shaped recess in the connecting rod small end with a hole communicating with the gudgeon pin and small end bush. Access to the lubricator reservoir was, according to the original frame drawing of January 1870, by a long slot cut through the footplating above it, permitting the spout of an oilfeeder to pass through. But this long slot shown on No. 1's drawing was

changed later to the row of five short slots she now carries, an arrangement which was eventually provided on all 8-footers.

The cylindrical extension, or boss, on the crosshead in which the piston-rod was cottered, was an example of the fine clearances which were necessary on the 8-footers. Two small flats had to be machined at top and bottom of this boss to clear the nuts on the piston-rod packing glands. The notch at the rear end of both slide bars, to clear the connecting-rod at top and bottom crank centres, fitted very snugly round the connecting-rod in these positions. To an observer it seemed as if it must be too narrow for the rod!

The rear step was of a similar shape to the present one, but rather smaller and lighter, without the front guard plate. The more massive steps were substituted on No. 1, as on all the other early

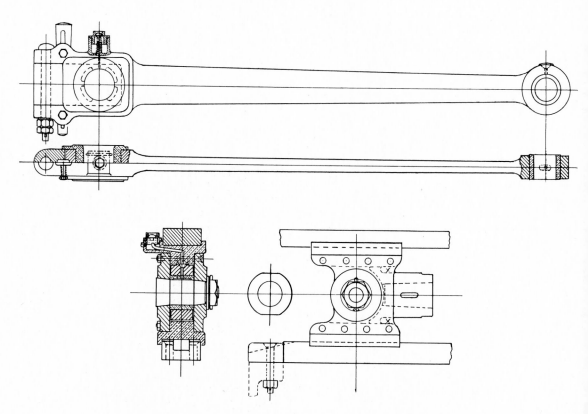

Connecting rod and crosshead for 8ft. singles Nos. 1–1002. Crosshead drawing shows the flats on the piston rod socket and (dotted at X) the outline of the crossheads on the earlier engines Nos. 1–550. The rear end of the lower slidebar is also shown, with its notch to clear the connecting rod on bottom centre. The connecting rod increases in thickness as well as in depth, from the small end to the big end. The round headed bolts which hold the brass slippers were always most carefully finished flush, and were quite invisible on the actual crossheads

8-footers, when vacuum-brakes were added to the engine, from May 1876 on. The steps then became a frame member, supporting the main brakeshaft fulcrum bracket and taking the pull of the brake rigging. The safety-valve casing was smaller than at present and housed two spring balance valves,

No. 1's crosshead. This although following the Stirling design generally, differs in the dimensions of the piston-rod boss, which has an end collar and appears to be a little larger in diameter than the original. Note that the cheeseheaded bolts holding the slippers to the crosshead are so finished off as to be quite invisible. The original 1870 fish-bellied slidebars are still in position

No 1's big end. The fitting has been carried out in a slovenly manner. The two brasses should be butted together with no gap, or they will 'work' in the fork of the big end. The oil well cap is of Ivatt, not Stirling, design

the levers of which extended into the cab, diverging in plan slightly to right and left to clear the whistle, which was then in a central position on the crown of the firebox casing. From 1877 onwards, starting with engine No. 69, these spring balance safety-valves were replaced by a pair of Ramsbottom valves, requiring a rather larger and more handsome brass casing. The whistle was then moved a few inches to the right, the driver's side, to clear the single cowtail lever of the Ramsbottom safety-valve. In all probability No. 1 received her larger safety-valve casing and Ramsbottom valves in May 1877, when a new longer firebox was fitted to her original boiler barrel.

The vertical Friedmann injectors first fitted were arranged between the driving wheel and the trailing wheel, outside the frame and below the footplate. They were ahead of the cab, so that adjustments to the water control involved leaving the cab and edging along the outside platform. This feature

No. 1's eccentrics. The main portion of the two sheaves was originally cast in one piece. The helical driving wheel springs date from not earlier than 1887, and may have been an Ivatt alteration. There is a strengthening patch on the main frame visible. Note that the boiler lagging had to be cut away to clear the inner eccentric strap

was retained to the end of Stirling's superintendency on all the 8-footers, though the vertical Friedmann injectors were replaced by horizontal injectors from 1874 onwards.

Concerning features of design not externally visible, No. 1 and the next four engines had bogie frames in which the plan view of the frame stays which carried the socket for the bogie pivot was in the form of an X, with the socket at the crossing of the two diagonals, whose ends were attached to the bogie side frames. But here, too, as in so many other details, No. 1 was unique. The main weight on the 8-footer bogie was taken at the main frames through a bracket and pad, very similar to the arrangement on the G.W.R. 4—6—os of Church-ward and Collett, directly on to a bracket fixed to the bogie frames and immediately above them. The pivot of the bogie was also intended, thanks to springiness and consequent slight deflection under load, to take a share of the weight. Now, on the bogies with X frame stays, there was a strut, from the crossing of the X members to each side frame. On No. 1 this was a rectangular bar on edge, on the other four engines a bar of circular section. No. 1 still has this original bogie of hers, so that there cannot have been much wrong with the

No. 1's bogie stays. These are the diagonal form of bracing used on the earliest engines, and all but the transverse stays (just this side of the steamchest drain pipe) are the original 1870 parts. The transverse stays replaced the rather weaker original ones at a very early date. The centre pin, with its nut and seating, remains just as in 1870

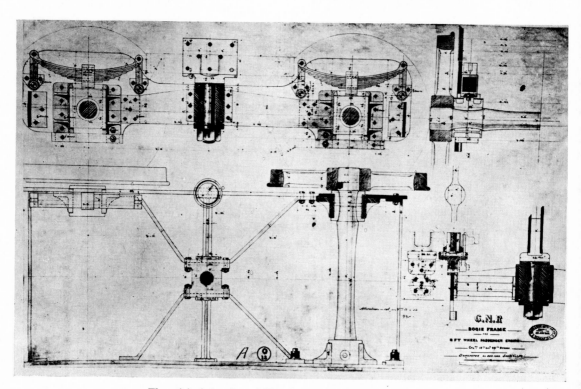

The original drawing of No. 1's bogie, dated December 1869

design on the score of length of life. The 6 in. by $\frac{3}{4}$ in. strut originally fitted has, however, been replaced by a stronger one, $1\frac{1}{8}$ in. thick, probably in the first few months of No. 1's existence. Nevertheless, a new design of staying, by means of gusset plates lying horizontally between the frames, was introduced in 1873. This remained the standard for all later engines, even the larger No. 1003 class of 1894-95, though these differed in detail and were more robust than the earlier engines' bogies.

It is a curious fact that, though Stirling provided rear sanding-gear for every other class of engine he built, he did not do so for the 8-footers. The box between the driving splasher and the cab was a dummy on the 8-footers, and on them only. There seems to be no good reason for the absence of rear sand, and no doubt, had it been provided, it would have been used as on the other single-wheelers to lay a track of sand on the rail and wheel tread when backing on to a train, so as to obtain the best possible adhesion on starting.

In her first eight months at work, No. 1 completed 32,000 miles of running, just about the average rate of mileage covered during the first ten years of her existence. It does not look as if her 'teething troubles' kept her out of service anything more than a negligible proportion of the eight months.

No. 1 was fitted with a new firebox of increased length in May 1877, thereby increasing the full weight of the engine from 38 tons to 39 tons 9 cwt. The frames, of course, would have needed lengthening by 8 in. to accommodate the longer firebox. It should be borne in mind that welding a piece of $1\frac{1}{4}$ in. thick wrought iron plate into the two halves of a frame, cut to permit this, was in 1877 a perfectly reasonable blacksmith's job. As will be seen, a similar process was carried out at different times in later days, even after Stirling's death.

There is little doubt that it was at this 1877 general repairs that No. 1 was first fitted with brake rigging and the bellows type of simple vacuum brake cylinder. The first 8-footer which had this earliest type of brake when built was No. 221, turned out new in July 1876. It was a 'Heath Robinson' sort of contraption, with bellcranks, links and double-ended levers to transmit the pull from the two ends of the cylinder, which was itself mounted transversely between the frames, its axis parallel with the trailing axle.

In 1880, however, No. 1's original boiler was adjudged to be due for replacement, having covered 432,972 miles, and her frames had also been giving trouble, possibly due to the cylinders working loose; a defect on the early 8-footers which was remarked

No. 1's boiler front.   This is an Ivatt straightback boiler, and the combination ejector and brake valve was a late Stirling addition.   The blower pipe passes to the left handrail; the steam pressure gauge is piped to the base of the whistle stand outside the cab.   Only one water gauge is fitted, although several general arrangement drawings about 1885-1890 showed two water gauges and no pet cocks. The original 1870 cab still remains, but the raising of the boiler centre line in 1880 has required the notching of the angle surrounding the boiler, to clear the cab window frames.   The thumbscrew to clamp the regulator in any given position has been removed

upon in 1908 by the then shedmaster at Hitchin, Mr. Hawkins, who must have been at least 60 years of age at that time and who had been closely associated with the running of the Stirling singles throughout their existence. There were other occasional defects in the earlier engines, which were dealt with as they became apparent, and modified similarly on the later engines of the class when built. Pistons occasionally tended to work loose on the piston-rods, and the frames sometimes developed cracks behind the driving wheels. New frames were strengthened at this point in 1877, and a further modification was made here in 1884.

One other minor point, hardly a defect, was that the stay heads on the firebox sides tended to rub against the inside of the main frames, as traces of wear in the expansion brackets developed in service. The main frames of No. 1 and all the other 8 ft. singles were only 4 ft. 0½ in. apart as compared with 4 ft. 1½ in. on all other Stirling engines; and on No. 1 as originally built the frames were parallel throughout their length. From 1880 on, and on No. 1 when rebuilt in that year, the frames ahead of the smokebox were set inwards so that at the bufferbeam they were only 3 ft. 11¼ in. apart, to give a little more side play to the leading bogie wheel.

It looks as though Stirling in developing a 4—2—2 from a 2—2—2 had reckoned that no actual side play need be provided, and that the bogie would only pivot to the very small extent that flange clearance between the rails would permit; very much as the Gooch Broad Gauge 4—2—2s on the Great Western Railway had a rigid wheelbase overall. But the Broad Gauge engines' driving wheels had blind, flangeless tyres; and Stirling evidently found very soon—very likely from derailments at points—that he would have to provide at least some flexibility over his wheelbase. There can be no doubt that the special 4 ft. 0½ in. dimension between frames was originally intended to accommodate the little bit of side play that the dimension of 4 ft. 5⅝ in. between tyres would need when the engine came on a curve and the bogie rotated just a trifle on its pivot, as well as the side play provided in the trailing wheel axlebox guides.

One result of this feature was that the expansion brackets of the 8-footer boilers would normally be too narrow for the frames of the 7 ft. 6 in. singles of 1886 and that the boilers of the latter would not go into an 8-footer's frames anyway.

No. 1 was thoroughly rebuilt and left Doncaster works on December 20, 1880 with a brand new set of deeper frames, new trailing wheels 4 ft. 7 in. in diameter, and a new boiler 4 ft. 2 in. in diameter; and with a new pair of front buffers of much neater design than her original ones. Moreover, her 11 splasher slots were closed in with a backing plate painted the dark green★ of the tender

★ In later years some, if not all, of the engines had the dark green of the slots changed to black.

panel surround and edged with black with a white line. The pitch of the boiler was raised to 7 ft. 3¼ in., the wheel tyres still being 2½ in. thick. But by the next time No. 1 needed a new set of tyres the standard thickness had been increased to 2¾ in. and the pitch rose accordingly by another quarter of an inch to its final figure, 7 ft. 3½ in.

The simple vacuum brake was still fitted, but it was replaced some years later—either in 1885 or in 1887—by the automatic brake with a vertical cylinder and a simplified rigging. At that time double heading with the 8 ft. singles was strictly forbidden, and the brake pipe was therefore not carried forward to a hose connection on the front bufferbeam, which would be necessary to permit of double-heading, with the pilot engine driver in charge of the braking, until 1894.

From 1880 to 1886, or perhaps even later, No. 1's chimney was still of the built-up type, though fitted with a liner, which her original chimney lacked; but one of the cast-iron chimneys which superseded the built-up type was provided during the late 1880s. A second cast-iron chimney, with a deeper top, was fitted about 1895, or perhaps a year or two earlier, and at about the same time her front footplate angle iron, ahead of the smokebox, which had remained unchanged since 1870, was replaced by the deeper and more graceful curved design. The lining out of the backed-in driving splasher slots was omitted, the whole of the splasher being painted the light green of the boiler and cab. The vacuum brake-pipe was carried forward, between the frames and under the driving axle, to the front bufferbeam, a sign that the old days of one engine, one train, had gone and that double-heading was now permitted. Side chains were added to the front bufferbeam, and the size of the letters and numerals on the beam was reduced, so that the front number could be

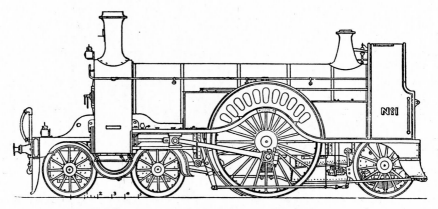

No. 1 as running 1895–1904, with unlined splasher slots and vacuum brake connection on front bufferbeam

accommodated above the level of the side chains. Previously these numerals had been the same 6 in. size as those on the cab sides.

The diameter and stroke of the cylinders, which had previously always been recorded on the front bufferbeam above the main draw chain and hook, were still painted on, but when side chains were fitted the location of this information was changed to a lower position on the bufferbeam, near the bottom edge and either between the main draw hook and the left side chain, or between the left side chain and the left guardiron. There seems to have been no direct ruling on which of these two positions should be chosen. This method of recording the cylinder size—or sizes, for if the cylinders differed in diameter the legend would indicate this fact, thus

$$\left. \begin{array}{l} R \quad 18'' \\ L \quad 18\tfrac{1}{4}'' \end{array} \right\} \times 28''$$

—was dropped in 1907 when side chains were once again dispensed with and the bufferbeam numerals reverted to their old position and size.

At a still later general repair, almost certainly in 1903, No. 1's wrought-iron driving-wheels and laminated bearing springs were replaced by cast-steel wheels and Timmis helical springs. It is probable that these wheels and springs were taken from No. 777, which was condemned at this time. The wrought-iron wheels thus replaced were not the original ones, but a pair of improved and rather stronger design, with larger axle bosses, which seem to have appeared first in 1884. Unfortunately drawings are not available to enable precise dating to be given. From early photographs it seems likely that the wrought-iron driving-wheels were strengthened in stages, and then in 1887 were replaced by the cast-steel design, with oval section spokes in place of rectangular. These steel wheels were used on old engines requiring new driving-wheels as well as on new construction. Although these cast-steel wheels did not appear on a new 8-footer until 1887, the drawing is dated November 1885, so that it is quite likely that they were used as replacements for earlier engines during 1886.

As regards the gradual change in design of the wrought-iron wheels, all the increased dimensions had only to 'fit in the air', and could, in a hand-made blacksmith's job like forging these wheels, be changed as thought desirable between the fabrication of each pair of wheels.

No. 1's 1880 boiler lasted until 1889, when it was replaced. It had been in service for 409,767 miles. This new, third boiler was replaced in 1900, after 378,611 miles, by a second-hand boiler, from

No. 664, which had already done 129,400 miles. It lasted No. 1 until she was withdrawn from service on September 23, 1907, by which time her chimney seemed also to have been practically worn out, the deep top having been scoured away by the blast of the engine and levelled down to a shallow top, similar in appearance to the Ivatt large 'Atlantics', a detail which definitely spoiled No. 1's looks. She still carries this chimney, but the boiler with which she did her exhibition and special running in 1925 and 1938 was specially fitted to her in May 1925 for the Darlington Centenary celebrations and the procession of historic locomotives in which, of course, she figured.

There is only one record of the performance of No. 1 when she was in regular service; but fortunately it is an outstanding one, logged by the Rev. W. J. Scott, from Grantham to Doncaster. A fully detailed record is not available; but Scott was, of course, a most experienced observer, and the figures quoted can be taken as absolutely accurate. On this run No. 1 had a load of 200 tons, tare, and got away in grand style down to the Trent valley, passing Newark, 14·6 miles, in 15 min. 2 sec. at 70 m.p.h. On the level across the Trent valley the speed was well sustained, and she covered the 6·3 miles from Newark to Carlton in 5 min. 58 sec. Still better was the climb to Markham, with no

No. 1's works plate, dating from April 1870. In cast brass, with the letters polished and now painted white. The black lining-out of the spokes, and the black-and-white lining-out of the driving wheel splasher slots are well shown

lower speed than 50 m.p.h. and with a fast subsequent descent, Retford, 33·1 miles, was passed in 33 min. 58 sec. The maximum did not exceed 72 m.p.h., but a high average was maintained onwards to Doncaster—indeed the last 17·4 miles to the stop took only 17 min. 33 sec. Thus the excellent time of 51 min. 31 sec., start to stop, was achieved over the 50·5 miles from Grantham to Doncaster. This run alone is enough to show by how much the 8-footers could exceed their designed performance target of 51 m.p.h., with a load of 150 tons. On this occasion No. 1 averaged 58.8 m.p.h. with a load of 200 tons.

No. 1's mileage from 1870 to 1907 was 1,404,663. This was probably the highest figure for any Stirling single, the runners-up almost certainly being No. 8, the second 8-footer built, and No. 21 or No. 61, the 7 ft. singles, although in the absence of complete mileage records it is not possible to say definitely.

After withdrawal, No. 1 was not scrapped but put aside until 1909 when she was sent to the White City for exhibition alongside the Ivatt large 'Atlantic' No. 1442 at the Imperial International Exhibition at Shepherds Bush. For this purpose No. 1 was stripped of her brake rigging, her rear 'sandboxes' and the backing plates of the slots of her driving splashers. Her 1880 buffers were replaced by a dilapidated pair of the 1870 type. The idea, of course, was to restore her as far as possible to her condition as first built in 1870, but the attempt was as half-hearted as all such attempts elsewhere have since been.

The bogie, in almost every detail, was '1870', except that the leading ends of the splashers had been cut back. The crossheads were not her original ones; possibly they were from a scrapped engine with a running number not lower than 662. She had her 1880 mainframes, 8 in. longer than the 1870 frames, with the boiler centre line raised 2½ in. and the boiler itself 1½ in. larger in diameter, and with a firebox 8 in. longer than her original one. Her chimney was, of course, a one-piece cast-iron one, instead of a three-piece built-up one. Her safety-valve casing was much larger and covered Ramsbottom and not spring-balance valves. Her trailing-wheels were 4 ft. 7½ in. in diameter instead of 4 ft. 1 in. and the springing here and the shape of the frames was different. Her cab footsteps were of much more substantial design than the originals. Her injectors were of modern design. It is true that she had a pair of old wrought-iron driving-wheels fitted, but these were not of the original design and the bearing springs were helical, not laminated. Finally, a Sturrock tender of a type never allotted to an 8-footer, and previously used on the old 0—4—2 engine No. 112A of 1849 in her last days as the Doncaster carriage shunter, was provided. At this time the official story was that all copper and brass from the boiler had been removed and that this was a mere shell.

After the close of the Exhibition No. 1 was brought to Kings Cross shed, stowed away in a corner and allowed to accumulate dust and rust for the next 12 years. She was brought out of the shed in October 1921 and cleaned up to serve as a photographic foil for No. 1000, the first Gresley 3-cylinder 'Mogul', and again in 1922, this time as a foil for No. 1471, the second Gresley 'Pacific'. Three years later she was provided with a boiler

No. 1 and L.N.E.R. 4470, 1925. (Not, as it might appear, No. 1 and G.N.R. 1470.)

*No. 1 on special down train on 30 June
1938, between Potters Bar and Brookmans Park*

with three washout-plugs along each side of the firebox casing, and was run in steam in the procession of historic locomotives at Darlington in 1925, with the L.N.W.R. *Cornwall* ahead of her and the Midland Johnson single-wheeler behind her. For this occasion the brake rigging was replaced and the brake pipe extended forward to a hose connection on the front bufferbeam, just as had been done in 1895.

In her final condition she was used once again as a photographic foil, this time in June 1925 for the first Gresley 'Pacific', *Great Northern*, then numbered 4470. It was probably intentional that the angle from which the photograph was taken leaves only the numerals —470 visible, tending to mislead the casual viewer into thinking it a genuine Great Northern photograph of 1922.

After the Centenary celebrations, No. 1 was placed in York Railway Museum, where she remained until Mr. E. G. Marsden, then the Information Agent of the L.N.E.R., had the brilliant idea of running her in steam with a train of 1888 period carriages, both as a contrast to the new carriage stock which Sir Nigel Gresley was then about to put in service for the summer timetable of 1938 and as an indication of the development of travelling comfort in the 50 years since the 1888 Race to Edinburgh. As a publicity device it was most original and successful, though, for some of us,

No. 1 captured and held the limelight almost entirely for herself.

Mr. Marsden has related how doubtful and anxious he was of what reception Sir Nigel would accord to his idea, and how enthusiastic the great man at once became. No. 1 was taken to Doncaster and given what the Doncaster record calls a 'heavy repair'. Since the engine was only in the shops between June 16 and 29, it is clear that the minimum was done to put her into running order again. In fact, on her first trip she ran a driving axlebox hot, and this proved a most awkward job to handle at the Kings Cross locomotive shed, for the 8 ft. diameter wheel was too big for the drop-pit used normally for working on casual wheel and axlebox repairs; and No. 1 had to have her front end lifted high on a crane all the while work was being done on the troublesome axlebox. The opportunity was taken to refit big end brasses at the same time, and an examination of these and of the crank pins showed how badly worn—practically worn out— these parts were.

Nevertheless, though her boiler pressure had been reduced to 140 lb. per sq. in., No. 1 went successfully through her publicity run and worked a series of excursions during the succeeding three months, with no failure on her part; though it is true that her wretched tender let her down on one occasion by developing such a ferocious leak in its rusted-away tank plates that a trip had to be abandoned for lack of water. A layer of concrete in the tank bottom cured the leak.

Apart, indeed, from an intermittent lack of lubrication to the piston-rod packing-glands, which caused steam leakage, No. 1 surprised everyone by her performance and her consistent reliability. She needed working only very lightly to keep time, and usually ran well before time, with her load of seven 6-wheeled carriages weighing about 100 tons. The maximum speed attained was approximately 70 m.p.h., but that this was not higher was due to consideration for the passengers in the rough riding 1888-type stock.

The log of her first special trip, in June 1938, is given below. The load was seven 6-wheeled coaches, weighing a little less than 100 tons. With such a light load there was, of course, nothing exceptional about her performance, other than the mere fact that she was still able to do it. Nevertheless, the climb to Potters Bar was 'none so bad'.

L.N.E.R. KINGS CROSS—STEVENAGE
Load: 100 tons
Engine: 4-2-2 No. 1 ex York Railway Museum.

Dist. Miles		Actual m. s.	Av. Speed m.p.h.
0·0	KINGS CROSS .	0 00	—
2·6	Finsbury Park .	6 15	—
3·5	Harringay .	7 28	45
5·0	Wood Green .	9 11	57
6·5	New Southgate .	10 52	47 min.
9·2	New Barnet .	14 16	48
10·6	Hadley Wood .	16 00	50
12·7	Potters Bar .	18 38	49
14·5	Brookmans Park .	20 36	56
17·7	Hatfield .	25 01	eased
22·0	Welwyn North .	31 52	—
23·5	Woolmer Green .	34 06	—
25·0	Knebworth .	37 15	—
		sigs	—
26·7	Langley Jc. .	39 01	—
28·6	STEVENAGE .	43 00	—

After this brief and most unexpected reappearance No. 1 returned to York Museum, but she was not to remain there long undisturbed. Soon after the outbreak of war in 1939 all the engines then in the Museum, including of course No. 1, were removed to various small locomotive sheds in the North East and in the remoter parts of the Border country. No. 1 was housed at Ferryhill (Co. Durham) and remained there throughout the war.

It was a wise move: although the Museum itself was not damaged, the York locomotive sheds received a direct hit and a Gresley A4 'Pacific' was damaged irreparably. No. 1 is back at York now and it is to be hoped that no shortsighted and philistine decision on the part of authority will permit of her destruction at any time in the future. With the myopic and defensive attitude of so many responsible people today the threat to the continued existence of No. 1 and other preserved steam locomotives is by no means an empty one.

No. 1 was the first of a most successful class of locomotive, which during nearly 30 years ran most of the express trains of the Great Northern Railway, with economy and reliability at higher speeds than any other trains in the world. Designed to take trains of 150 tons at average speeds of around 51 m.p.h. between stops, they performed this work with a more than adequate margin of power; but when loads increased to 250 tons and average speeds to 55 m.p.h., they began to be outclassed and, as is shown in a later chapter, while on occasion they were able to handle such trains satisfactorily, they could not be relied upon to do so in all conditions of wind and weather.

Perhaps this is a suitable place to deal with the question of whether in 1870 Stirling may not have given consideration to a 4—4—0 type of engine before coming down in favour of a 4—2—2. Some years ago a dilapidated drawing of an outside-cylindered 4—4—0 came to light at Doncaster. This drawing had no reference number or title, was dated simply 1870 and was signed 'J. C. Park'. A tracing, or rather a drawing, was made from it by the late J. N. Maskelyne and was reproduced in the Stephenson Locomotive Society Journal in 1952; this led to a certain amount of correspondence, mostly on the irrelevant point of just how little Stirling actually concerned himself with his designs. Looking back over the years, and after having studied very many drawings indeed, both arrangements and details, the authors have been forced unconditionally to take the view that no detail ever got on a Stirling Great Northern engine without his knowing and approving it. There was no laissez faire about Patrick Stirling.

Of this 4—4—0 design, it may be said that the driving-wheels were 7 ft. in diameter and the bogie-wheels about 3 ft. 9 in. The firebox was 6 ft. 2 in. long. The cylinders may have been 28 in. stroke, but it is not possible to be certain about this. Now, No. 1 was completed and out of works on April 20, 1870, and her firebox was only 5 ft. 6 in. long. The first 6 ft. 2 in. firebox was that fitted to the second 8-footer, No. 8, completed towards the end of

December 1870. Moreover, those original detail drawings of No. 1, some of which are still in existence today, are dated 1869, showing clearly that the original design was conceived in 1869, not 1870. So that we are forced to the conclusion that the 4—4—0 was a design produced *after* No. 1 had been completed. Since, when first built, No. 1 was not an immediate success, it is possible that J. C. Park, then the Chief Draughtsman at Doncaster, sketched out his idea of what he thought was needed. It is even possible that he showed it to Stirling and that it was turned down. But it is certain that the 4—4—0 design was not a product of Stirling's brain, or in the least in line with his ideas at the time.

So much thought went into the mechanical ideas behind No. 1, that a relatively minor point such as the original firebox on No. 1 being a little too small for the work she was intended to do, would never lead to a complete changeover in design. Especially, indeed, to a design involving the coupled wheels which were probably at that very time beginning to prove so troublesome and expensive on Sturrock's last design, the 7 ft. 2—4—0s, Nos. 264 to 269. Within the next few years all of them were rebuilt

as single-wheelers—a crowning argument against the idea that Stirling in 1870 could have ever contemplated building a top-link passenger engine with coupled wheels.

But if Stirling had dismissed the thoughts of a Great Northern 4—4—0 from his mind, this may not have been entirely true of the Doncaster drawing office staff. Park left for the North London Railway in 1873, and in October 1876 a senior draughtsman at Doncaster, known today only by his initials 'J.L.C.', certainly took the trouble to copy out the leading dimensions and constructional specifications of a batch of 20 4—4—0s designed by S. W. Johnson, which the Midland Railway had 'tendered' out and of which Dübs & Co. commenced delivery in 1877.

It is possible that 'J.L.C.' was impressed by the leading particulars of this Midland bogie engine with 7 ft. coupled wheels and a larger heating surface than Stirling ever achieved on his passenger engines. But it was another 20 years before the first Great Northern 4—4—0 appeared, and the dimensions of Ivatt's No. 400 of 1896 were quite different from the Johnson engine—and mostly smaller.

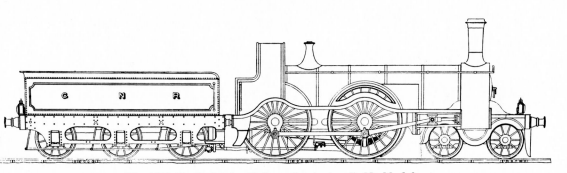

The 1870 'Park' 4-4-0. Redrawn by the late J. N. Maskelyne

CHAPTER 6

THE EIGHT-FOOT 4-2-2s: DECEMBER 1870 TO 1893

The 8-foot singles—1870 to 1879

No. 1 had been in service since April 1870 and her first few months had shown up her potentialities and defects, so that by the autumn of that year Stirling was prepared to go ahead and build further engines of the same general design, in which the known defects would be eliminated. The complete success and reliability of the improved design were not, however, to be achieved at once. For the next six years there was to be change after change, mainly in the minor details of the design, as experience and increasing mileage showed up points of weakness. It was not until 1877 that Stirling felt satisfied, for the time being, to put in hand a batch as large as eight engines; though the completion of these was spread over about 18 months. Previous to this the production had averaged little over two *per annum*, though it had begun to increase—three engines having been built in each of the two years, 1875 and 1876. Even at this stage finality had by no means been reached, and in two years more a new general arrangement drawing was needed to cover still further changes.

Nos. 8 and 33

No. 8, the second engine of the class, was completed at Doncaster and out of shops in December 1870. The actual date for No. 8 can only be inferred, since the first note of her repairs in the remaining official records is dated February 21, 1888, when she was rebuilt in line, in most particulars, with the later engines of the class. However, her Doncaster works number was 61, and engines with the works numbers 60 and 62 were both recorded as out of works on December 31, 1870.

The third 8-footer, No. 33, was completed and out of shops on March 15, 1871, and in all respects —except perhaps one minor one—was a twin of No. 8. From this time onward, for many years, the 8-footers, and indeed, almost all Great Northern engines, were built in pairs, each engine of a pair being usually identical with the other. Between successive pairs of engines of the same class, however, there were often—indeed, almost always— minor differences, and sometimes quite important changes had been made.

Because No. 1's most serious defect had been poor steaming, a new boiler was designed for No. 8, with a different tube arrangement giving a larger heating surface, and a much longer firebox, this involving longer main frames and wheelbase.

For both Nos. 8 and 33, Stirling broke his rule of simplicity of boiler construction, and included a water midfeather in the copper firebox. The midfeather was in fact a direct substitution of the otherwise standard and universal brick arch, in the same position in the firebox and inclined at the same angle. It was open, on the water side, to the front and sides of the inner firebox, and thus was a different and rather more simple arrangement than Sturrock had used on some of his own express engines in 1860, and far less complicated than the McConnell arrangement which had been tried out experimentally in 1855 on a Sturrock six-coupled goods engine, No. 328.

Both the 1855 and the 1860 designs had basically consisted of a vertical 'water leg', extending from the crown of the copper inner firebox right down to the foundation ring, dividing the grate into two separate halves, each requiring its own firehole. The midfeather was rendered more complicated and awkward to make, by its upper half being stopped short of the tube plate, so that the tube arrangement could be exactly as for a normal boiler with a brick arch.

It does not seem that Stirling's midfeather was entirely satisfactory. At least one of the two engines fitted with it, probably both—though it is here that No. 8 may have differed from No. 33—originally had the boiler feed water delivery put through clackboxes on the sides of the firebox opposite the tip of the midfeather, instead of the usual position well forward on the sides of the boiler barrel.

In February 1871 *Engineering* published a sectional general arrangement drawing and an outside view (engraved from a photograph) of No. 8, which showed the clackboxes on the firebox sides. In September 1871 *The Engineer* published its own engraving of the same outside view, and also a 'Portfolio Supplement' of a sectional general arrangement drawing modified to show the boiler feed piped to clackboxes on the side of the barrel exactly as on No. 1. Evidently trouble had already been encountered with the feed delivery into the firebox sides, due no doubt to the burning of the plates locally, arising from the rapid deposition of scale around the point of entry of the feed water; a state of affairs which was inevitable and, one would have thought, foreseeable and obvious.★ But most probably the hope of improving the water

No. 3 in 1872–3, exactly as built, almost certainly at Grantham. The fireman rose to be a top-link driver, who retired before the first World War. The photograph, faded almost to nothing, was obtained from his grand-daughter over twenty years ago

circulation at the midfeather outweighed the risk of trouble for the first month or two. Certainly, Stirling in September 1871 was putting a good face on it and stating that he was thoroughly satisfied with the midfeather, and that a number of boilers were being built with the device.

★ Yet Dean on the G.W.R. tried the same position of the clacks on the firebox sides some 15 years later.

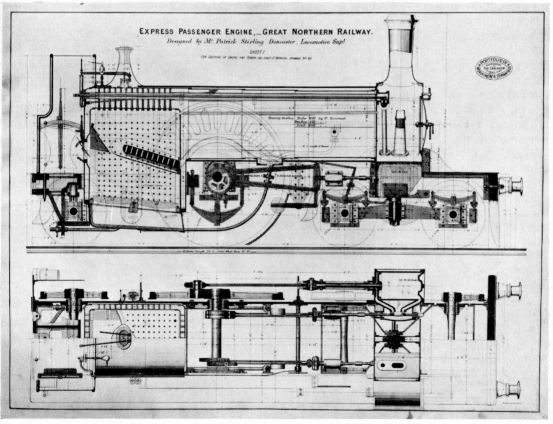

General arrangement drawing of No. 33, 1871, showing water midfeather, but with boiler feed water delivery at front end of barrel

E

THE STIRLING SINGLES

No one knows how long these midfeathers survived. An optimist might give them two years, but the probability is that before that period had elapsed the midfeathers would have been removed, and the copper fireboxes either patched or renewed and standard brick arches fitted. There are no records left to tell us definitely.

COMPARATIVE BOILER DIMENSIONS

Engine	No. 1	No. 8
Tubes: Number . .	175	217
Outs diam. in. .	$1\frac{5}{8}$	$1\frac{9}{16}$
Heating surface sq. ft. . .	$875\frac{1}{2}$	1043
Firebox: Length . .	5ft. 6in.	6ft. 2in.
Grate area sq. ft.	15·8	17·75
Heating surface sq. ft. . .	$92\frac{1}{2}$	122
Total heating surface sq. ft.	968	1165

To accommodate the longer firebox, the trailing wheelbase was also increased by 8 in. from 8 ft. to 8 ft. 8 in. The pitch of the new boiler was raised by 1 in., to 7 ft. 2 in. All other frame and motion particulars were unchanged from No. 1, except that normal design 'D' valves replaced the original balanced slide-valves. The blast-pipe was kept at the lower position to which No. 1's had been altered, and this remained standard thereafter.

The steam chest covers were shown on the general arrangement drawing altered to flat plates; this would have made it impossible to assemble the valve spindles, and is an obvious draughtsman's error. It is a curious point that *Engineering* showed the covers correctly, while *The Engineer* followed the Doncaster drawing.

There was a minor change in the bogie framing, the transverse members between the pivot block and the sideframes being altered from a flat bar to a round bar section, $2\frac{1}{2}$ in. diameter.

Nos. 2, 3, 5, 7, 22 and 48

There was a pause of nine months before the next 8-footer was completed at Doncaster, long enough for Stirling to decide, no doubt as a result of bitter experience, against any further use or development of the water midfeather provided on the previous two engines. The decision was final and, after this early experiment, no Stirling engines, single-wheelers or coupled, were built with midfeathers or, indeed, with any departure at all from the simplest firebox arrangements practical. All had a normal brick arch and deflector plate at the firehole.

Stirling was evidently satisfied that the size of boiler carried by Nos. 8 and 33 was all that was required for the foreseeable future; and, in fact, the firebox dimensions and barrel length remained unchanged until 1894. It may be remarked, in passing, that *The Engineer* had criticised them as too small as far back as 1871.

Nos. 2 and 3 were the next two engines built, similar in every respect to Nos. 8 and 33, except for the return to the conventional brick arch. They were completed at Doncaster in December 1871 and March 1872 respectively, although the exact dates are not known.

At some time between 1871 and 1874 the arrangement and diameter of the boiler tubes was altered again, this time a reduction in number to 183, while the diameter was increased to $1\frac{3}{4}$ in. It looks as if Stirling's early experiment with small diameter tubes, commencing with one of the 7 ft. singles, had not really proved satisfactory in the end, for the $1\frac{1}{4}$ in. tubes had come to stay—at least

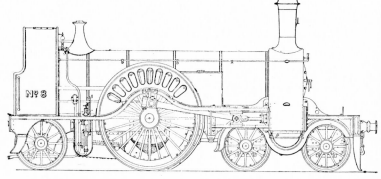

No. 8, as built, 1870, with water midfeather in firebox, and with feedwater delivery into side of firebox

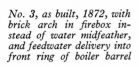

No. 3, as built, 1872, with brick arch in firebox instead of water midfeather, and feedwater delivery into front ring of boiler barrel

as far as the long barrels of the 8-footers were concerned.

But which was the first engine to receive these $1\frac{3}{4}$ in. tubes can now be only a matter of guesswork. The first indication still available as evidence of the change is a piece of paper pasted over a small portion of the firebox drawing including the midfeather, on which the new tube arrangements were noted. Unfortunately there is no date assigned for the change to 183 tubes, though a later change to 170 tubes is dated January 31, 1879, thus providing the necessary clue to the first engine with the 170 tubes.

The earliest general arrangement drawing showing the 183 tubes is dated August 1874, so that there is therefore the possibility that No. 48, completed in the October, may actually have been the first engine built with $1\frac{3}{4}$ in. tubes. But it is much more likely that this new tube arrangement applied to all the engines of the batch, from No. 2 in 1871 onwards. The reversion to the use of a brick arch had involved considerable internal changes in the firebox and in the positioning of the firebox stays. To change the tube arrangements was a relatively minor job; and for new work, apart from the experiments on just a few engines, Stirling had already adopted $1\frac{3}{4}$ in. tubes as his standard. The pitch of the boilers of these six engines remained at 7 ft. 2 in., as on Nos. 8 and 33.

A change in the design of the bogie framing was introduced at about this time, probably on No. 5, out of shops, new, in August 1873, which henceforth remained the standard for all 8-footers subsequently built; though the bogies already in service were not altered. The original diagonal bar staying was altered to plate gussets, lying horizontally above the bogie axles. The side frame-plates of the bogie remained unaltered, so that from the outside it was not possible to note any change.

No. 5 was quickly followed by No. 7, in September 1873, but there was a six months gap before No. 22 appeared, in March or April 1874, and a further gap before the next engine, No. 48, was completed, in October 1874. This was a year in which Doncaster works were fully occupied, not only in turning out new coupled engines, but also in rebuilding old Sturrock engines to Stirling standards.

The first five 8-footers had had the weight on the driving wheels adjusted by set-bolts, bearing on the ends of the plate springs through the spring shackles, which were loaded in compression. On No. 5 this method was changed, and the actual process of adjustment simplified, by using one set-bolt only, bearing on the underside of each spring buckle, the connection to the axlebox being made through a rather elaborate tension member, almost a framework, which also served as a guide through which the spring buckle and the plate spring itself passed.

At some time in 1873 or 1874 the old Friedmann injectors were replaced by horizontal ones, probably still Friedmann's. Once again the doubt remains, on which engine was the change first made? It can only be said that No. 48 is the most likely candidate, but that either No. 22 or even No. 34 might possibly have been the first engine with the new injectors.

In any case, within a few years, probably by the end of 1881, all those engines at first fitted with Friedmann injectors were having them replaced by the less temperamental Sheward and Gresham type, and later by Gresham and Craven injectors, which remained the standard for Stirling engines of all classes.

In 1877, No. 5 had a major alteration carried out on her inner firebox. From No. 8 on, the height above the boiler centre line of the firebox crown had been fixed at $9\frac{1}{2}$ in. For some reason, possibly as a result of damage due to the water level being allowed to get so low that the crown was burned, No. 5 had the height of the crown of her firebox reduced to $7\frac{1}{2}$ in. Trouble from burnt firebox crowns, due to the greater deceleration of the new continuously braked trains, was certainly occurring at about this time. No other engines, as far as can be traced, were altered similarly and new boilers were still being made with the crown at the $9\frac{1}{2}$ in. dimension until 1880, when the height was reduced by 1 in., to $8\frac{1}{2}$ in. To complete the picture, the next change was to a height of $6\frac{1}{2}$ in., in 1884; and the $7\frac{1}{2}$ in. dimension of No. 5 was never used again.

No. 48 was one of the engines involved in the Abbots Ripton accident of January 21, 1876. She had only been out of Doncaster shops two months after her first general repair, and went back again for a further two-and-a-half months, the repairs found to be necessary after the accident including a new cylinder.

Nos. 34, 47, 53 and 62

The next pair of engines, Nos. 34 and 47, out of Doncaster shops new in May 1875 and on June 14, 1875 respectively, did not differ from No. 48 in any major particulars, apart from the raising of the pitch of the boiler by another $\frac{1}{2}$ in., to 7 ft. $2\frac{1}{2}$ in. No brakes of any sort had been fitted so far on any 8-footers as built, but these were the last of the class to be built without brakes. No. 47 was the first of the class to be shown at a public exhibition: she

was sent to the Railway Jubilee Exhibition, held at Darlington in 1875.

No. 53, completed on November 9, 1875, was the first engine of the class to be stationed at Kings Cross. She ran daily between London and Grantham for a number of years, and was the regular

No. 53, as first equipped with brakes, 1877-8

engine on the 7.15 a.m. down Leeds express as far as Grantham, returning with the corresponding up express. She was very well looked after, and was probably the very last 8-footer to run with the driving splasher slots lined out. Kings Cross kept them repainted up till 1898 or 1899, six or seven years after most of No. 53's sisters had lost this decoration.

No. 62 was completed on February 14, 1876, and was the twin of No. 53.

Nos. 221 and 94

The result of the Newark brake trials in 1875 was a decision by the Great Northern Board of Directors to equip all their passenger stock with the simple, or non-automatic, vacuum-brake. In future all new passenger engines would be fitted with brake blocks and rigging and vacuum-brake cylinders, and all existing passenger engines would be brought into line and similarly equipped at their next general overhaul at Doncaster.

No. 34, about 1877, after fitting with non-automatic vacuum brake. Compare photograph above with line drawing, right

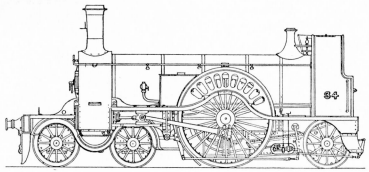

The drawing for the layout of the vacuum-brake arrangements for the 8 ft. singles was made in May 1876, and the first engine to be built new with brakes was No. 221, completed on July 29, 1876. She was followed on October 9, the same year, by her twin, No. 94.

Both these engines included a major change at the rear end, in the substitution of 4 ft. 7 in. diameter trailing wheels for 4 ft. 1 in., a design change made in order to provide an improved form of rear springing for the 8-footers to which eventually every earlier engine of the class was altered to conform.

The original springing must have almost inevitably provided a 'lively' ride at the cab end. It was Stirling's first standard for the trailing wheels of all inside-framed tender engines, and he continued to use it throughout his lifetime on some classes. It consisted of a set of six volute springs, nested in two batches of three, right and left of the centre

line of the engine, and cradled in a transverse channel-iron, bearing on the top of the trailing axle-boxes through a vertical post, or strut, at each end. A similar, but inverted, channel formed in the drag-box casting passed the weight of the rear end of

No. 94 as built 1876. One of the first engines built with the larger trailing wheels and fitted with vacuum brakes. She was a Kings Cross engine, but this photograph seems to have been taken at Doncaster

the engine through the volute springs to the axle-boxes and wheels. Such a type of springing, though sensitive to track irregularities, had no appreciable 'damping' inherent in its make-up, and the change to the new design, with a longish plate spring beneath each axlebox, must have meant a great improvement in the comfort of the footplate; even though the term 'comfort' might nowadays be regarded strictly as relative to previous conditions—and not in the least comparable with the stuffy total enclosure of a diesel cab!

The large diameter of the trailing wheels was necessary, to enable the plate springs to be under-slung, while giving the required track clearance below them.★ The position of the firebox ruled out the combination of inside bearings to the trailing wheels with plate springs above the axleboxes. Here, once again, a more or less accidental change in the outward aspect of the 8-footers enhanced their appearance of compactness and beauty.

But the addition of the vacuum brake apparatus itself certainly had a most detrimental effect on the simplicity of outline of the right-hand side of the engine. The vacuum ejector, then a most bulky and clumsy bit of apparatus, was the villain of the piece. On front-coupled engines this had been tucked away behind the front bufferbeam, below footplate

The original drawing showing the 1876 layout of vacuum braking on 8-footers, using a double-ended non-automatic vacuum cylinder

★Nevertheless, seven years later, Stirling contrived to get the same type of springing on 4 ft. 1 in. trailing wheels, on his later design of 0—4—2 mixed traffic engines introduced in 1883. Drawings of these engines have all been destroyed, so that it is not possible to compare the two designs and see just how it was done.

level. Only a short, curved section of the ejector exhaust-pipe could be seen, where it entered the lower part of the front of the smokebox below the door. This was also the original layout for the 8-footers, Nos. 221 and 94, but, for some reason not readily apparent, it was changed, and the ejector was moved so that it stood on the right-hand side of the smokebox, its base resting on the smokebox wrapper plate at the level of the footstep, originally provided to help the enginemen to circumnavigate their engines safely. The ejector steam-cock, which had previously been mounted on the side of the smokebox, and the steam pipe from the cock to the ejector were moved rearwards to the front ring of the boiler barrel. The brake pipe was brought up between the frames ahead of the driving-wheels and then horizontally forward outside the frames above the footplate to the ejector on the side of the smokebox. But the brake pipe was not carried forward to the front bufferbeam, for double-heading was strictly forbidden.

It almost seems as if Stirling was proud of this eyesore, for the ejector itself, a brass casting, and the copper steam-pipe and brake-pipe (where this was visible) were kept brightly polished. A crude form of passenger alarm communication was provided by a cord, passing from the train, above the tender, and connected to the top of a long vertical lever, mounted just ahead of the cab and pivoted at its lower end. This lever abutted near its pivot against a stop clamped on the long rod, running the length of the boiler barrel, from the cab to the ejector steam-cock, which the driver normally pulled to apply the brake by supplying live steam to the ejector, and of course pushed in order to shut the steam-cock. Theoretically, by pulling on the cord a passenger could open the ejector steam-cock, thus applying the brake, and whilst the cord continued to be pulled the driver could not close the cock. In practice no doubt the stretch of the cord would have enabled the driver to take control, but at least his attention would have been drawn definitely and clearly to what had happened. Unless in the dark he had failed to observe the altered position of the lever after operation by the passenger, he would not, as nowadays, have been in some temporary doubt as to whether a more or less normal brake-pipe leak might have been responsible for the relatively slow change in vacuum on the driver's gauge.

The vacuum-brake cylinder was mounted transversely behind the trailing axle between the frames and was of the old 'collapsible sack' type, provided halfway along its length with a foot for fixing—in this case, at first, to the underside of the 'drag-box' casting—and for the brake-pipe connection. The cylinder was double-ended and was of indiarubber, the external circular plate ends and a series of internal metal rings preventing the indiarubber from collapsing flat when a degree of vacuum was created by the ejector. Instead, the ends were drawn towards the middle, the rubber creasing similarly to a bellows. To each end of the cylinder was connected one end of a bell crank lying horizontally, the other end of which through a universally-jointed link pulled on the top end of an arm on a transverse

No. 69, probably in 1881, with new frames, but with her original boiler and open splasher-slots

horizontal brake shaft, carried at its ends on brackets bolted to the reinforced cab footsteps. A short arm near each end of this shaft was connected via the brake pull rods to the brake hangers and brake blocks. It sounds even worse in description than the

No. 93 at York, probably about 1887; splasher slots have been filled in, and later design of brake gear fitted, but she still has her original shallow frames and smaller diameter boiler, and the 'dummy' rear sandboxes have not yet been added

drawing itself looked, and that was bad enough! And all this complication merely in order to enable an unsuitable double-ended cylinder to be used. This cylinder was 20 in. outside diameter and there was plenty of room to have mounted two vertical half-cylinders of this general design, pulling direct on arms of the transverse main brake-shaft; when later the automatic brake was fitted only one vertical cylinder, 21 in. in diameter, connected thus was needed and this simple layout became standard, all the older engines being altered in accordance.

No. 221 was rebuilt twice, receiving new deeper frames and new cylinders in March 1888. She had already received a new 4 ft. 2 in. diameter boiler in October 1882, which was replaced by a new, similar one in May 1893. Her final rebuilding was carried out in 1899 by Ivatt and will be dealt with in the chapter devoted to rebuilt engines. No. 94, on the other hand, retained her original frames throughout.

Nos. 69 and 98

These two engines were completed at Doncaster within a week or two of each other and carried consecutive works numbers, 219 and 220 respectively. No. 69 was out of works, new, on February 19, 1877 and No. 98 shortly after. Once again, the actual date cannot be given in her case; there are no records in existence. Both engines were stationed at Peterborough and both were among the shortest

lived of the earlier 8-footers, No. 98 being scrapped in May 1900 and No. 69 in June 1901.

No. 69 was the first 8-footer to be built new with Ramsbottom safety-valves instead of the old twin spring balance safety-valves. The Ramsbottom valves had been tried out during the previous year or so on other classes of Stirling engines.

A new drawing was made specially for the main frames of these two engines. Unfortunately it is no longer in existence, and it is not possible to say just how these frames differed from the earlier ones. The probability seems to be that the profile at the cylinders was not changed, but that the depth of the frames over and behind the driving wheel hornguides was increased. There had been trouble here on earlier engines. The later engines of the following series were also fitted with these stronger frames and some of them lasted the life of the engines; but Nos. 69 and 98 do appear to have both received new frames early in life, probably both around 1882.

Among the chronological puzzles occasionally posed by photographs of the 8-footers, there is an early one of No. 69, which happens to show the original open slots in the driving splasher. The closing of these slots by fitting backing plates was not put in hand until the end of 1880: the building dates of engines of several classes settles the dividing line between slotted and plain splashers for new engines quite clearly. Of course, engines with slotted splashers already in service would not have had the backing plates added until they next were sent to Doncaster for repairs, which might be two or even three years later; although there is the possibility that simple jobs such as fitting splasher-slot backing plates would be delegated by Doncaster works to such running sheds as Peterborough, where No. 69 was stationed, and Kings Cross, both fully equipped in those days to carry out even general repairs. In this photograph of No. 69 the frames at the smokebox are of the type fitted on engines only between 1880 and 1883; in particular on Nos. 662-71 when built, and for several 'rebuilds' including No. 1. It is recorded that No. 69 was at Doncaster from September 1879 to March 1880 for general repairs, when she received a new right-hand cylinder; the next visit to Doncaster works being between June and November 1882. It seems very nearly certain that on one of these two occasions she was given new frames.

But if the new frames had been fitted at the earlier visit when she was ex-works in March 1880, then the well-established and accepted story that such frames were first introduced when No. 1 was rebuilt in December 1880 would be completely upset. And if the frames had been fitted at the later visit, in June 1882, then why are the splasher-slot backing plates absent on this particular photograph? Various theories can be put forward to support either occasion as the likely date of frame change, but in the absence of concrete evidence one way or the other—and the official repair books omit reference to any change of frames on No. 69—then this must remain a puzzle.

This case illustrates the importance of the evidence provided by old photographs and the difficulty in assessing such evidence in the absence of official records which are no longer in existence. This particular query may not seem a matter of great moment so many years later, with all the engines except No. 1 long resolved into scrap and the metal used again unrecognisably; but if history is to be recorded, it is perhaps just as well that it should be stated accurately, even if uncertainties have to be accepted as unresolved.

Nos. 544-49, 60, 550, 93 and 95

There are few changes to record on the next engines of the class to be built. In fact, the only points to be mentioned are that the last two engines, Nos. 93 and 95, received cabs in which the side sheets were longer, below waist level, than on any previous engine, a change which was continued thereafter on all succeeding 8-footers; and that the number of boiler tubes on these two engines was reduced from 183 to 170, not by altering the spacing of the tubes, but merely by omitting 13 of them. The most likely reason for this change is that trouble may have been experienced with cracks developing in the tube plate between the flanged corners and the outer row of tubes. To leave solid metal in this area could be counted on to eliminate or reduce such trouble.

Nos. 544 to 547 had consecutive Doncaster works numbers, but their appearance new was spread over almost six months, and they were turned out in

pairs on August 8 and September 4, 1877, and on November 27, 1877 and January 24, 1878. No. 548 was out of shops new on May 6, 1878 and Nos. 549 and 95 on June 26, 1878 and April 23, 1880, but we can only say that Nos. 60, 550 and 93 seem to have been completed in September 1878, December 1878 and December 1879 respectively.

The four engines Nos. 544-47 received new frames or new part frames in the 1880s, but for some reason the succeeding four engines, Nos. 548, 549, 60 and 550, all retained their original frames throughout their existence. A possible reason for this is given in Chapter 12.

No. 60 had the melancholy fate of being the first 8-footer to be withdrawn from service, in September 1899, less than three months after No. 221 had been very thoroughly rebuilt by Ivatt with a new domed boiler, special new cylinders with balanced slide-valves exhausting (like the slide-valve 'Atlantics') through the back, a special water circulating pipe and all 'modern conveniences'. It is probable that the ordering of the first batch of Ivatt small 'Atlantics'—the 'Klondykes'—was the reason for No. 60's early withdrawal.

No. 60 is also the subject of a chronological puzzle. The two photographs of her show rather conflicting aspects of the way in which the older 8-footers were brought up to date, to be in line with the current practice of the time. The earlier photograph of No. 60 shows a cast-iron chimney, of the 1885 type, but the brake rigging is of the simple vacuum type and there are no 'dummy' sand-boxes. The later photograph shows the older, built-up type of chimney, but the brake is the automatic version and the dummy rear sand-boxes are fitted. Still, several 8-footers were running right up to the last with built-up chimneys, including No. 549 of the batch now under consideration; and probably so was No. 60, but there is no evidence left to prove it; and though the late Mr. J. F. Vickery thought this was the case, he unfortunately could not be sure, nearly 60 years afterwards, when the question was raised with him.

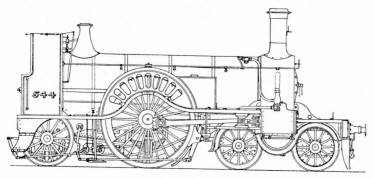

No. 544, as built, 1877, with Ramsbottom safety valves and the larger trailing wheels, but still with shallow frames and non-automatic brake

No. 662 at Boston, about 1898. One of the earliest engines to be withdrawn

A curious minor point about the early 8-footers, applicable to all engines built up to 1880, was that no particular care seems to have been taken in the exact pitching and positioning of the snap-head rivets attaching the footplate angle-irons to the platforms themselves. This had the effect of causing variations in the height and position of the two footsteps on the platform on the curve of the raised footplate immediately above the driving axle. No. 60 was specially identifiable by the exceptional positions of her footsteps, but on one or two of the other engines the position of the footsteps, combined with some other peculiarity, aided identification in photographs where the number was not clearly decipherable.

Nos. 662-71

These ten engines were the first to be built new with deeper frames at the smokebox. The thickness of the frames on the general arrangement drawing is shown as 1 3/16 in., whereas all previous and later engines had 1¼ in. frame plates. This drawing, however, is one of those on which there are a number of obvious errors, and it is likely that the 1 3/16 in. thickness is another of them, especially since No. 1's frames, of exactly the same design, are 1¼ in. thick.

They had the larger 4 ft. 2 in. diameter boiler, the bogie frames were strengthened, the crosshead design was revised to provide a neater outline, and the vacuum brake cylinder was changed to the piston type arranged vertically, with a consequent simplification of the actual brake rigging. Conical

buffers of a neater design were fitted. The injector deliveries were taken to the sides of the mud collector at the lowest point of the middle ring of the

No. 664 as built, 1881. The first engine with the plain driving wheel splasher and the oval brass Doncaster works plate

No. 665 at Kings Cross, probably about 1888, but certainly with no changes apparent externally from her original condition

boiler barrel instead of to a clackbox on the side of the front ring. It is probable that this was a really useful arrangement and that a good proportion of the scale and dirt deposited in the boiler by the feed water was actually left in the mud drum and

No. 667 at Kings Cross, about 1900.   She appears to be one of the engines fitted with the chimney originally intended for the No. 1003 class, appreciably shorter than the cast-iron chimney normally fitted to the earlier 8-footers

could easily be removed when the boiler was washed out through the manhole provided in the base of the drum. It was only after seven years that this method of delivering the feed water was changed, No. 775 being the first engine with the new arrangement, a combination steam-valve and clackbox being provided on the 'boiler-front' in the cab,

from which the feed water passed to the boiler through an internal pipe, terminating at a point along the length of the barrel above the mud collector.

The fireboxes on Nos. 662 to 671 were fitted with a more elaborate firehole door than on either earlier or later engines, the flap being hinged in their case at the top, and giving an opening through the upper half of the main firehole door instead of the lower half as in the usual Stirling arrangement. This meant that the lower lip of the hole through which the fireman had to put his coal when firing was just about 2 ft. above the cab floor, instead of about 1 ft. on the earlier engines and about 18 in. on the engines following the No. 662 series. The necessary additional lift of the coal very definitely involved harder work for the fireman. Of course the 6 ft. 2 in. firebox of the 8-footers needed very little physical energy to be put into the propulsion of the coal to the front end—very different from the task of the fireman of a Great Western 'King', for example, with its 11 ft. 6 in. firebox, burning most of the coal in the forward half of the box. Also the coal consumption in the heyday of the Stirling singles was only in the order of 30 lb. per mile, so that even with the higher lift required, the effort of firing was not very great. The Stirling footplate inside the cab was always at the level of the outside platform, 4 ft. 2 in. above rail level.

The curve of the upper edge of the main frames ahead of the smokebox and above the footplate on these ten engines differed from that on later engines. The drawings show exactly similar radii

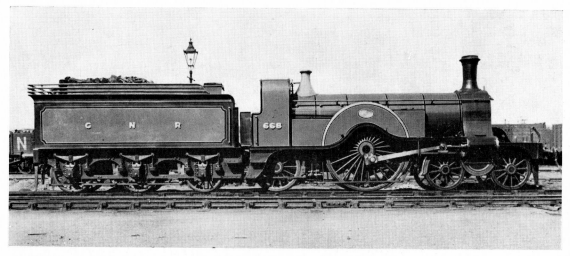

No. 668 at Peterborough 1911.   With botched-up chimney base, fitted at Doncaster to replace the correct one, which had worn out.   The boiler, ex 778, was in 1925 fitted to No. 1 and is still carried by her.   A secondhand crosshead has been fitted, from a scrapped early 8-footer.   The tender is a Stirling one, of 1890–93 type

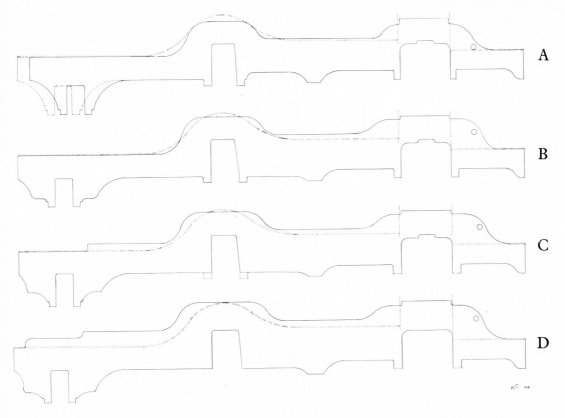

THE DEVELOPMENT OF THE MAIN FRAMES OF THE 8-FOOT SINGLES

The four drawings show the steady increase in frame dimensions of the 8-foot singles from 1870 to 1895. All drawings are to the same scale, and the thickness of the frame plates remains at 1¼ inches throughout. The line of the footplate has been shown chain-dotted, and forms a datum line which indicates just how the frame strengthenings were carried out. The outline of the footplate is the same for the upper three frames shown, but on the lowest frame, that for the No. 1003 class, the curve above the driving axle is higher, and so is the line of the footplate above the slide-bars.

A shows in full lines the frames of No. 1 as built, with the short firebox and trailing wheelbase. The chain dotted lines at the rear end show the increase in length to accommodate the longer firebox used on No. 8 and all subsequent engines up to 1893. This longer frame is correct for Nos. 2, 3, 5, 7, 8, 22, 33, 34, 47, 48, 53, 60, 62, 69, 93, 94, 95, 98, 221, 544-550 as built.

B shows the strengthened, deeper frames used first on No. 1 when rebuilt in 1880, and used on new engines Nos. 662-671. The horns projecting downward at the cylinder have been strengthened; the upper edge of the frame from the cylinder to behind the driving axle box is higher, but the rear portion of the frame still continues at footplate level. The anchorages for the ends of the rear wheel laminated springs have caused a change in the frame shape here. In front of the smokebox the higher top edge of the frame has a 'plunging' shape, so that the location of the point at which the frame passes below the front footplate is the same as on the original No. 1 frames.

C shows in full lines the frames used on Nos. 777, 778, 1001 and 1002, which were built new with helical springs for the driving wheels. The horns, shown dotted, at the driving axle were required on Nos. 771-776, engines built with laminated driving-wheel springs. Most of the earlier engines rebuilt by Stirling received new frames of one or other of these two versions, depending on whether helical or laminated springs were used. The trailing wheel spring anchorages are modified to suit stronger spring brackets with adjustable spring-links. The rear portion of the frame is raised well above footplate level, necessitating—on the official drawing at any rate—a slight notch at the front end of the expansion bracket where the top edge of the frame curves down to the rear of the driving axle.

D shows the very considerably deeper and stronger frames on Nos. 1003-1008. The alteration to the cylinder design on these engines, with the port face and steam chest no longer vertical, but inclined so that the upper edge of the port face is further away from the actual cylinder, improved the layout of the exhaust passage so that the central small notch in the frame above the cylinder is no longer needed. The frames have been made higher yet at both cylinder and driving axle, and the trailing portion of the frame is again raised higher above the footplate.

Note: It has not been possible to show all the holes drilled through the frames, the position of many of these not being dimensioned on the drawings still available.

for both types of frame, but Nos. 662 to 671 and those earlier engines rebuilt before 1884—like No. 1 —had a more 'plunging' effect in their appearance. The curve was an S with radii of 1 ft. 4 in. for both convex and concave parts of the curve. On

No. 669 in about 1899, with cast-steel driving wheels replacing the original wrought iron ones, and with auxiliary axlebox lubricators

No. 771 about 1899. Although there are several photographs of this engine on trains, there does not appear to be a really satisfactory 'portrait' of her

these rebuilds and on the No. 662 series the concave curve centre seems to have been struck only about 15 in. above the footplate, so that there was not the smooth blending into the footplate level which was apparent on the later engines, from 1884 onwards. It is probable that this derived originally from the new frames made for No. 1 in 1880, since the distance which the frames extended forward of the smokebox above the footplate was the same for the original shallow frames as for the new deep frames which succeeded them. These frames were the first to be set inwards between the smokebox and the front bufferbeam, where the distance between frames had been narrowed to 3 ft. 11¼ in. to increase front bogie wheel clearance.

Nos. 662 and 663 were the last engines of the class to be fitted with slotted driving-wheel splashers. There is indeed quite a possibility that the slots were filled in before the engines were completed, both on these two engines and on the two 6 ft. 7 in. coupled engines, Nos. 207 and 212, under construction at the same time. The cabs were the

same as on the immediately preceding engines, with the 3 in. longer cab sides, although the roofs were still the same length as on No. 1 and all her sisters so far constructed.

On No. 664 there was also a notable step forward in the modernisation (for those days) of the appearance of the 8-footers. The slots in the driving splashers had been abolished, and the plain splasher was decorated with an oval brass plate on which the works number and date of the engine were engraved as well as the words 'Great Northern Ry. Co. Makers Doncaster Works'. A dummy rear sand-box was added between the driving-wheel splasher and the cab, tidying up the appearance. The chimneys were still of the built-up type, but the boiler pitch having been raised a further ¾ in., to 7 ft. 3¼ in., the chimney overall length was correspondingly shortened.

The vacuum ejector was still mounted on the right side of the smokebox, and the brakes were still the simple vacuum type. It is fair to say that pencil sketches made on the 1874 general arrangement drawing show several attempts to tuck the ejector away into a less conspicuous position. Indeed, as has been mentioned, Nos. 221 and 94 at first had their ejectors placed below the footplate ahead of the smokebox, in the position adopted for all other classes of engine, but it was not long before they were moved to the standard side position on the 8-footers.

No. 664 was sent to the Stephenson Centenary Exhibition at Newcastle in 1881. She was a Doncaster engine, and it is perhaps an indication that Stirling may have had a special feeling for certain individual engines of the class that No. 1, the first to be built, No. 47, the first to be on public exhibition, and No. 664, the first with closed splashers and herself also an exhibition engine, were all stationed at Doncaster, where of course Stirling would see

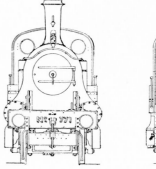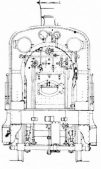

(LEFT) *Front view of No. 771 as equipped in 1892.* (RIGHT) *Cab view of No. 776 as built, 1887*

them almost daily. It is worth recalling that Stirling was in charge of the Locomotive Running Department as well as of the Doncaster Works. But No. 776, six years later, did not become a Doncaster engine after her exhibition at Newcastle; she was sent to Peterborough. No new 8-footers were, in fact, shedded at Doncaster after No. 670 was sent there new in 1882.

Nos. 664 and 665 were twins, but on Nos. 666 to 671 the cab roofs and the upper part of the cab-sides were made 3 in. longer, this being the same amount that had already been added to the lower part of the cabsides on the previous four engines. Apart from the removal of the vacuum ejector to the inside of the cab and the replacement at varying dates of the built-up chimneys by cast-iron ones, little change occurred throughout the life of these engines. No. 666 indeed always retained the narrow, straight footplate angle-iron ahead of the smokebox, although the other nine engines were given the later form of angle, with the curve behind the bufferbeam following the line of the bogie splasher, which itself was cut short by a small amount at the leading end.

No. 668 survived all the other engines of the series by over six years. She had made the fastest run between London and Grantham in the 1895 Race to Aberdeen, and undoubtedly this was the main reason for sparing her until June 1912. Most of the series were withdrawn in 1903-04, but Nos. 663 and 666 remained in service until 1906. No. 668 had a cast-iron chimney in 1895, but this was replaced about 1905 by a second built-up one.

It was while this series of 8-footers was being put in hand that David Joy, the inventor of the radial valve gear which was standardised on so many engines on different railways between 1880 and 1920, approached Stirling on using the Joy valve-gear on an 8-footer. Stirling sent him drawings in December 1882, and Joy managed to lay out the gear to his satisfaction, though—not surprisingly —he found it 'awfully difficult—no room between the wheel and the motion-plate'. But Stirling's reaction was unfavourable and most characteristic: 'Naa, mon, I canna spile my grand engine with the likes of that machinery outside o' her'—and no Stirling engine ever had Joy valve-gear or indeed any valve-gear during his lifetime other than the Stephenson link motion.

It is worth pointing out that the Joy valve-gear would have involved new cylinders with valves on top, an awkward steam and exhaust-pipe arrangement, the latter too high in the smokebox to get a properly positioned blast-pipe with easy curves in the exhaust 'breeches pipe'. The external curves of the smokebox would have had to be suppressed or

No. 772 at York, about 1888–90. The exhaust pipe from the vacuum ejector, unique on the 8-footers, runs from the cab to the smokebox externally, crossing over the handrail The standard combination ejector was later fitted, the exhaust pipe from which passes inside the boiler from the cab to the smokebox

at least drastically altered. Moreover, the special virtue of the Joy gear, that on *inside-cylinder* engines it permitted longer axle and big end bearings, had no application at all on the outside-cylinder 8-footers, whose bearings were not restricted by any constructional design difficulties.

On the subject of the steam distribution, the present writer was told, many years ago, by William Theobald, then Chief Locomotive Inspector on the London, Tilbury & Southend Railway, that in his younger days he had taken the opportunity of riding on as many types of locomotive as possible, among them the Stirling 8-footers; and that he had asked his Great Northern opposite number Inspector friends about the valve-setting, and if it was the best possible. The reply was that in the early days of the 8-footers, a large number of tests of different valve settings had been carried out, and the setting which gave the best all-round result had been adopted and standardised. It is a pity that no records of this remain.

Here again, it may be worth while stating that valve setting on any locomotive is not a case of a hard-and-fast, obviously ideal, setting. If the leads at front and back of the slide-valve are made equal then port openings and cut-offs at front and rear will not be the same. If cut-offs are made the same, then the other two factors will be affected; and similarly, if port openings are made equal, it will be to the detriment of lead and cut-off equalisation. The shorter the connecting rod and the eccentric rods, the worse the irregularities will become. So that for any engine, to get the optimum results will mean a juggling with those three factors in setting the valves; and the best setting for each case will depend also on what speeds the engine will require to run at, and within what range of

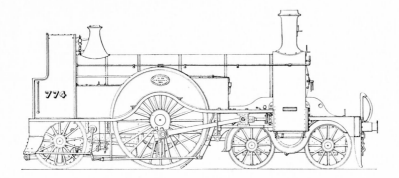

No. 774 as running in 1900 with vacuum brake hose connection on front buffer-beam

cut-offs it will normally be working. With the short-travel, flat slide-valves of Stirling days, unsatisfactory valve setting could make all the difference. Even on such comparatively recent designs as the Great Western 'Castles' it made the difference between a good engine and a relatively poor one.

Nos. 771-74, 775-78, 1001-02

Although these three batches of the 18 in.-cylinder 8-footers differed from one another in minor details, they differed even more from the earlier engines of the class. The frames were deepened behind the driving wheels so that, under the expansion brackets on the firebox sides, they were no longer level with the outside platform but were $4\frac{1}{2}$ in. above it. The engines were consequently known as the 'high framed' 8-footers, the older engines being referred to as 'low framed'. In later days this was an important difference from the

point of view of the works, because boilers were no longer immediately interchangeable between engines; but in Stirling's day it did not matter, since each engine retained its boiler, once fitted, until the boiler was worn out and replaced by a new one—never by a second-hand one.

There was also the change in the profile of the main frames ahead of the smokebox, the curves giving a more 'flowing' appearance, which was referred to in dealing with Nos. 662-71. The running plates to the rear of the smokebox were made $1\frac{1}{2}$ in. wider than on the earlier engines, but the main increase in width was that of the cab, from 6 ft. 0 in. to 6 ft. 8 in. The side elevation was the same as on Nos. 662 to 665, with a narrower upper portion than on Nos. 666 to 671.

The bogies were slightly different, the four plate springs being reduced from 2 ft. 6 in. to 2 ft. 4 in. in length, while the number of plates remained the same.

No. 776, photographed in grey when new, before being sent to the Newcastle Exhibition in 1887. The works plate for No. 777 has been put on in error

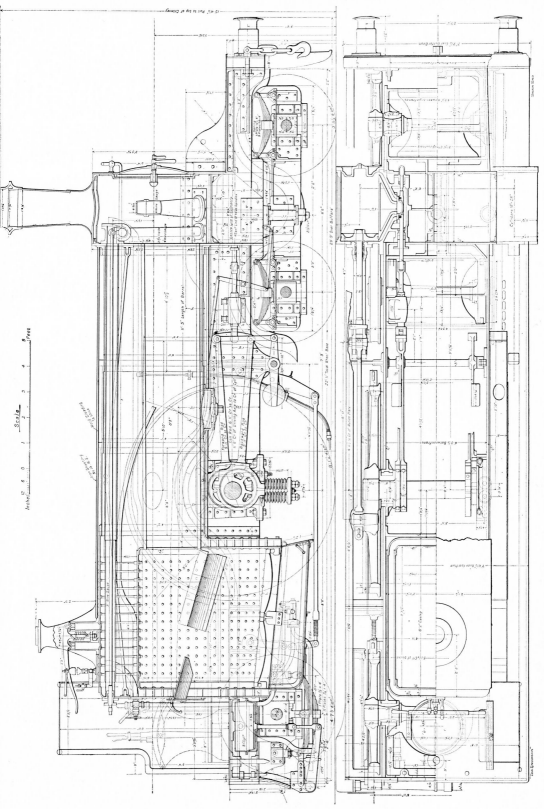

General arrangement sectional drawing purporting to show No. 776. The cab, however, is incorrect; the lower portion should be 3 in. longer. The safety valve casing is of the shape used only before 1883. The detail of the bogie splasher is incorrect both front and rear. Note that the frames have an additional transverse horizontal plate stay immediately behind the smokebox. This was introduced at the end of 1880 and used thereafter on all engines of the Class

The injector delivery on Nos. 771-74 was still into the sides of the mud collector, but, commencing with No. 775, the clackboxes were placed on the 'boiler-front' in the cab and the feed was delivered halfway along the barrel through internal pipes. The pitch of the boiler remained, for a year or two, at 7 ft. 3¼ in., but with No. 775 the wheel tyres were increased in thickness from 2½ in. to 2¾ in. and the pitch went up to 7 ft. 3½ in., the final dimension for the class, for all the older engines received the thicker tyres as their old ones wore out.

A retrograde step in design was first put into practice on this batch, but eventually became standard for all new and replaced pistons. Each piston was still fitted with two Ramsbottom packing rings, but instead of each ring sitting in its own groove, as hitherto, one wide groove was provided to accommodate both of them. This sounds innocent enough, but in fact there is an appreciable falling-off in steam-tightness when the two rings are put in one groove. The main cause of leakage is the inevitable side clearance of the rings. There is always a certain amount of rubbing on the faces of the rings, tending to cause wear, and the total side wear is therefore more rapid with the two rings in one groove; moreover, it all takes place in the one groove. The 'labyrinth' effect of rings in separate grooves is lost. The space between the inside of the piston ring and the bottom of the ring groove is, of course, necessarily so great as to form a free path for steam leakage across the groove.

The steam chest covers on these engines each had two substantial lifting eyes cast on the back, to assist in lifting the covers into position. From this time onwards, all new cylinders, whether for old or new engines, were equipped with these lifting eyes. It is said that it had already been the practice at some running sheds to add screwed-in lifting eyes to the covers as a worthwhile aid to fitting.

No. 777 at Kings Cross, about 1895. The engine, like No. 776, received a built-up chimney when first constructed, but it was replaced after about 10 years by a cast-iron one, of the type originally intended for the No. 1003 class

No. 771 was the last 8 ft. single to be fitted with the old simple vacuum brake, and was new, out of shops, on November 7, 1884. No. 772, completed on March 18, 1885, was the first to be built with the automatic brake. She was, from the first, fitted with a combined ejector and brake-valve, and in her case only, for the first few years, the exhaust-pipe from the ejector passed externally along the boiler to the smokebox. It actually crossed over the handrail about three feet ahead of the cab, to lie snugly close to the boiler barrel, and must have been an occasional source of emotion in the enginemen if by chance their hands grasped the hot exhaust-pipe momentarily instead of the handrail. This arrangement did not last very long, however, and the internal exhaust-pipe, passing inside the boiler barrel which was used on No. 773 and all subsequent engines—and eventually also on all earlier engines —was later fitted to No. 772. No. 771 was the last engine of the class to be fitted when new with taper shank buffers. No. 772's buffers, though of the parallel socket type henceforward adopted as standard, were unique in having a half-round beading round the end of each socket.

Hitherto all 8-footers had been built new with the then standard built-up type of chimney, but No. 773 shocked and distressed the admirers of the class, both inside and outside the Doncaster works, by appearing, on August 6, 1885, with a slim cast-iron chimney, henceforth to be, with a few exceptions, the standard chimney for the class. It was at first felt to be quite out of keeping with the essential dignity of the class. But the new chimney, if not so impressive as its predecessor, was perhaps more in line with the remarkable degree of neatness which all Stirling's engines exhibited after 1885. Even the buffers contributed their little share, the final parallel shank design being first used on No. 773. Again, quite a number of the older engines received these parallel shank buffers when rebuilt in the 1880s.

No. 774, out of shops new on December 1, 1885, was the 'twin' of No. 773, and was the last 8-footer to have wrought-iron wheels and dry-sanding. She became one of the more famous of the 8-footers, because for some ten years she was the latest of the class to be stationed at Kings Cross, and her regular driver, Sam Watson, taking her over new, remained her driver for the next 16 years. An exceptionally fast 'runner', it is very likely that Sam was the driver who achieved the highest speed ever recorded with an 8-footer, 85·7 m.p.h., and that his beloved and cherished No. 774 was the engine which did it.

There was a further point of difference between Nos. 773-74 and all the 8-footers which had preceded them. This was the adoption of mild steel for frames and boilers, instead of the wrought-iron hitherto used. There had been a considerable reduction in the cost of steel during the previous few years, and the changeover to steel frames and boiler reduced the cost of Nos. 773-74 by nearly £200 as compared with the previous pair of 8-footers. Stirling was in process of changing to steel for all his engines, and it happened that No. 773 was the first new 8-footer to use the new material. All subsequent 8-footers had steel frames and boilers.

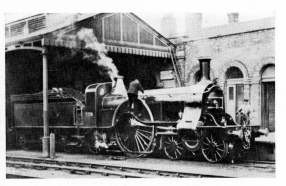

No. 778 at Lincoln about 1899. The driver is filling the auxiliary oilboxes for the driving axleboxes which were fitted to the engines by Ivatt

No 8-footers were built in 1886, but No. 775 was completed on January 20, 1887, and in having cast-steel wheels and steam sanding-gear represented another stage in the 'modernisation' of the 8-footers. No. 775 was the engine which, in the 1895 Race to the North, put up the highest average speed between Grantham and York, covering the 82¾ miles in 76 min., an average speed of 65·3 m.p.h. Even with the 101-ton train of the occasion, that was a really good performance; but it did not earn her the late survival of No. 668, though she did last nearly a year longer than the other straight-back engines of the same batch. She was officially broken up on November 7, 1905.

The final 'modernisation' of the class came with the next engine, No. 776, completed on March 26, 1887, which differed from No. 775 in having Timmis helical springs for the driving wheels in place of the laminated springs hitherto used. No. 776 was intended for exhibition at Newcastle and was therefore fitted with the dignified built-up chimney, no longer standard because of its high cost, but eminently suitable for an exhibition engine. It seems clear, not only from the case of

No. 776 but also, as will be seen later, in connection with Nos. 1003-08, that Stirling himself, as an artist, preferred the built-up type and used it when a reasonable excuse gave him the opportunity. Two of these built-up chimneys were made—the usual Doncaster practice of 'pairs'—but the second one was apparently not ready in time for No. 775, and was used on No. 777, which was ex-works September 21, 1887.

There was only one point of difference between No. 776 and No. 777. The latter engine had the old soft packing for her piston rods, with adjustable glands: No. 776 had the new metallic packing with the non-adjustable glands which this packing required. This one detail makes it clear that the official photograph, taken in neutral colours prior to exhibition, does really show No. 776, even though at the time of the photograph she was carrying No. 777's works plate, with the works number clearly shown as 441, instead of 433, No. 776's works number. It seems likely that No. 776 proved somewhat of a 'rush job' as she neared completion and the time of the opening of the exhibition became imminent, and the wrong works plate may have been a mistake due to haste. It was certainly put right later. In 1890, three years after the Newcastle Exhibition, No. 776 was again exhibited, this time at Edinburgh.

Helical driving wheel springs were used not only on all subsequent engines, but also on several older engines when they were rebuilt in the late eighties. They were almost certainly adopted with the idea of keeping the adhesion weight as nearly constant as possible by eliminating the internal friction of a laminated spring. They may also have cost slightly less.

No. 778, the last of this batch of four engines, was completed on November 26, 1887. During her relatively short life of less than 17 years she carried three boilers, a second-hand one from No. 3 being put on in November 1898 and replaced by a new boiler in August 1900. This final boiler was transferred to No. 1 in 1925, was used on her reappearance in steam again in 1938, and is still carried by her in the York Museum.

No. 773's second boiler, which was fitted in March 1896, had the distinction of being the very last boiler built for an 8-footer to the Stirling drawing and specification. After No. 773 was scrapped, it was laid aside for over three years before being fitted to No. 221, which carried it for a further two years before this engine also was scrapped.

It will have been noted that Nos. 775-76 and 777-78 could not have been called 'identical twins', even though their differences were not major ones.

F

THE STIRLING SINGLES

Nos. 1001-02

There was a break of nearly six years, from November 1887 to August 1893, before the next new 8-footer was completed at Doncaster, to be followed by her twin in December the same year. These were the very last of what might loosely be called the original design to be built. During those six years Stirling had built no fewer than ten express passenger engines, all 7 ft. 6 in. single-wheelers, and, if anything looked certain, it was that this was now the preferred design and that the 8-footers were a class in process of being superseded, with a very strong probability that no more of them would ever be built.

The underlying cause for Nos. 1001 and 1002 being brought into existence is an unusual one; the only parallel instance is that of No. 92, constructed to use again a sound pair of expensive driving-wheels. In the case of Nos. 1001 and 1002 it was not wheels but main frames which were already cut and finished and were not required for any other engine. It will be remembered that frame plates were usually machined eight at a time, for use on four engines. It happened that when the renewal of defective frames on the older 8-footers had been completed, there were, at the beginning of 1893, two sets of frame plates over. These had been cut in 1892, and there was no indication that they would ever be needed for any of the existing engines. But Stirling did not ask the Board at once for authority to build these new engines and charge their cost to the Capital Account. He decided to treat them as replacements for two old Sturrock engines, single-wheelers rebuilt from Sturrock's last express passenger engine design which had first appeared as 2—4—0s. They were 27 years old, and the excuse was a sound one, though later on

Stirling told Rous-Marten that he had 'found they were good for some years yet'. The new 8-footers were therefore numbered 264 and 265, and ran for some months with these numbers. They were the first 8-footers to be built as replacements for over 13 years, the last previous such engine being No. 95 built in April 1880.

In January 1894 Stirling got authority to construct 20 new engines on Capital Account and decided to transfer the two 8-footers, Nos. 264-65, to this Account, so that early in 1894 they were renumbered 1001 and 1002, the first four-figure numbers carried by any Great Northern engines. But there was an old Doncaster drawing office convention that if drawings were made for a series of engines of which the running numbers were not yet chosen, the drawings would refer to them as 'for engines Nos. 1000, etc.'; there was thus a faint spice of familiarity in the numbers of 1001 and 1002. It is a pity that no photographs exist showing them with their first running numbers.

Only in one minor point did they differ from their immediate predecessors. Their cabs were provided with horizontal handrails along the sides, similarly to the 7 ft. 6 in. singles and to all the other contemporaneous Stirling engines. They were the first 8-footers to be so fitted, and Stirling never added these handrails to any of the earlier engines. Ivatt, however, in rebuilding No. 544 with a domed boiler, added the horizontal handrails to the existing Stirling cab, and the four domed 8-footers to which he gave new cabs, Nos. 22, 34, 95 and 221, all received the additional handrails with the new cabs.

No. 1001 was the last engine of the original design to remain in service, being withdrawn on July 2, 1912, having survived No. 668 by just a month. She was, like No. 668, a Peterborough engine, and suitable work for them on the Lincolnshire branch lines was still available, a circumstance which no doubt had some bearing on their continued existence so long after all their sister engines had been withdrawn. Another factor may have been that Peterborough always looked after their single-wheelers and, even in their last days, those Stirling 8-footers and 7 ft. 6 in. engines which were lucky enough to be shedded there were never allowed to become 'run down'. They were maintained just as Stirling would have wished them to be, right up to the end.

As we turn to the work of the 8-footers in their very earliest days we find that no one seems to have recorded any performances for posterity. The first performance recorded seems to have been a note in *Engineering* at the time, that a special train convey-

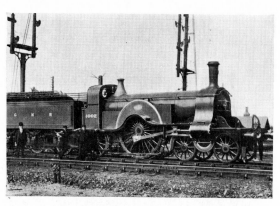

No. 1002, about 1900. The last of the 18-inch cylinder engines, the forty-seventh of the class to be built

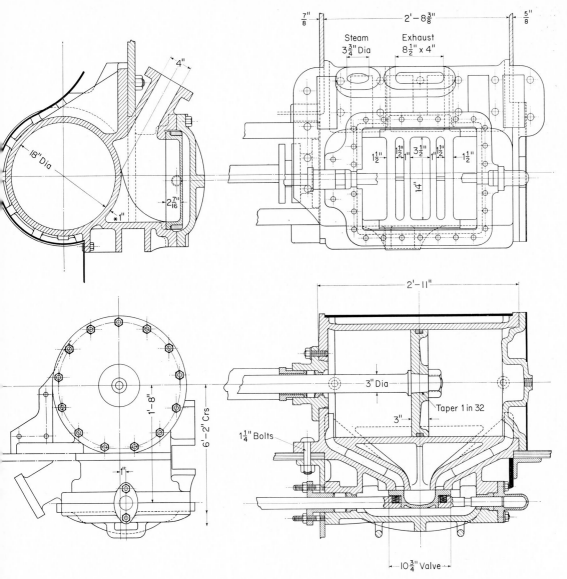

Cylinder for 8 ft. 0 in. Passenger Engine, 18 in. dia. x 28 in. stroke (engines up to and including No. 1002). Nominal piston clearance at ends of cylinder ⅜ in. ★This dimension, which does not appear on any existing drawing, is 1 in. to scale

ing the Prince and Princess of Wales from Kings Cross to Retford on August 16, 1875 covered the 138·6 miles in an inclusive time of 142 min. with one stop to change engines. No details or engine numbers are given, but in the *Railway Magazine* many years later the engine from Kings Cross to Peterborough was given as No. 22, and the time as 76 min. for the 76·4 miles. This was undoubtedly a remarkable run for the period, though the load

was most probably a light one. Nevertheless, a running average of just about 60 m.p.h. for such a distance, with only handbrakes working on wooden brake-blocks on the tender and the guard's van, or vans, and on a Royal train too, was altogether exceptional. Very soon after this, in October 1875, No. 22 was recorded as having run from Kings Cross to the Peterborough stop in 92 min. for the 76·4 miles, an average speed of 49·8 m.p.h. The load of 18 coaches seems exceptionally heavy for those days, certainly not less than 180 tons and very likely well over 200 tons. The next recorded performances were with the same engine; she may have had at that time a driver of outstanding merit —or daring.

Summary details of these runs are given in the accompanying table, but noteworthy are the details of climbs out of London to the Potters Bar summit shown in the supplementary table, which includes the work of engine No. 48 as well.

EARLY RUNS FROM KINGS CROSS TO PETERBOROUGH

76·4 miles—booked time 90 min.

Engine No.	Load tons	Overall Time Min.	Av. Speed m.p.h.
22	160	89	51·5
22	150	88¼	51·8
22	120	78½*	53·1
22	190	89	51·5

* to passing Holme, 69·4 miles.

KINGS CROSS TO POTTERS BAR, 12·7 MILES, START TO PASS.

Engine No.	Load tons	Times m. s.
22	190	20 15
48	135	17 40½

To set these runs in their correct perspective, it is necessary to add that in the heyday of the Gresley 'Pacifics', 20 min. was considered a good average time to Potters Bar with the East Coast and Leeds expresses of 470 to 520 tons.

By far the greatest number of logs and notes of performances by the Stirling singles come from the records left by the late Charles Rous-Marten. He was fortunate in being allowed, apparently, to ride on the footplate or in the train, almost at his own discretion; and on one or two occasions he did endeavour to persuade the driver to get the very highest speed possible out of the engine. But Rous-Marten does not fail to point out that the 8-footers were designed to haul the heavy trains—of their period—and not just to run very fast with light trains. In fact, he says: 'Even in those days, that is, the quarter-century 1869 to 1894, there were few Great Northern fast expresses which could be called really light, except perhaps two of the Manchester expresses, which rarely exceeded 100 tons.' And these Manchester expresses were in the earlier days the preserve of various classes of rebuilt Sturrock engines, rather than the Stirling singles.

Only a few of the runs recorded by the late A. C. W. Lowe remain, since his early log book covering most of the Stirling period has been lost. One of the three remaining logs is quoted later, as are several recorded by the Rev. W. J. Scott, and by E. L. Ahrons.

The late James F. Vickery has contributed also a number of 'run of the mill' trips he made behind Stirling singles, mostly in their later days. In no case did the driver know he was being timed or that there was someone he knew on the train.

But Rous-Marten is *the* outstanding authority on the work of British locomotives from the early 1880s onwards. With credentials from the New Zealand Government he made an elaborate inspection of all the British railways during 1884 and 1885, including in his report particulars of speeds obtained on different railways. The 8-footer, No. 665, gave him 80 m.p.h., his highest speed then on the standard gauge; he did however record just about the same speed with a Johnson Midland 4—4—0, and also with a Broad Gauge 4—2—2 single on the Great Western. Rous-Marten's records, as published, were not given in the detailed manner that has become usual in more recent times, but they certainly give an excellent impression of the competent way in which the 8-footers performed the duties allocated to them. In the majority of his early notes Rous-Marten did not quote the engine number, which was regrettable in that each of the Stirling singles had a strong individuality. Printed opposite are summary details of some of Rous-Marten's runs with anonymous 8-footers.

Most, if not all, of these runs were made in the days when Stirling was still at the head of affairs, and the engines either gained time or at least had no time booked against them; but it was different after Ivatt took charge, and adhesion weights were reduced and the loads increased. The following three cases, in all of which time was lost, may have had bad weather as their extenuation, but Rous-Marten gave at first only the unfortunate outline. 8-footer No. 3 lost 6 min. 20 sec. between Kings Cross and Peterborough with a load of 230 tons, taking actually 89 min. 20 sec. Although they refer to the 7 ft. 6 in. singles described in the next chapter, the other two runs may be mentioned here. No. 233 lost 7 min. between Kings Cross and Peterborough, with a load of 256 tons, taking actually 92 min. No. 875 took 139 min. Peterborough to York with a load of 256 tons, losing

Route	Load tons	Dist. Miles	Time m. s.	Start to stop Av. Speed m.p.h.
Kings Cross—Grantham . . .	175	105·5	120 42★	53·2★
" "	120	105·5	114 50	55·1
Peterborough—Grantham . . .	120	29·1	33 08	52·8
Grantham—Retford . . .	148	33·1	32 40	60·8
Peterborough—Finsbury Park . .	130	73·8	79 22	55·8
Grantham—Kings Cross . . .	90–120	105·5	112 to 115†	56·6 to 55·1
Doncaster—Grantham . . .	155	50·5	56 19	53·8
Grantham—Peterborough . . .	155	29·1	30 17	57·6

★ Net time of 119 mins.
† Range of times on a number of runs.

(probably) about 14 min.

When these were published, in *The Engineer*, they drew a strong protest from 'Retired Observer', who seemed to have been rather more than just an observer, almost up to the date of his letter. He wrote: 'Mr. Rous-Marten does not say anything about the coal. I have seen some funny stuff on Great Northern tenders. Fuel used is now—(1898) —much worse than that formerly obtainable, and I have had many complaints of trains losing time due to "grates clinkered and could not keep steam", these all on big-boilered engines.

'To rebuild the older engines (i.e. Stirling's engines) with a steam dome has not been an improvement, as I have seen more engines, having domes, splashed by priming than those without domes. With domes, the usual practice is for the enginemen to fill their boilers, fill their fireboxes and then fill their pipes.'

Rous-Marten, in the *Railway Magazine* a year later, seemed to have re-quoted the last two of these runs, though since there were minor discrepancies between his two articles and the engine numbers were not quoted in the *Railway Magazine*, this cannot be taken for granted. The time from Kings Cross to Peterborough in the latter case was quoted as 90 min. 25 sec., the load 260 tons and the train the 7.45 p.m. The Peterborough to York run was identical in both articles, and Rous-Marten concluded by saying: 'Both these time losses were due to slow starts.' It should be noted that both Nos. 233 and 875 were fitted with steam-sanding, whereas No. 3 had dry-sanding.

There can be no doubt that Rous-Marten was deeply impressed by the poor performance of No. 875. Over two years later still, he was again quoting it in the *Railway Magazine*, though once more with discrepancies. 'One of the Great Northern 7 ft. 6 in. singles of the 871-880 batch ran from Peterborough to York, 111·8 miles, in exactly 2 hrs. with a load of 230 tons. In a second trip, the very same engine

with the same load took 139 min., because some trifling showers had fallen.'

Perhaps a correspondent, writing in *The Engineer* over the *nom-de-plume* of 'Runnning Shed', may have hit the bull's-eye with his comment on the Stirling 8-footers: 'They keep time like clocks with 13 on, but are all over the place with 14.' In other words, they were reliable in their ability to keep time under all conditions of weather with up to 200 tons load, but with heavier trains than this time-keeping would depend to some extent on the weather conditions. And, it may be said again, to no little extent on the skill and judgment of the drivers.

It will have been noted that the weight per coach has increased in these later instances appreciably above the weights of the coaches in the 1870s. Brakes, lavatories and steam-heating all contributed to this.

To complete the record of day-to-day overall performance, the following runs, noted at a rather later date than those previously quoted, are added. They represent excellent work with trains that were very heavy for single-wheelers. No. 667 ran from Peterborough to Doncaster, 79·6 miles, start to stop, in $93\frac{1}{2}$ min. with a load of 276 tons. There was a strong side wind. No. 1001 ran from York to Peterborough, with a load of 250 tons, in the actual running time of 123 min. 46 sec. for the 111·8 miles. There were two stops, at Doncaster and Newark, so that, although the periods during which the train was at rest are omitted, the train was twice brought to a dead stop and restarted. With a load of 250 tons, the effect of such a stop could not be appreciably less than 4 min. as compared with a run through the station at speed, so the net time for this run might well be only 116 min. Rous-Marten does not give any particulars of the run from Peterborough to Kings Cross, but simply says that the train made up 14 min. from York to Kings Cross.

Some further performances of the 8-footers in

85

Ivatt's time were recorded in greater detail by J. F. Vickery. Two runs on the 8.1 p.m. up from Grantham, which was allowed 33 min. start to stop for the 29·1 miles to Peterborough, show the fast running habitually made down the Stoke bank. These runs were clocked in 1901-03. As Vickery recorded times only at the stations, the times passing Stoke summit box are missing.

The consistency of the times, as between the two runs, will be noted, and on a third journey not tabulated, with engine No. 33 and a load of 120 tons, Tallington was passed in 23¼ min. The lighter load, however, permitted of a faster start up to Stoke, and Corby was passed in 12 min. exactly. Lower speed than on either of the tabulated runs was made thereafter down to Peterborough.

One of the most detailed records of the work of one of the 8-footers was also made by Mr. Vickery on the 8.40 p.m. from Peterborough to Kings Cross in April 1903.

This was really an exposition of an 8-footer running under ideal circumstances. Vickery does not mention the weather, so presumably it was not unfavourable. But with a load not far short of 200 tons the engine was skilfully handled to make a very brisk start from Peterborough, and the 1¾ min. lateness with which the train had left Peterborough had been recovered by Hitchin. Then checks supervened; but so fast was the downhill running from Potters Bar, with its maximum of probably 80 m.p.h. near Wood Green, that the booked time of 85 min. would have been maintained but for the

succession of checks and stops inward from Finsbury Park. The driver was reported to be Sam Watson, one of the most able enginemen of his day.

G.N.R. 8.40 p.m. PETERBOROUGH—KINGS CROSS
Load: 168 tons tare, 185 tons full
Engine: 4-2-2 No. 774

Dist. Miles		Sch. min.	Actual m. s.	Av. Spd m.p.h.
0·0	PETERBOROUGH	0	0 00	—
3·8	Yaxley		6 11	36·9
7·0	Holme		9 09	64·6
12·9	Abbots Ripton		15 31	55·7
17·5	HUNTINGDON	20	20 16	58·1
20·4	Offord		22 54	66·2
24·7	St. Neots		27 00	62·9
32·3	Sandy		34 19	62·3
35·3	Biggleswade		37 19	60·0
44·5	HITCHIN	49	47 05	56·6
47·8	Stevenage		51 39	43·3
51·4	Knebworth		55 44	52·9
54·4	Welwyn		58 39	61·8
			sigs.	
58·9	HATFIELD	64	63 04	—
63·9	Potters Bar		70 37	—
67·2	New Barnet		74 22	52·8
69·9	New Southgate		76 57	62·8
71·4	Wood Green		78 09	75·0
72·3	Hornsey		78 50	79·5
			p.w.s.	
73·8	Finsbury Park		80 30	—
			sig. stop	
76·4	KINGS CROSS	85	89 19	—

Net time: 82¼ min.
Net average speed: 55·7 m.p.h.

G.N.R. 8.1 p.m. GRANTHAM—PETERBOROUGH

Engine No.		47		664	
Load, tons		161		153	
Weather		Strong side wind, heavy showers		Dry but dull	
Dist. Miles		Actual m. s.	Av. Speed m.p.h.	Actual m. s.	Av. Speed m.p.h.
0·0	GRANTHAM	0 00	—	0 00	—
3·5	Great Ponton	6 55	30·0	6 49	30·2
8·4	Corby	13 02	48·4	12 46	49·9
13·3	Little Bytham	17 14	69·6	16 59	69·1
16·9	Essendine	20 11	72·9	19 50	75·5
20·7	Tallington	23 27	69·7	22 59	72·3
29·1	PETERBOROUGH	32 00	—	31 36	—

CHAPTER 7

THE LATER 7 ft. 6 in. 2-2-2s

Nos. 238 and 232

THESE engines represented a complete change of practice in Stirling's express engine designs, and were the first inside-cylinder single-wheelers since No. 39, the last 7 ft. engine, and No. 92, hitherto the only 7 ft. 6 in. engine, were completed at Doncaster at the end of June 1870.

In 1884 Stirling was still under pressure from the directors to economise as far as possible. On the 8 ft. singles the only outward sign of this was the change from the massive looking, three-piece, built-up chimney to the neater but less impressive cast-iron, once-piece chimney, commencing with No. 773 which was being built at the same time as No. 238. But it was Nos. 238 and 232 which were the first express engines actually in service with the cast-iron chimney.

The old Sturrock singles of 1860-61, Nos. 229-40, had by this time reached the end of their expected period of life, and it was sensible to replace them by new engines rather than spend a considerable sum of money in renewing them over the succeeding years. Stirling's new engines were thus of dimensions rather larger than the Sturrock rebuilds, but still a little smaller than the 8 ft. engines, and, what was of great importance, costing much less. Nevertheless, Stirling later explained that these 7 ft. 6 in. engines, and the succeeding similar but rather larger 7 ft. 6 in. engines, were intended primarily for use on the hillier sections of the line.

A further point of engineering technique had come to the fore at this time, the development of the manufacture of steel plate so that its price fell below that of wrought-iron. Stirling had used wrought-iron for both frames and boilers up to this period, and its good qualities (relative freedom from corrosion and fatigue, and its convenience for welding under the smith's hammer) had contributed

No. 238, the first 'intermediate' 7ft. 6in. single, as built 1885, with dry sanding front and rear and the cylinder displacement type lubricator on the front of the smokebox. The lubricator on the side of the smokebox waist comes into action when running with steam shut off

to the trouble-free life of Stirling's engines. But the claims of higher tensile strength and less cost could not be denied and the frames and boilers of Nos. 238 and 232 were made of steel. Their wheels, however, were wrought-iron, and such evidence as still exists indicates that the driving-wheels were the same type as No. 92's new pair of 1882 design. Indeed, it may well have been the manufacture of this replacement pair of 7 ft. 6 in. wheels which put the idea of an up-to-date version of No. 92 into Stirling's mind. The carrying wheels were the same as the leading wheels of the standard 2—4—0 engines.

No. 232, the second 'intermediate' 7ft. 6in. single, as running about 1903, with Ivatt modifications and chimney. Steam sanding for forward running has been provided, and the rear sandbox reduced in size

Nos. 238 and 232 were completed at Doncaster works on June 30 and August 1 respectively, both in 1885. The general arrangement drawing, so often dated *after* the completion of the first engine, in this case is dated December 12, 1884, and shows one or two details, such as the cab-footsteps, different from those on the completed engines. The feed water delivery, as shown on the drawing, was put into the boiler through clackboxes on the sides of the barrel, exactly as on the coupled engines of that date; and no rear sand-gear was shown, though this was added on the engines during construction. But No. 92 had footsteps of similar shape, clackboxes on the boiler barrel and no rear sanding-gear, just as shown on the general arrangement for Nos. 238 and 232. It thus looks as if it had been the original intention to build an up-to-date version of No. 92. The leading wheelbase, 9 ft. 9 in., was the same as No. 92's, the boiler barrels were the same length, 10 ft. 6 in. and, of course, the same standard 4 ft. 2 in. diameter; but the alteration in cylinder size, from 17½ in. by 24 in. to 18½ in. by 26 in.,

precluded using any motion parts to No. 92's drawings. Connecting rods, eccentric rods, crank axle, were all different from No. 92's.

The depth of the inside firebox below the boiler centre line was 5 ft. 6 in., as on No. 92's original boiler, but the height of the crown above the centre line was only 6½ in. It has been noted in an earlier chapter that the firebox crowns became lower and lower as Stirling grew older, and one is almost forced to the conclusion that some of the early renewals of a cylinder, shown in the repairs book from time to time on all classes of Stirling engines, may well have been due to fracture caused by water carry-over from a boiler with too high a water level, and that the firebox crowns on new engines were made lower so as to reduce the risk of this by increasing the steam space in the boiler. Rous-Marten once quoted Stirling as saying: 'Why should I put on domes? Look at those Great Eastern engines over there. They all have domes and the drivers complain that they are always priming on account of the Doncaster water. But my engines use the same water and they do *not* prime.'

This may well have been true as a general rule, but with a dirty, foamy boiler any engine, even the largest modern types, will prime; and the original high water level of Stirling's 'straightback' boilers not only meant a small steam space above the water,

No. 230 at Kings Cross in 1892. The earlier form of steam sanding is fitted, with the air intake above the sandbox. The rod for operating the rear dry sander is missing—perhaps located out of sight but more probably because the rear sand gear was out of order

No. 233, rebuilt by Ivatt, near Peterborough in 1910-11. Although fitted with a new domed boiler the original Stirling smokebox has been retained

but also caused the area of the water surface to be seriously reduced, due to the inward curve of the boiler above the centre line. Stirling always emphasised that with the collection of steam through the $\frac{5}{8}$ in. diameter holes of a perforated steam-pipe running the whole length of the boiler, he was collecting steam from the whole surface of the water, and therefore minimising the local disturbance of the water by violent ebullition immediately below the opening of a dome, this violent ebullition being the main factor in causing priming. Obviously the larger the water surface area the less risk of priming there would be.

The present writer, when travelling daily into London on the Great Northern main line, can recollect several cases, between 1903 and 1908, of Ivatt engines priming, but only one case of a Stirling engine doing so. It is true that during this period Ivatt's engines were becoming an ever increasing proportion of the locomotive stock, but in early 1903 there were nearly twice as many Stirling engines at work as there were Ivatt engines. Of course, all the 'straightback' boilers then in existence were of the latest designs, with the low firebox crown and the larger steam space, but these boilers were smaller than any of the Ivatt boilers and the engines were engaged on the same duties; certainly the Stirling engines of the mixed traffic and suburban tank classes were driven very hard indeed throughout their latter days, just the circumstances in which priming is most likely to occur.

Concerning the increase in cylinder dimensions over No. 92, it will be remembered that even as far back as 1871, Stirling had gone on record as saying

No. 234 at Kings Cross, about 1900

that the 17 in. x 24 in. cylinders of the 7 ft. singles had been found too small for the power needed, so that an increase in size was the logical step to take, even though the larger diameter involved a cross-section of the steam ports, where they lay parallel to the cylinder barrel, which must have been a headache to the foundry. It is purely surmise, but the short life of most of the earlier cylinders of this design could possibly be due to defective castings which only revealed their defects on a rebore.

Nos. 238 and 232 were both stationed at Doncaster when built, and were almost certainly first used on Leeds trains, where the gradients were rather steeper than on the main line, but the distances less, so that the shorter fireboxes and rather smaller grates would not put the engines at any great disadvantage. It was probably these services which Stirling had in mind when he referred to using these engines on the hillier parts of the line.

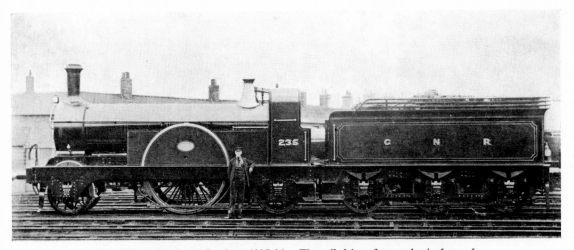

No. 235 at Peterborough, about 1895-96. The tall driver figures also in front of 8-footer No. 98, taken about the same time. His name is not known. The Stirling curved cab roof must have been barely high enough for him

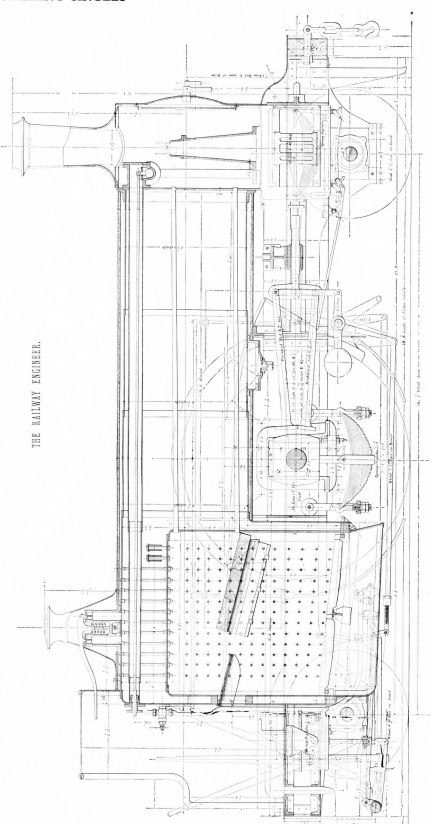

THE RAILWAY ENGINEER.

General arrangement sectional drawing purporting to be of No. 234. This drawing is, to scale, of the two 'intermediate' 7 ft. 6 in. singles, Nos. 238, 232, but has had the dimensions altered to apply to No. 234, a longer engine. The dry sand gear shown is correct for Nos. 238, 232, but No. 234 and all subsequent engines had front steam sanding gear. The bridle-rod was actually arched over the driving wheel transverse break rod. The safety valve casing is of the earlier shape, abandoned in 1884

As on the other single-wheelers, a small amount of side-play was allowed, in this case on the leading wheels, amounting to 7/16 in. each way, to ease the long wheelbase round curves. On the 8-footers this side-play was only provided at the trailing wheels, and it might have been expected that this practice would extend to the 7 ft. 6 in. engines. Still, the slidebars and crossheads of the 8 ft. engines, with their small clearance from the face of the bogie wheels, were probably the reason for the difference in practice. It must be remembered that the bogie on the 8-footers had no transverse play at all, merely pivoting on the fixed centre-pin.

A curious point about these two engines, Nos. 238 and 232, which applies also to most of the engines of the succeeding similar but slightly enlarged class, is that they received 18 in. by 26 in. cylinders as renewals when the original cylinders wore out. Whether this was due to the short expectation of life of the 18½ in. cylinders, because the cylinder walls, even when new, were on the thin side, cannot be stated with certainty; but it seems likely. The alternative explanation, that the engines with the larger cylinders were more prone to slipping, cannot be quite ruled out. The weights on the driving axles of the 8-footers were officially the same (17 tons), as on the 7 ft. 6 in. engines, but it is possible that in practice the fact that the axle of the latter engines was a cranked one and that all, not only part, of the torque of the engine was taken through it to the wheels may have led to a decision to keep axle loading a little less on the inside-cylinder engines than on the 8-footers. In their later days the 7 ft. 6 in. engines certainly did seem to slip more readily and frequently than the 8-footers; but their cylinders were at that period mostly about 19 in. diameter, after several reborings.

One of the chief practical improvements on Nos. 238 and 232 was that they ran rather more freely than the 8-footers, due to their larger steam and exhaust ports combined with smaller cylinders. The comparative figures are:

8ft. engines:	Steam ports 14in. × 1½in. with semi-circular ends,
	Exhaust ports 14in. x 3½in.,
	Volume of cylinders, 18in. diam. 7,126 cu. in.
7ft. 6in. engines:	Steam ports 16in. × 1½in. again with semicircular ends,
	Exhaust ports 16in. × 4in.,
	Volume of cylinders 18½in. diam. 6,994 cu. in.
	18in. diam. 6,617 cu. in.

Against this improvement in steam distribution, however, must be set two other factors. The actual passages through the slide-valves and exhaust cavity to the blast-pipe were rather more restricted and subject to eddies than on the 8-footers, and the blast-pipes—no doubt due to the smaller grates on Nos. 238 and 232—were $4\frac{5}{8}$ in. diameter as compared with $4\frac{3}{4}$ in. diameter on the outside-cylinder engines. Still, a $4\frac{5}{8}$ in. diameter blast-pipe orifice would not appreciably increase back pressure, unless the engine were being driven all out in an attempt to achieve the highest possible speed.

Both No. 238 and No. 232 received new straight-back boilers in 1895, and both in the course of their lifetime received new cylinders. Indeed, No. 238's

No. 237, about 1896, with large built-up chimney, the only straight-back 7ft. 6in. engine to be so fitted

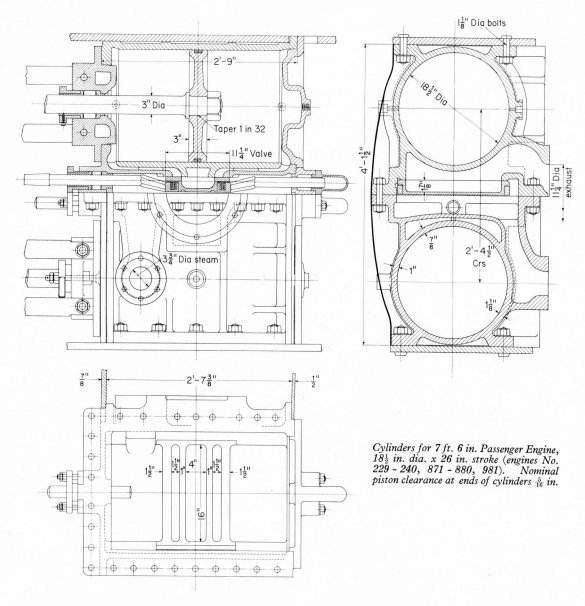

Cylinders for 7 ft. 6 in. Passenger Engine, 18½ in. dia. x 26 in. stroke (engines No. 229 - 240, 871 - 880, 981). Nominal piston clearance at ends of cylinders $\frac{5}{16}$ in.

first pair of cylinders lasted less than four years, and she received yet another replacement pair in 1901.

Perhaps this was the reason why she remained in service two years longer than No. 232, whose original cylinders were replaced by new ones in 1899. No. 232 was broken up in June 1906; No. 238 lasted until November 1908.

Both engines had had the usual Ivatt alterations made to them. Front sandboxes had been removed to a position below the footplate; rear sandboxes had been cut down in size; and the leading and trailing wheel plate springs, longer than the original

ones, and no doubt affording the enginemen a better ride, had been brought above the footplate for improved accessibility. It is curious to note that on the Gresley double-bolster bogies on L.N.E.R. coaches, the springs are just as much tucked away out of sight as on the Stirling outside-bearing leading wheels—yet this more modern design did not come in for adverse criticism, at least, not while the designer was still in office. And the trailing wheel springs of, for instance, the London, Tilbury & Southend tank engines, from 1880 to 1930, were certainly even less accessible, and more awkward to replace.

The No. 234 class

These were an enlarged version of Nos. 238 and 232, and the first engines of the class were completed at Doncaster rather less than a year after the original, smaller pair of engines had gone into service.

It has usually been accepted that it was the good

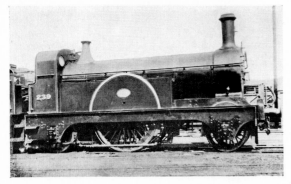

No. 239 about 1901. Still in Stirling condition, the front vacuum hose connection and brakepipe having been added by him in 1894-95

results achieved in service by Nos. 238 and 232 which led Stirling to consider building these larger engines of the same type, which would use the standard 8-footer size boiler, rather than multiplying the original two. But in fact drawings were being made of details for the larger engines before No. 232, the second engine of the original type, was completed. The date of the new frame drawing, for instance, is August 1885, the month No. 232 was out of shops new, and there must have been other, preliminary drawings and sketches prepared before this date, perhaps even before No. 238 had gone into service. Unfortunately the records are incomplete and this must be left as a surmise.

Nevertheless, it is clear that Stirling did not wait for any appreciable practical test of the two intermediate engines before pressing on with their larger successors. The two classes were so similar in nearly all respects that it did not prove necessary to redraw many of the details: the existing drawings were used, with the necessary altered lengths added, and with the references 'For engines Nos. 1000 and 1001' against the dimensions for Nos. 238 and 232, and 'For engines Nos. 1002 and 1003' against the dimensions for the larger engines. This was usual Doncaster drawing office practice, until the running number of the proposed engine had been allotted and could be added to the drawings, and the four-figure number deleted.

It seems clear that the enlarged engines were put in hand so that they could rank with the 8-footers in top-link main line work, and, in addition, do the special jobs for which Nos. 238 and 232 had been constructed at least as well as those two engines. And they would be cheap to build.

To the question, 'Why did not Stirling see this in 1869-70, and build enlargements of his 7 ft. singles or of the 7 ft. 6 in. single No. 92?' the answer is clear enough. First, the adhesion weight permitted would be less than for an 8 ft. diameter wheel, and Stirling would be reluctant to exceed this on a cranked axle, while he would have no compunction in doing so on a straight axle. In those early days crank axles were a real nightmare to the locomotive superintendent; hoops were shrunk round each crank, not only to relieve the stresses in the webs due to working conditions, but also in the hope that if—or, perhaps, when—the crank axle did fail the pieces would be held together at least long enough to enable a stop to be made safely after the symptoms had been observed on the footplate; and even, with luck, to hold back the total failure of the axle until a routine shed examination would reveal the existence of a crack. Stirling's choice of an outside-cylinder engine with a leading bogie in 1870 had paid good dividends in reliability and economy in repairs, as well as in performance and prestige.

Conditions had begun to change in 1884. Steel manufacture was no longer an art, but had become a straightforward technical industry, and crank axles were more reliable than they ever had been. And there were the practical examples of Nos. 238 and 232, performing their duties so satisfactorily.

It has been indicated above that the standard 8-footer boiler—judged from the side elevation—was adopted. The frames of the inside-cylinder

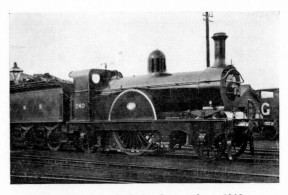

No. 240, as rebuilt by Ivatt, about 1903. Still retaining the Stirling smokebox and door

engines were 1 in. farther apart than those of the 8-footers, and the firebox of the new boilers was made correspondingly wider, so that the grate area was increased from 17¾ sq. ft. to 18·4 sq. ft. The extra width, of course, prevented any of these boilers from being used on 8-footers. In addition, the firebox casing was 4¼ in. deeper than the narrower 8-footer firebox; this was made possible partly by the higher pitch of the boiler, which was now 7 ft. 6 in. The barrel, 11 ft. 5 in. long, was 11 in. longer than No. 238's (or No. 92's), so that the leading wheelbase was lengthened by 11 in., all of which was added to the connecting rods and eccentric rods. Since the firebox was 4 in. longer, the trailing wheelbase was correspondingly increased by just that amount.

The blast-pipe remained the same diameter, 4⅝ in.; the later standard parallel shank buffers were adopted. There was a change from the piston type to the diaphragm type of vacuum-brake cylinder, and rear-sanding was provided. It is just possible that this last feature came about more or less accidentally. Dry front-sanding was at first proposed, but before any of the enlarged engines were built, this was changed to steam-sanding. The levers and gear were in existence, all ready for the front dry-sanding, but no longer needed. They could be, and were, used to provide rear dry-sanding. In spite of the general arrangement drawing showing front-sanding only, Nos. 238 and 232 had been built with dry-sanding front and rear, both operated by the same rodding, which had to be pushed, from a central position, to operate rear-sanding and pulled to operate front-sanding. The carrying wheels were, like those of Nos. 238 and 232, interchangeable with the similar wheels on the 2—4—0s.

It has been said that the connecting rods were lengthened by 11 in. as compared with Nos. 238 and 232, but that is only true of the first 15 engines. They were shortened by ⅛ in. from 6 ft. 8¼ in. to

No. 871, the first of the 1892 batch of 7ft. 6in. singles, at Hatfield 1900. Apart from the front hose connection and side chains on the front 'buffer beam, she is just as originally built

6 ft. 8⅛ in. on the last six engines, Nos. 876 to 880 and 981. There were other minor differences between engines within the class, in the usual Stirling fashion.

The first two engines of the enlarged design, Nos. 234 and 229, were completed at Doncaster on June 19 and July 27, 1886. They differed from the later engines in having plate springs to the driving wheels and also in the details, at first, of their steam-sanding gear, which were eventually brought in line with the later version used on the other engines of the class.

No. 234 was one of the engines whose cylinders were renewed exceptionally soon, in three years to a day, in fact. The other engines were No. 238 in under four years, No. 239 in three years, and No. 876 in less than three years. None of the cylinders in the engines built up to 1889 seems to have lasted the normal life-span of ten years, and all the replacements made up to about 1903 were made 18 in. diameter. Bird states that the cylinders of Nos. 871 to 875, built in 1892, were actually made 18 in. diameter new, and Rous-Marten quotes No. 874's cylinders as 18 in. diameter in 1895, no doubt having read this dimension from the bufferbeam. These would have been the original cylinders at that date. Yet the records are insistent that the cylinders on this batch were 18½ in. by 26 in., and that it was the replacement cylinders which were 18 in.

After Nos. 234 and 229, there followed, in pairs, eight further engines only differing from the early engines of the class in having helical springs for their driving-wheels, and without the changes in detail between succeeding pairs which had characterised the early 8-footers. In order of building they

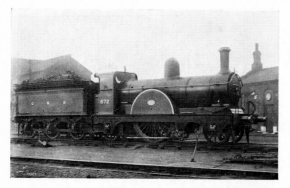

No. 872, as rebuilt by Ivatt at Kings Cross in 1908. With Ivatt smokebox door and smaller rear sandboxes

were Nos. 237, 230 completed on March 22 and April 16, 1887 respectively; Nos. 236, 239 completed on September 24 and November 23, 1887; Nos. 231, 233 completed on February 9 and April 18, 1888; and Nos. 235, 240 completed on November 5, 1888 and January 10, 1889 respectively. All these engines started life with wrought-iron wheels throughout, although the 8-footers had changed to steel wheels with No. 775 in January 1887, the engine which also inaugurated the use of helical driving-wheel springs on the 8-footers.

No express locomotives at all were built for the next three years, but a further series of 7 ft. 6 in. engines was then put in hand, of which the first, No. 871, was completed on January 26, 1892. This series was not built in pairs, as had been the case with the 8-footers and the earlier 7 ft. 6 in. singles, but in a batch of five. No. 871 was followed by Nos. 872, 873, 874 and 875, completed respectively on February 23, March 30, May 9 and June 30, 1892. These five engines were built new with cast-steel wheels throughout. A few of the earlier engines also received cast-steel driving wheels at a later period of their existence. On the whole, their wrought-iron wheels lasted appreciably better than those of the earlier 8-footers.

After a gap of nearly two years, a further six engines were constructed, the last engines of the 2—2—2 type to be built in Britain, or, it is believed, anywhere in the world. The first of this batch, No. 876, completed on April 19, 1894, was followed by the remaining five engines in the next three months. No. 877 appeared on May 12, Nos. 878, 879 and 880 on June 11, 15 and 30 respectively, and No. 981 on July 16. It is obvious that they were hurried through so as to be able to take their part in the summer service of 1894, when the commencement of double-heading would inevitably have led to a

No. 875 at Grantham. about 1896

serious shortage of main-line express engines. They were the first Stirling top-link express engines to be built new with the automatic vacuum-pipe carried through to the front bufferbeam, and with the side chains and small numerals on the bufferbeam. They also had flanged smokebox frontplates, this change eliminating the use of angle-iron to join the smoke-box front plate to the wrapper plate.

Although none of these six engines was originally fitted with Davies & Metcalf exhaust steam injectors four (Nos. 876, 878, 880 and 981) were so fitted in the early part of 1896. This was undoubtedly a tribute from Ivatt to the esteem in which he held these engines, for no other straightback engines were ever so fitted; though all the 8-footers and 7 ft. 6 in. engines rebuilt by him received them.

In about 1898, No. 880 was fitted for a time with the Macallan variable blast-pipe. This was a device by which a smaller diameter cap could be superimposed, at the driver's discretion, above the normal blast-pipe, which was made rather larger in diameter than standard.

Domed boilers were fitted on a much larger proportion of the 7 ft. 6 in. singles than on the 8-footers, a further indication of Ivatt's views. Nos. 233, 235, 236, 237, 240, 871, 872, 873, 876, 877 and 880—11 engines out of 21—received domed boilers, No. 237 as late as September 1910. Ten of these boilers had the larger grate area of $20\frac{1}{4}$ sq. ft., which the $1\frac{3}{4}$ in. water legs of the earlier Ivatt boilers provided, against the 18.4 sq. ft., not only of the Stirling boilers with 3 in. water legs, but also of the second Ivatt domed boilers fitted later to Nos. 871 and 877 and the final one fitted to No. 872, actually her third domed boiler. All the domed boilers were pressed to 170 lb. per sq. in.

A peculiarity about the final domed boilers fitted to these last three engines was that they were from a batch of six which had been ordered originally as

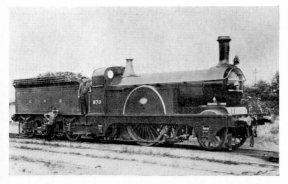

No. 873 at Cambridge about 1898. The vacuum brake pipe to the front buffer beam, added 1894-95, can be seen just below footplate level outside the outside frames

straightback boilers for fitting to 8-footers. A last-minute design change resulted in this batch being altered to carry domes on the middle ring of the barrel, which had three rings. In this respect they were unique, and the dome was of necessity positioned 15 in. further forward than on the earlier domed boilers of this type, which had two barrel rings with the dome on the ring next to the firebox.

In addition to these domed boilers, Ivatt also built a number of otherwise similar straightback boilers for the class. Both varieties had washout plugs on the sides of the firebox, a feature introduced on the G.N.R. by Ivatt, so that even the Ivatt straightback boilers on this class could be distinguished from their Stirling counterparts. There were, however, instances of Stirling boilers on other classes, in particular the No. 1003 class 8-footers, having washout plugs fitted to the firebox sides after Ivatt took over.

It has been pointed out that at first the cylinders on these engines seem to have given trouble and had abnormally short lives. To set against this, it can be said that towards the end of their days their cylinders were bored out, as wear took place, to rather larger diameters than Stirling permitted. For instance, No. 880's cylinders were recorded as being $19\frac{1}{8}$ in. diameter in March 1907, and she continued at work, still with these cylinders, until August 1911. Since the barrel thickness over about one-quarter of the circumference was only $\frac{7}{8}$ in. originally, the wall must have been reduced to a nominal 9/16 in.

The cylinder drawing dated September 1884, made for the earliest engines and not altered in any way, certainly shows the diameter as $18\frac{1}{2}$ in., and so do the original general arrangement drawings both for Nos. 238 and 232 and for the enlarged engines. Yet on the tracing made from the general arrangement of the latter the draughtsman has shown a fine careless unconcern for exactitude by dimensioning the cylinders as $18\frac{1}{2}$ in. on the actual part and 18 in. in the title of the drawing! It is necessary to study all Doncaster drawings of those days with grave suspicion; there is usually something wrong somewhere, which has to be checked and crosschecked from other drawings, records of repairs, photographs, and so on, if one is to avoid being trapped into a mis-statement. It used to be said that first a sketch was made, then the part was made, and, last of all, the drawing was made. But such cavalier treatment could only apply to relatively uncomplicated items which fitted mainly 'in the air'.

When built, all the engines of the class had the then new cast-iron chimneys, a little shorter than the chimneys on the 8-footers and having a deeper top above the lip, a feature which seemed to add a hint of compactness in their appearance. These special chimneys were used later, apparently more or less at random, on a number of 8-footers, and were a feature which seemed to enhance the appearance of these engines also. From about 1893, for two or three years, No. 237 received a chimney of the massive looking, built-up type; not the type used on the last batch of 8-footers, Nos. 1003 to 1008, but the longer chimney of the 8-footers of 1880 to 1884, which must have exceeded the nominal official height to the top of the chimney—13 ft. 4 in.—by about 2 in. It is a curiosity that the old 'Jenny Linds', Nos. 201 and 202, when rebuilt by Stirling also measured 13 ft. 6 in. from rail level to top of chimney. Some of the 7 ft. 6 in. engines rebuilt with domes were fitted with cast-iron chimneys moulded to give the appearance of built-up ones. These were Nos. 235, 877 and 880. The others received plain chimneys of the Ivatt pattern —not with the shallow top of the large 'Atlantics',

No. 876, fitted with exhaust steam injector, at Peterborough about 1899. This injector was fitted to a number of the 7ft. 6in. engines by Ivatt, from 1896 on

but with less taper than the Stirling cast-iron chimneys and rather clumsy curves at lip and base.

One of the domed 'rebuilds', No. 872, was actually rebuilt completely at Kings Cross shed, the new boiler, cab, sandboxes and details being sent from Doncaster. Great care was taken with the painting of the rebuilt engine, and the base of the dome was edged with black with a white line, a style of painting which only appeared on one other engine on the G.N.R., No. 93, the first 8-footer to be rebuilt with a domed boiler.

The best engines of the class came in for a St. Martin's summer of main-line usefulness for several years from about 1910 on, when a series of light, fast trains was put on between Kings Cross and Sheffield and Bradford in competition with the Great Central Railway. The engines used were Nos. 872, 873, 876 and 877, all with domed boilers and working in a link with the Ivatt singles, Nos. 263 and 264.

Although the 7 ft. 6 in. singles were all still in service five years after the first 8-footer had been scrapped, they had all been withdrawn before the end of 1913, when there were still a few 8-footers running. The last three to go were Nos. 235, 237 and 872, all condemned on the same 'circular notice' dated December 24, 1913. The first to go

was No. 231 in April 1905, and the last straightback engine of the class in service was No. 234, the first engine to be built, condemned in November 1912.

No. 981 at York, September 1904. An unusual state, Ivatt leading springs, exhaust steam injector and auxiliary oilboxes on front sandbox, but otherwise in Stirling condition

Turning now to actual performances, there are first of all some early runs clocked by Rous-Marten, of which only summary details are available, and no engine numbers, but which nevertheless show excellent work:

Route	Load tons	Dist. Miles	Time m. s.	Av.Sp. m.p.h.
Kings X—Peterborough	120	76·4	83 10	55·1
Kings X—Grantham	135	105·5	116 49	54·2
Grantham—Doncaster .	175	50·5	52 02	58·2
Peterborough—Kings X	155	76·4	81 27	56·3

In later days these 2—2—2 locomotives were performing splendidly with considerably heavier trains, as the following summary shows:

No. 877, as built, about 1898, with flanged smokebox front plate and front vacuum brake hose connection

Route	Engine No.	Load tons tare	Dist. Miles	Actual m. s.	Av. Speed m.p.h.
Kings Cross—Grantham . . .	878	214	105·5	115 48	56·0*
Kings Cross—Grantham . . .	231	222	105·5	115 27	56·5*
Grantham—Doncaster . . .	231	222	50·5	54 08	59·5*
Grantham—Peterborough . .	235	168	29·1	30 37	57·9
Peterborough—York . . .	233	230	111·8	120 33	55·1

*Average calculated on net time.

G

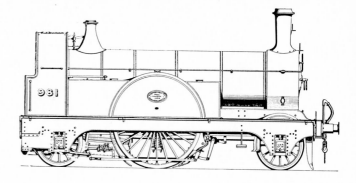

No. 981 as built, 1894. The very last engine of the 2-2-2 type ever to be constructed

As a fairly complete record of a run on the 5.29 p.m. up from Peterborough, the accompanying log provides as fine an example of the work of the 7 ft. 6 in. engines as could be desired. It was logged in May 1904 by J. F. Vickery. Note should be taken of the very good start over the level Fenland stretch, to Holme, and of the average speed of 56·4 m.p.h. maintained over the 43·5 miles from Offord to Potters Bar. Although this length includes some favourable stretches, in the aggregate it is markedly adverse, and includes the long climb of six miles at 1 in 200 from Three Counties to Stevenage. Hitchin station lies in the middle of this ascent. Although Vickery did not record the passing time at Stevenage, his time at Knebworth is enough to indicate the excellence of the work on the bank, and the

average speed of 56·4 m.p.h. previously quoted represents extraordinarily fine performance for a 2—2—2 engine hauling 275 tons.

Regarding the rebuilt 7 ft. 6 in. engines, Rous-Marten gives notes of a run with No. 877 on the 10.20 a.m. from Kings Cross to Nottingham and Sheffield. The load was 170 tons (2 twelve-wheeled, 2 eight-wheeled, and 2 six-wheeled), the weather was drizzly and the rails were slippery. The engine gained just over 4 min. on booked time and Rous-Marten commented: 'The driver, having 88 min. allowed from Kings Cross to Peterborough, had things easily in hand and never pressed his steed.'

Dist. Miles		Actual m. s.		Remarks
0·0	KINGS CROSS .	0	00	
12·7	Potters Bar . .	19	00	Min. rate 43·7 m.p.h.
17·7	Hatfield . .	24	25	
31·9	Hitchin . .	38	57	Max. speed 77·6 m.p.h.
58·9	Huntingdon .	63	27	
76·4	PETERBOROUGH	83	54	

G.N.R. 5.29 p.m. PETERBOROUGH—KINGS CROSS

Load: 1 twelve-wheeler; 5 eight-wheelers; 6 six-wheelers
249 tons tare, 275 tons full
Engine: 7ft. 6in, 2-2-2 No. 231

Dist. Miles		Sch. min.	Actual m. s.		Av. Sp. m.p.h.
0·0	PETERBOROUGH	0	0	00	—
3·8	Yaxley . .		6	30	35·1
7·0	Holme . .		9	49	58·2
12·9	Abbots Ripton .		16	22	54·1
17·5	HUNTINGDON	21	21	39	52·3
20·4	Offord . .		24	17	66·5
24·7	St. Neots . .		28	30	61·3
32·3	Sandy . .		36	04	60·3
35·3	Biggleswade . .		39	05	59·8
44·5	HITCHIN . .	52	49	17	54·1
51·4	Knebworth . .		58	09	46·6
54·4	Welwyn . .		61	30	53·7
58·9	HATFIELD .	69	65	21	70·2
63·9	Potters Bar . .		70	34	57·6
67·2	New Barnet .		74	08	55·4
69·9	New Southgate .		76	30	68·4
72·3	Hornsey . .		78	30	72·0
73·8	Finsbury Park .		79	57	62·1
76·4	KINGS CROSS .	91	84	10	—

No. 880, as built, at Hatfield about 1897. Fitted with Macallan's variable blast-pipe, the operating rod for which can be seen below the handrail

In 1910, when a new train for Bradford and Leeds was put on, leaving Kings Cross at 2.15 p.m. and running non-stop to Doncaster, two of the rebuilt 7 ft. 6 in. engines were used turn-and-turnabout with Ivatt single-wheelers. The loads were light, the timings quite fast, and Nos. 872 and 876, the engines concerned, were completely masters of the job. The logs of runs with both these engines are given below, with No. 872 as far only as Grantham.

The driver of No. 876 obviously knew that he could take things comfortably to Potters Bar, and still have plenty of time in hand.

The scheduled time for this train, from Kings Cross to passing Grantham, was 112 min., so that No. 872 had not only regained all the $7\frac{1}{2}$ min. delays, but was nearly $\frac{3}{4}$ min. ahead of booked time by Grantham.

Another example of performance is that of No. 878 on the 9.45 a.m. dining-car express from Kings Cross to Leeds with 214 tons; she reached Grantham in 115 min. 48 sec. in spite of a relaying slack at Potters Bar. The $15\frac{1}{4}$ miles of the Stoke bank took 18 min. 39 sec.

ENGINE No. 872

Load: 141 tons (4 coaches)

Dist. Miles		Sch. min.	Actual m. s.	m.p.h.*
0·0	KINGS CROSS	0	0 00	—
2·6	Finsbury Park .		5 17	—
5·0	Wood Green .		7 52	60
9·2	New Barnet .		12 37	50·5
12·7	Potters Bar .		16 44	52
17·7	Hatfield . .	22	21 09	80
25·0	Knebworth .		27 19	64
			p.w.s.	
31·9	Hitchin . .	36	33 23	
			dep.	
35·7	Three Counties†		40 52	—
44·1	Sandy . .		51 09	72
51·7	St. Neots . .		57 43	71
58·9	Huntingdon .	60	63 27	78
63·5	Abbots Ripton .		67 47	61
69·4	Holme . .		72 24	80
76·4	Peterborough .	78	79 25	—
84·9	Tallington .		89 22	67
88·6	Essendine .		92 58	60
92·2	Little Bytham .		96 39	52
97·1	Corby . .		102 44	45·5/51·5
100·1	Stoke Box .		106 19	46
102·0	Great Ponton .		108 20	72
105·5	GRANTHAM .	112	111 19	
			PASS	

* Max. and min. speeds by stop watch.
† Signals to a dead stand for 1 min. 27 sec.

ENGINE No. 876

Load: 135 tons (4 coaches)

Dist. Miles		Sch. min.	Actual m. s.	m.p.h.*
0·0	KINGS CROSS .	0	0 00	—
2·6	Finsbury Park .		5 30	—
12·7	Potters Bar . .		18 40	$43\frac{1}{2}$
17·7	Hatfield . .	22	23 40	74/54
31·9	Hitchin . .	36	36 50	$80\frac{1}{2}$
			signal check	
58·9	Huntingdon .	60	62 10	—
69·4	Holme . .		—	79
76·4	Peterborough .	78	78 40	—
105·5	Grantham . .	112	110 50	—
120·1	Newark . .	127	125 00	—
138·6	Retford . .	147	144 55	—
156·0	DONCASTER .	165	163 45	

*Max. and min. speeds by stop watch.

No. 237 near Werrington, 1912. This was the only Stirling 7ft. 6in. singlewheeler to be rebuilt with domed boiler while retaining the original cab. All the other engines with domed boilers received new Ivatt cabs

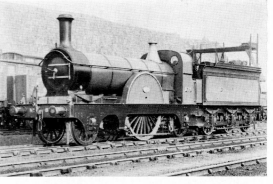

No. 879 at Hitchin in 1908, with Ivatt modifications. Driver Clark, shown in this photograph, was probably the driver on the occasion described in Chapter 13, when over 60 m.p.h. was reached between Hornsey and Wood Green on a suburban train

CHAPTER 8

PERFORMANCE: SPEED: COAL CONSUMPTION

Maximum Speeds

FOR details of the maximum speeds attained by Stirling engines, we have to depend once again on Rous-Marten. All his best speeds were attained on up trains between Stoke Summit and Essendine or Tallington.

In 1884 the highest speed he had attained was with No. 665—80 m.p.h. with a light train; but he comments that with a heavier train on another occasion the same engine was only able to reach 74 m.p.h. This was of course with a boiler pressure of not more than 140 lb. per sq. in.

But in 1892, when he was again in England and recording locomotive performance, he had many cases, both with 8-footers and with 7 ft. 6 in. engines, of over 79 m.p.h. on both up and down trains.

Then on an up train down the Abbots Ripton bank, he noted, with an 8-footer, 76·5, 78·2 and 80 m.p.h. over the last three successive miles of the bank. This was soon equalled by several other 8-footers and a 7 ft. 6 in. engine, both on down trains at Arlesey and up trains at Essendine.

It was not long before these speeds were exceeded, and several engines of both the classes were timed at 81·8 m.p.h. on up trains descending the Stoke bank. The loads were 110-140 tons.

Then, in his own words, 'On one occasion I made a special effort to exceed that apparently fixed rate of speed, 81·8 m.p.h., which I had attained on several railways. Travelling on one of the newest of Mr. P. Stirling's splendid 8 ft. single express engines'—either No. 1001 or 1002—'we attained 80 m.p.h. down the gradient of 1 in 200 near Little Bytham. In reply to my question, the driver, a very intelligent man, said that in his opinion the engine was doing "about her best". He gave, however, a little more steam experimentally, when the speed rose to 81·8. But a second addition of steam was followed by a drop to 78·2, apparently due to back pressure. The line became more level and no increase could be obtained. It is my impression, in view of later occurrences, that had the first additional steam been given at an earlier and steeper portion of the incline, the maximum of 81·8 might have been passed. But the driver's knowledge and practical experience led him to err on the side of excessive caution. Hence this remains my maximum so far with the 8 ft. engines.' Rous-Marten gave the boiler pressure on the foregoing runs as 160 lb. per sq. in. for both 8 ft. and 7 ft. 6 in. engines.

Then, in 1894, a second opportunity occurred, this time with a 7 ft. 6 in. engine, apparently when he was travelling in the rear vehicle of the train.

No. 666 on down train at Hadley Wood about 1899

No. 879 on down express at Hadley Wood about 1898

100

'After passing Corby at 70·6 m.p.h. the speed rapidly increased to 73·5, 75·0, 76·6, 78·2, 80·0, 81·8, 82·4, 83·7, and finally 84·1 m.p.h., several quarter-miles being covered in 10·7 seconds apiece, and two miles consecutively in 42·8 seconds.'

There was a third occasion, and Rous-Marten was this time riding on the footplate of the same 7 ft. 6 in. engine. 'The weather was perfectly calm and fine, and the load lighter by one coach than the previous time, but the maximum speed was once again 84·1 m.p.h., sustained for two miles. The maximum was attained somewhat more quickly with the lighter load, and the speed diminished rather more slowly as the falling gradient merged into the level road. But only three secs. were gained from Stoke to Little Bytham and two secs. gained Essendine to Tallington. The time for the 3 m. 52 chains from Little Bytham to Essendine was 2 min. 39 sec.=82·6 m.p.h., the highest recorded up to then. There was entire and remarkable steadiness alike on the footplate and in the train' ('in the train' of course referring to the previous

occasion). In this last case the time from Grantham to Kings Cross, start to stop, was 104 min. 17 sec. for the 105 m. 28 chains; and the driver, also 'a very intelligent and capable man', was of opinion that giving a little more steam would have reduced the time per mile by about one sec., provided he received special authority to get the most out of the engine. This would have meant an increase in the speed to just over 86 m.p.h.

The complete logs of these two runs are given below. Rous-Marten quotes the cylinders as being $18\frac{7}{8}$ in. diameter by 26 in. stroke. As the trips were made in 1894, the engine must have been one of the earlier batch, Nos. 229-240; the $18\frac{1}{2}$ in. cylinders must have done a great deal of work to have needed reboring to $18\frac{7}{8}$ in. diameter. The later engines of the class at this date would have had cylinders still of the nominal size. It is indeed a pity that the actual engine number was not mentioned. No. 237, from the evidence of her dates for general repairs and cylinder renewal, seems the most likely engine.

G.N.R. 4.18 p.m. GRANTHAM—KINGS CROSS
Engine: 7ft. 6in. 2-2-2 Single

| Load, coaches . . . . | 7 | | 6 | |
| Load, tons . . . . | 100 | | 85 | |

Dist. Miles		Actual m. s.	Av. Speed m.p.h.	Actual m. s.	Av. Speed m.p.h.
0·0	GRANTHAM . . .	0 00	—	0 00	—
3·5	Great Ponton . . .	6 08	34·2	5 59	35·2
5·4	*Stoke Box* . . .	8 45	43·6	8 29	45·7
8·4	Corby	11 47	59·4	11 29	60·0
13·3	Little Bytham . . .	15 47	73·6	15 28	73·8
16·9	Essendine . . .	18 26	81·7	18 07	81·7
20·7	Tallington . . .	21 23	77·3	21 02	78·3
29·1	PETERBOROUGH . .	29 11	★	28 57	★
36·1	Holme	37 49	48·6	37 16	50·4
42·0	Abbots Ripton . .	44 09	55·9	43 08	60·3
46·6	HUNTINGDON . .	48 52	58·6	47 37	61·7
49·5	Offord . . .	51 31	66·3	50 01	72·5
53·8	St. Neots . . .	55 57	58·3	54 07	62·9
58·0	Tempsford . . .	60 23	56·8	58 06	63·2
				sig. stop	—
64·4	Biggleswade . . .	67 44	52·2	sig. stop	—
				sig. stop	—
68·5	Arlesey . . .	72 39	50·1	76 58	—
73·6	HITCHIN . . .	78 47	49·8	82 54	51·5
76·9	Stevenage . . .	83 19	43·7	86 59	48·4
80·5	Knebworth . . .	87 25	52·7	90 54	55·2
83·5	Welwyn . . .	90 49	52·9	94 07	56·0
87·8	HATFIELD . . .	94 48	64·7	97 48	70·0
92·8	Potters Bar . . .	100 14	55·2	102 57	58·3
100·5	Wood Green . . .	107 23	64·6	109 36	69·5
101·4	Hornsey . . .	108 07	73·7	110 19	75·3
102·9	Finsbury Park . .	109 28	66·7	111 34	72·0
105·5	KINGS CROSS . .	112 57	—	115 03	—

★ Slack to 10 m.p.h. through Peterborough.

THE STIRLING SINGLES

At some time subsequent to 1894 Rous-Marten must have had faster trips, both with 8-footers and with the 7 ft. 6 in. engines, for he wrote later that in 1901 he had timed them at 84·9 and 86·5 m.p.h. respectively, and still later, that the maximum speed he had ever timed an 8-footer at was 'just about 86 m.p.h.'. This must, in all probability, have meant timing the engine over half a mile, in 21·0 seconds, since Rous-Marten is said to have used a chronometer graduated in fifths of a second, and 10·5 seconds for the quarter-mile would not have been available on such an instrument, recording only 10·0, 10·2, 10·4, 10·6, 10·8 and 11 secs. for quarter miles around such speeds. The 86·5 m.p.h. of the 7 ft. 6 in. engine meant a 10·4 sec. reading for the quarter-mile. There was certainly very little in it either way.

It is indeed a pity that Rous-Marten apparently never rode on No. 34 or No. 221 after they were rebuilt with 175 lb. per sq. in. boilers and with the direct exhaust slide-valves. If, with a suitably light load, Rous-Marten could have been at the elbow of a driver on one of these engines, urging him to try just a little more steam, from Stoke down to Tallington, even the most pessimistic of engineers would agree that a speed of 90 m.p.h. could almost certainly have been reached. But this must remain for ever another of the 'might-have-beens'.

A point which seems never to have been mentioned, in discussing maximum speeds and speeds up the banks of the Stirling engines, is the effect on the performance of the engines of their being equipped with a reversing hand lever, and not with a turnscrew or power reverser. At anything over, say, 40 m.p.h. it is very nearly impossible to 'notch up' an engine, that is to reduce the percentage cut-off of steam in the cylinders, by tugging at the lever, even with steam shut off. At high speeds and

No. 670 in about 1896. One of the very few 8-footers which appears never to have received a cast-iron chimney

with steam still on, and with flat slide-valves it is quite beyond the strength of a man. And it is very tricky to attempt to increase the cut-off by lowering the lever to the next notch. If the catch misses the notch by ever so little, the lever will as often as not fly into full gear, and both the driver and the fireman together will have to struggle their hardest to bring the lever back, with steam shut off, to its running position.

The natural effect of this characteristic was that the driver of a Stirling engine would, at a comparatively low speed, notch up the engine to the extent that he would regard as satisfactory for climbing the banks, and then ease back the regulator as required, when the top of the bank had been attained and the engine began to gain speed. This was not an uneconomical procedure, for the throttling of the steam through the partially closed regulator would dry the steam thoroughly and even superheat it to a small degree. But it did mean that it was by no means certain that the reversing lever setting was the best to attain the highest speeds, especially with Stephenson link motion, where the lead increases as the cut-off is reduced, with most complicated effects on the flow of both live and exhaust steam.

Rous-Marten's 'intelligent driver' would have only tried opening further a partially closed regulator. It is quite possible that the engine would have run faster by combining this with dropping the reversing lever a notch—but it is as certain as anything can be that he would not have considered attempting this with steam on at 80 m.p.h.

So many of the logs quoted in this book show the characteristic of the speed varying closely in accordance with the gradient condition that the reason has deserved mention. With a screw reverser, a modern driver would tend to alter its setting, little by little, as the road conditions changed, and so flatten out the variations in speed.

Nos. 7 and 669 on down express—probably the afternoon Scotsman—at Oakleigh Park, 1900

No. 230 at Harringay on down express, about 1899

It is a pity that no logs are available where the details of the working of the engine—cut-offs, regulator openings, boiler pressures, and so on—are recorded. Without such particulars, and an appreciation of their why and wherefore, any log must fail to give a complete picture of the engine performance and of what extra effort, if any, it might have been capable.

Coal Consumption

On matters of coal and oil consumption by the Stirling singles, little exists in the shape of results of trials or monthly coal consumption sheets for one shed or another. However, in *Engineering* in 1868 the coal consumption of the 7 ft. singles was given as 21 lb. per mile. And there is, on a sheet of foolscap paper at Doncaster, a summary of the results of some Indicator trials with a 'No. 1 Class' engine, number not given. The results are neither dated nor signed, and include, not only irrelevances such as the weight of the boiler, but also some wrong calculations, one of which goes so far as to give the specific coal consumption as 2.02 lb. per I.H.P. hour! Since the boiler pressure was only 140 lb. per sq. in. it is probable that the date of the test was before 1885. At 50 m.p.h. a sample card gave an average indicated pressure of 55 lb. per sq. in., this corresponding to a total I.H.P. of 692. The coal consumption, of best Yorkshire hard steam coal, was 28.4 lb. per mile, the water evaporation 28 gallons per mile. The total weight of the train of 15 vehicles was 213 tons, including the engine and tender, which together weighed probably about 68 tons. The average speed was given as 50 m.p.h., but the conditions and location of the test are not mentioned.

There is also a report, dated May 13, 1885, from Stirling to his Locomotive Committee, dealing with the coal consumption of an 8-footer, No. 771, on two of the Sheffield to London expresses, the 12.5 and the 3.3 p.m. trains. The 12.5 included a dining car, weighed 87 tons, and was booked at an average speed of 50.8 m.p.h. The 3.3 weighed only 75 tons, but the average speed of this train was higher, 53.4 m.p.h. The same engine and crew were used and the test was carried out between Grantham and Kings Cross, two runs on each train being made, under the supervision of an inspector. The fuel was 'carefully weighed' on each occasion. The result was unexpected, the coal consumption coming out at 19.4 lb. per mile on the heavier but slower train, and at 22.2 lb. per mile on the lighter, faster train; which—as Stirling put it—'shows how expensively increased speed is obtained'.

In *The Engineer* in 1891, the coal consumption of the 7 ft. 6 in. engine No. 234 was given as 30.6 lb. per mile, and the oil consumption as 4 pints per 100 miles—the latter presumably for engine and tender, not for engine only. The average loads were given as 177.6 tons—almost certainly tare loading—booked at speeds of over 50 m.p.h. between stops.

These were all quite good and reasonably economical coal consumptions for saturated engines with the given loads and speeds, and compare favourably with those of engines on other railways under similar conditions at that time.

The only directly comparable figures, however, as between Stirling engines and one belonging to another railway are the results of a series of trials conducted, also in 1891, with an 8-footer No. 34,

No. 545, on down express at Hitchin about 1900. This is the better of the only two known photographs of this engine.   She has received an Ivatt smokebox door but in all other outward respects is just as in late Stirling days

a 7 ft. 6 in. engine No. 240 and a North Eastern two-cylinder compound single-wheeler No. 1519, also with 7 ft. 6 in. wheels. These trials covered six days working for each engine, on the same trains, in successive weeks. The Great Northern engines were all stationed at Doncaster, and the trials were conducted from there. As an example of daily turns for top-link enginemen in those days, they are worth noting:

		Mileage
7.45 a.m.	Doncaster to Leeds (a slow train)	28
10.00 a.m.	Leeds to Peterborough, with one stop at Grantham	108
3.00 p.m.	Peterborough to Doncaster, non-stop	80
	Daily total mileage	216

The load on the up train was invariably '10', equivalent in those days to a tare load of 140 to 150 tons. On the down train, it varied from '12' to '15', as the average of the week's loading, that is, from 170 to 225 tons tare.

The weather, of course, varied during each week as well as between the different weeks. No. 34 had 'rough' weather each day on her week, but kept time on all trips, although her load on the down train averaged 210 to 225 tons, the heaviest average of the three weeks. Not unnaturally, the coal consumption was heavier than that of No. 240, which not only had rather lighter loads on her down trips, ranging between 170 and 195 tons, but also managed to lose a total of three minutes on the 18 journeys she made. Her driver, J. Jones, also acted as pilotman on the North Eastern No. 1519 throughout her week, and reported at the end of that week that he never wanted to ride on another compound. She was very rough at speed, and the North Eastern man said the road was bad—he may have been right—and that the coal was inferior in size and quality to North Eastern coal. No. 1519 was worked in nearly full gear most of the time,

No. 231 on up Manchester express passing Hatfield, August 1891

No. 776 on up express approaching Hadley Wood, 1903. The specially short chimney can be noted

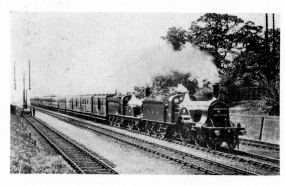

Down express at Hadley Wood, hauled by No. 774 and 872, about 1900

No. 773 on up train—probably a Leeds or Manchester express—at Ganwick, about 1898

No. 550 about 1892-93, with new cast-iron chimney and larger diameter boiler, but still with her original shallow frames, which lasted her till the end

and went back to the Gateshead shops after the trials!

The particulars of the trials were sent to the writer many years ago by the late Hugh T. Gripper, who had been acting Shed Foreman at Grantham during 1891. Mr. Gripper had earlier served his apprenticeship under Stirling at Doncaster, and was actually working in the Pattern Shop when the first patterns for the cast-iron chimneys were made —and 'no one liked them'.

Stirling himself reported to his Locomotive Committee on these or similar trials during the same year, with a different 8-footer, No. 1, and different coal consumptions for all engines, though Nos. 240 and 1519 were still the other engines concerned. Both sets of figures are tabulated below. Stirling does not appear to have been perturbed by the amount of time lost by No. 1, and to have been concerned only with the lighter coal consumption of his engines as compared with No. 1519.

ENGINE TRIALS ON G.N.R. 1891

Engine No. and type	Driver's Name	Average Loading	Coal used lb. per mile	Oil used pt. per day	Remarks
34 (4-2-2) (Doncaster)	J. Cornthwaite	10 up 15 down	33·0	10	Time kept on all trains. Very rough weather all the time.
240 (2-2-2) (Doncaster)	J. Jones	10 up 12 and 13 down	29·1	9	Engine lost 3 min. during week. Strong side wind mostly.
1519 (4-2-2) North Eastern Compound	E. Shipley piloted by J. Jones	10 up 12 down	34·8	18	Moderate winds 4 days. Strong winds 2 days. Timekeeping fair. Note: This engine cost £2-12-6 more in 'stores', and consumed 3 tons 5 cwt. more fuel.
No. 1 (4-2-2) (Doncaster)	—	tons 189·1	31·1	10	47 min. lost during week, due to very strong winds.
240 (2-2-2) (Doncaster)	—	177·8	30·6	9	9 min. lost and 12 min. regained during week. Strong winds.
1519 (4-2-2) North Eastern Compound	E. Shipley	181·7	36·4	18	19 min. lost and 13 min. regained. Moderately strong winds.

THE STIRLING SINGLES

One can only comment that though the general flavour of the reports are strongly Great Northern, yet, making all allowances for this bias, the Stirling engines do seem to have had rather the better of it. Driver J. Jones was certainly out to show the utmost economy, and his efforts in the direction of 'coal dodging' were very likely the reason for the 3 min. booked against him.

No. 34 was last out of the shops previously after a general repair on September 20, 1890, No. 1 similarly on December 23, 1890, and No. 240 was out of shops, new, in January 1889 and did not return to the works for her first general repair until the end of September 1891; so that all the engines must have had quite an appreciable mileage behind them when they were used in this trial. Probably the report of No. 1519's return to the Gateshead shops was a mere rumour; but T. W. Worsdell, who had designed and built No. 1519 as a compound, had retired the previous year and been

No. 771 on up 'Flying Scotsman' starting out from Grantham about 1902. She is fitted with Ivatt smokebox door, but No. 876 (extreme right) though rebuilt with domed boiler, still retains her Stirling smokebox. No. 264, the Ivatt 7ft. 6in. single, was a London engine. Her driver was Sam Watson who had previously had 774 for many years

No. 664 at Grantham, northward bound, about 1891. This engine was stationed at Doncaster and seems to have been very rarely photographed. She is still fitted with the old type of vacuum ejector, but has been given a cast-iron chimney

No. 21, rebuilt by Ivatt, on down express at Harringay, 1898. The engine crew have observed the photographer, or perhaps may have a 'date' with him

succeeded by his brother, Wilson Worsdell, who in the course of the next few years converted all the North Eastern compounds into simple engines. Possibly Wilson Worsdell was not sorry that the result of the trials provided him with a further set of data in favour of simple engines. No. 1519 was built in 1889 and, like the Great Northern engines, also had a considerable mileage behind her at the date of the trials. In regard to Driver Jones's complaint of rough riding at speed, it is fair to mention that within a few years the inside bearings to her trailing wheels had been abandoned and new subframes with outside bearings provided, the reason given being to improve the riding of the engines. Yet the 8-footers had inside bearings to *their* trailing-wheels, and all observers from the footplate, including Rous-Marten, say that they rode very well indeed. Mr. Gripper, mentioned above, wrote: 'My rides on the 8-footers were a pleasure, and the riding was very easy, though cab protection was faulty—not enough overhang at the top for bad weather.' The present writer had asked about valve setting, but Mr. Gripper, then over 80, could not remember the details, though he said the setting was done with the lever in 3rd notch from full gear. But he went on to say that in running, 'after we got a move on, the lever was notched up and regulator opened up full' (this is not in agreement with the practice in later days). 'In spite of no steam dome, Stirling's engines were not given to priming. I remember at one time a signal box at Doncaster was newly painted white. A Great Eastern engine came along, priming badly, and made a mess of the box. Old Stirling was stated to have smiled when he saw the mess, though he did not often smile; he generally just glared at one.' It is possible that Stirling had this or a similar incident in mind when he spoke to Rous-Marten about priming, as recorded in Chapter 7.

It is only fair to quote T. W. Worsdell himself, on the use of domes, from a contribution he made to a discussion on American versus English loco-motives at the Institution of Mechanical Engineers in 1887. He said 'As regards steam domes, some wanted them and some did not. His own opinion was that with plenty of steam space a dome was unnecessary.'

He was at that time Locomotive Superintendent of the Great Eastern Railway.

No. 34, rebuilt, about 1899. This engine and No. 221 received new cylinders with the slide-valves exhausting straight through the back of the valve to the base of the blast pipe, similarly to the Ivatt Atlantics

No. 1003 on down Grimsby train, just North of Peterborough, 1912. Note: The smoke cloud was undoubtedly specially arranged for the photographer, the late Cecil Laundy

CHAPTER 9

PERFORMANCE:
THE 1888 AND 1895 RACES

In the competitive running of the East Coast and West Coast trains between London and Edinburgh which took place during August 1888, there was at first no real attempt on the part of the Great Northern authorities to make a Race of that part of the run for which they were responsible, i.e. from Kings Cross to York, with a change of engines at Grantham. It was only after a fortnight's running that there was any serious attempt to get the train in before booked time, and at no time can it be said that the engines were appreciably extended beyond most of their day-to-day working. There were, however, two runs which were noticeably better than all the rest. On August 13, No. 775 between Grantham and York suffered delays *en route* amounting to six min., and yet kept her running time. This performance, allowing for the delays and reckoning on net time and not on actual time taken, involved an average speed of 59·1 m.p.h. The other occasion was on August 25, when No. 233, with a train of seven vehicles, lighter by one coach than No. 775's load on August 13, ran from

Kings Cross to Grantham at an average speed of 60·2 m.p.h.

The running of the various engines for the whole of the period of racing is given in the table.

The thing that stands out above everything else in the table opposite is that the engines were completely masters of the job, and that in spite of the tightening of the schedule, it would have been easy, with the 7-coach load, to have improved still more on the booked timing, had the officials or the men considered it desirable. It should be noted that nine different Peterborough engines were allowed to participate. Very likely Nos. 775 and 777 were selected at Grantham as being the latest built engines stationed there. Since No. 775 had received her first general repair in April 1888, and No. 777 was out of shops, new, on September 21, 1887, both engines were in good condition. And as No. 95 also had recently, in May 1888, had a general repair, including a new boiler, it looks as if the Grantham engines may have been specially picked for the duty.

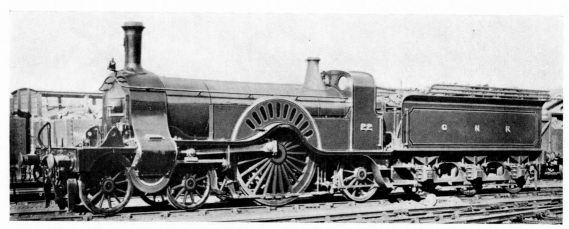

No. 22, about 1895. The engine did some of the best running during the 1888 'Racing'. In her very early days, too, she had put up some excellent performances

108

TABLE OF RUNNING BETWEEN KINGS CROSS AND YORK DURING AUGUST 1888
Average speeds calculated on net times

Date	Engine No.	Tare load tons	Kings Cross dep. a.m.	Grantham arr. a.m.	Avge. Speed m.p.h.	Remarks	Engine No.	Grantham dep. p.m.	York arr. p.m.	Avge. Speed m.p.h.	Remarks
1	671 (K's X)	120	10 00	11 59	53·1	arr. 1 min. early	3	12 02	1 33	54·5	dep. 2 min. early arr. 2 min. early
2	233 (P'boro)	135	10 00	11 58	53·6	arr. 2 min. early	3	12 02	1 33	54·5	dep. 2 min. early arr. 2 min. early
3	776 ,,	135	10 00	11 56	54·5	arr. 4 min. early	3	noon 12 00	1 31	54·5	dep. 4 min. early arr. 4 min. early
4	233 ,,	135	10 00	11 58	53·6	arr. 2 min. early	3	12 03	1 36	55·1	dep. 1 min. early arr. 1 min. late, 3 min. delays
6	98 ,,	120	10 00	noon 12 00	55·9	arr. 1 min. late 7 min. delays	777	12 04	1 36	55·1	dep. 2 min. late arr. 4 min. late, 2 min. delays
7	69 ,,	135	9 58	a.m. 11 54	54·5	dep. 2 min. early arr. 3 min. early	777	a.m. 11 59	1 31	55·1	dep. 3 min. early arr. 1 min. early 2 min. delays
8	48 ,,	120	9 59	11 56	54·0	dep. 1 min. early arr. 1 min. early	777	11 59	1 29	55·1	dep. 3 min. early arr. 3 min. early
9	776 ,,	135	9 58	11 55	54·0	dep. 2 min. early arr. 2 min. early	777	noon 12 00	1 30	55·1	dep. 2 min. early arr. 2 min. early
10	234 ,,	150	10 00	11 57	54·0	arr. 3 min. early	777	p.m. 12 02	1 32	55·1	—
11	776 ,,	120	10 00	11 55	55·0	arr. 2 min. early	777	a.m. 11 59	1 30	54·5	dep. 3 min. early arr. 2 min. early
13	237 ,,	120	10 00	11 55	55·0	arr. 2 min. early	775	noon 12 00	1 30	59·1	dep. 2 min. early arr. 2 min. early 6 min. delays
14	7 ,,	120	10 00	11 55	55·0	arr. 2 min. early	775	12 00	1 30	56·4	dep. 2 min. early arr. 2 min. early 2 min. delays
15	98 ,,	120	10 00	11 55	55·9	arr. 2 min. early 2 min. delays	775	a.m. 11 59	1 28	55·7	dep. 3 min. early arr. 4 min. early 5 min. delays
16	22 ,,	135	10 00	11 51	56·9	arr. 6 min. early	775	11 57	1 27	55·1	dep. 2 min. early arr. 5 min. early
17	22 ,,	120	10 00	11 55	55·9	arr. 2 min. early 2 min. delay	775	noon 12 00	1 29	55·7	dep. 2 min. early arr. 3 min. early
18	7 ,,	120	10 00	11 56	54·5	arr. 1 min. early	775	12 00	1 30	55·1	dep. 2 min. early arr. 2 min. early
20	233 ,,	105	10 00	11 50	57·5	arr. 5 min. early	775	a.m. 11 54	1 24	55·1	dep. 6 min. early arr. 6 min. early
21	237 ,,	105	10 00	11 49	58·0	arr. 6 min. early	775	11 54	1 22	55·7	dep. 7 min. early arr. 8 min. early
22	98 ,,	105	10 00	11 53	55·9	arr. 2 min. early	775	11 56	1 26	55·1	dep. 4 min. early arr. 4 min. early
23	233 ,,	105	10 00	11 48	58·5	arr. 7 min. early	775	11 53	1 22	55·7	dep. 7 min. early arr. 8 min. early
24	98 ,,	105	10 00	11 53	55·9	arr. 2 min. early	775	11 58	1 26	56·4	dep. 2 min. early arr. 4 min. early
25	233 ,,	105	10 00	11 45	60·2	arr. 10 min. early	775	11 51	1 30	55·1	dep. 9 min. early 9 min. delays
27	22 ,,	105	10 00	11 51	56·9	arr. 4 min. early	95	11 56	1 28	55·7	dep. 4 min. early arr. 2 min. early 3 min. delays
28	98 ,,	105	10 00	11 52	56·4	arr. 3 min. early	95	11 58	1 29	55·7	dep. 2 min. early arr. 1 min. early 2 min. delays
29	22 ,,	105	10 00	11 49	58·0	arr. 6 min. early	95	noon 12 00	1 30	57·7	dep. 2 min. early 4 min. delays
30	69 ,,	120	10 00	11 54	55·4	arr. 1 min. early	95	11 58	1 27	55·7	dep. 2 min. early arr. 3 min. early
31	98 ,,	105	10 00	11 50	57·5	arr. 5 min. early	95	11 54	1 23	58·3	dep. 6 min. early arr. 7 min. early 4 min. delays

But the Peterborough engines, which, after the first day, took the train from Kings Cross to Grantham, seem to have been random choices for the most part, probably the regular engine and crew whose turn it was for the job. No. 233 was practically a new engine, having less than four months' life behind her when the Race started. But the others were certainly by no means in mint condition. No. 69 went in for her next general repair in November 1888, and No. 48 had been out of Doncaster shops over three years since her last general repair there. Of course, Peterborough engines had a lot more work put in on them at the shed between general repairs than Grantham or Doncaster engines, but, even so, the fact that Nos. 8, 221 and 545 were then all so recently out of Doncaster works after repairs that they must have been in first-class condition, and yet were not used, does indicate that no attempt was made to select the best of the Peterborough 8-footers for the Race. In 1888 there were only three 7 ft. 6 in. engines stationed there, and all three were used, probably because they were allotted to the link of enginemen in whose duties the 'Racing' train was normally rostered.

The 1895 Race to Aberdeen was very similar to the 1888 Race in its gradual development, as far as the Great Northern was concerned. Booked times were set and were adhered to, even when there were moderate delays *en route*. But there was no attempt to run appreciably before booked times, even with a clear road. This state of affairs remained until the last week of the Racing, when it became clear that the West Coast working time-table had been completely thrown overboard for all practical purposes. But even then, the G.N.R. drivers were instructed by the Superintendent of the Line to use every care and not to go all out,

No. 775 at Kings Cross, about 1897. The engine has been 'tallowed down' after cleaning, and the thin layer of tallow has been worked into patterns by the cleaners: a style of finish more satisfactory to them than to the photographer

at least for the moment. It looks as if the G.N.R. authorities expected a week or two's further Racing, and wanted to have something up their sleeve to pull out if need be, while letting the West Coast people set the pace in the meantime. As it happened they left their final spurt—if, indeed, they had one in mind—too late.

The official timings for the running of the Racing train in 1895 do not seem to have been published, as they were in 1888. Against this, a number of detailed logs were obtained by such responsible and experienced recorders as Rous-Marten, the Rev. W. J. Scott and others, and from these a selection of the more enterprising runs has been made.

On the first night on which the East Coast made any acceleration of the 8 p.m. from Kings Cross to counter that of the West Coast, the Great Northern were certainly rather out of luck as far as Grantham. A late start, a fairly heavy train of 179 tons weight, an only moderate start out to Potters

No. 69 at Peterborough, 1889. In later years, a shorter chimney, new crossheads and curved front footplate angle were provided

No. 668, the engine which made the fastest run from Kings Cross to Grantham in 1895, photographed at Peterborough 1908-09. In Stirling condition except for Ivatt tender

Bar; a bridge repair at St. Neots involving single-line working, and crossing over to the up line and back again, of course at little more than walking pace; and finally being brought to a dead stand on an up gradient at Essendine for a 'tail lamp out'. From Grantham to York there were no out of course checks, but the running was certainly of the normal rather than the racing class.

On August 15, No. 22 was the engine from Kings Cross to Grantham, her load being 134 tons. She had run quite well as far as St. Neots, but suffered a devastating signal stop shortly thereafter, being brought to a stand for $2\frac{1}{4}$ min. at Blacklands Box, a slow train having been allowed to get on the road in front. There was also a slight signal check just before the Grantham stop. Probably $5\frac{1}{2}$ min. might be allowed for these delays, making the net time 111 min.

The runs of No. 668 on the final two nights of the Race were hampered by repairs to the Ouse bridge near Welwyn, where a permanent way slack was in force which was reckoned at the time to have cost 1 min. From an inspection of the speeds before and after the slowing and acceleration due to this slack, it seems that at least 1 min. 30 sec. may fairly be allowed.

The net average speeds are thus approximately 61·8 m.p.h. and 64·8 m.p.h. for the runs logged below. The load in both cases was 101 tons tare. The runs of No. 775 on the same two nights, from Grantham to York, are also tabled. On the last night there was said to have been a clear run, subject of course to the permanent speed restrictions at Doncaster and Selby, but on the previous night there had been a signal check outside York, estimated at the time as costing 1 min. But such a check, without any chance of recovery and with the train already slowing down for the coming stop, is extremely difficult to estimate. There is a further

factor, that on the last and fastest run of all No. 775 took $\frac{1}{4}$ min. longer from Selby to the York stop than she did on the previous night with its signal check. It raises a suspicion that there may have been something similar between Selby and York on that last night.

And that last run of No. 775 concluded the Racing as far as the Great Northern was concerned, for next morning the East Coast authorities decided to revert to normal working.

The question must inevitably arise, how much more had Nos. 668 and 775 in hand to improve on their last evening's performances. Sir Henry Oakley, the Great Northern General Manager, made the official position clear after the Race was over: 'The speed at which we ran last night was not higher than we run daily with our expresses from Yorkshire and Manchester, the only difference being that the lightening of the train to six carriages enabled us to run uphill almost as fast as we could run down. I did not, and do not, feel that there was any risk in the performance.' The element of a safety margin is underlined throughout that statement. There never was any all-out attempt by a Great Northern engine, and none would be permitted.

But a margin did exist: though only the drivers of Nos. 668 and 775 could have said by how much they might have expected to surpass their previous speeds and times, and they had hitherto had more discouragement than help from the authorities at Kings Cross.

It is true that there was a belated effort to tempt the Peterborough drivers into running faster. On August 16 there was a recommendation from Stirling to the District Locomotive Superintendent at Peterborough that the special conditions of the Racing might be allowed for in the distribution of coal premiums and that some pecuniary allowance, such as a 'quarter of a day's pay when they arrive on time', might be given; but since on almost every day's running they were already arriving on the booked time, this can hardly have been looked on by the men as an instruction, on the West Coast methods, to go as hard and as fast as possible. So long as the then Superintendent of the Line, F. P. Cockshott, was at Kings Cross each evening endeavouring to restrain the drivers and to impress on them the necessity for taking every possible care, a small financial reward for continuing to do what they were already achieving could be no temptation to go all out, against the almost certainty of a lasting black mark against them from the Superintendent.

And in the end it was the North British authorities, and not the Great Northern, who brought the Racing to a perhaps premature close.

THE RACE OF 1895
8 p.m. KINGS CROSS—GRANTHAM

Run. No.		1		2		3		4		5	
Date		22 July		29 July		15 Aug.		20 Aug.		21 Aug.	
Engine No.		545		874		22		668		668	
Engine Type		4-2-2		2-2-2		4-2-2		4-2-2		4-2-2	
Load tons tare		179½		179½		134		101		101	
Dist. Miles		Actual m. s.	Av.Sp. m.p.h.	Actual m. s.	Av.Sp. m.p.h.	Actual m. s.	Av.Sp. m.p.h.	Actual m. s.	Av.Sp. m.p.h.	Actual m. s.	Av.Sp. m.p.h.
0·0	KINGS CROSS	0 00	—	0 00	—	0 00	—	0 00	—	0 00	—
1·5	Holloway	—	—	3 58	22·7	3 31	25·7	—	—	—	—
4·0	Hornsey	7 45	31·0	7 27	43·2	6 43	46·8	—	—	—	—
9·2	New Barnet	—	—	—	—	—	—	—	—	11 35	—
12·7	Potters Bar	19 17	45·3	18 43	46·3	17 34	48·1	15 27	49·4	15 00	61·5
17·7	HATFIELD	24 34	56·7	23 44	59·8	22 44	58·1	20 12 p.w.s.	63·2	19 30 p.w.s.	66·7
22·0	Welwyn	—	—	27 41	65·3	26 57	61·3	—	—	—	—
31·9	HITCHIN	39 24	57·4	37 10	62·8	36 44	60·6	33 22	64·8	33 00	63·1
37·0	Arlesey	43 45	70·4	41 22	72·8	40 51	74·5	—	—	—	—
44·1	Sandy	50 07	66·8	47 36	68·2	47 06	68·1	—	—	—	—
51·7	St. Neots	57 20 p.w.s.	63·3	54 44	63·8	54 22 sig. stop	62·8	50 29	69·5	49 30	72·0
58·9	HUNTINGDON	64 32	—	61 37	62·8	65 17	—	56 58	66·5	55 30	72·0
63·5	Abbots Ripton	—	—	—	—	—	—	—	—	60 05	60·2
69·4	Holme	—	—	—	—	—	—	—	—	65 30	65·4
76·4	PETERBOROUGH	83 24	—	79 20	59·3	82 50	59·8	73 42	62·7	72 00	64·6
88·6	Essendine	98 00 / 102 00	STOP	93 07	53·3	96 27	53·7	87 14	54·0	84 30	58·6
100·1	*Stoke Box*	—	—	—	—	110 20 sigs.	49·7	99 38	55·7	96 00	60·0
105·5	GRANTHAM	125 31		112 44		116 29		104 41		101 00	
Net times (min.)		118		112¾		111		103¼		99½	

THE RACE OF 1895
GRANTHAM—YORK

Run No.		1	2	3	4	
Date		22 July	29 July	20 Aug.	21 Aug.	
Engine 4-2-2 No.		775	1002	775	775	
Load tons tare		179½	179½	101	101	
Dist. Miles		Actual m. s.	Actual m. s.	Actual m. s.	Actual m. s.	Av. Sp. m.p.h.
0·0	GRANTHAM	0 00	0 00	0 00	0 00	—
4·2	Barkston	—	—	—	5 40	—
14·6	NEWARK	16 00	15 27	14 31	14 00	75·0
20·9	Carlton	—	—	—	19 15	72·0
26·4	Tuxford	—	—	—	24 30	62·8
33·1	RETFORD	35 48	34 57	31 31	30 30	67·0
42·2	Bawtry	—	—	—	38 25	69·0
50·5	DONCASTER	52 49	51 59	46 59	46 00	65·7
57·5	Moss	—	—	—	52 00	70·0
64·3	Templehirst	—	—	—	57 45	70·8
68·9	SELBY	71 31	70 59	64 24	62 00	65·0
73·0	Riccall	—	—	—	66 30	54·7
78·5	Naburn	—	—	— sigs.	71 30	66·0
82·7	YORK	87 04	85 59	78 09	76 00	—

CHAPTER 10

THE LAST EIGHT-FOOTERS

The 8 ft. singles—Nos. 1003-08

FROM 1890 onwards, with the introduction of corridor stock, the weight of the Great Northern express passenger trains had been increasing year by year. The existing Stirling singles, which had hitherto always been comfortably up to their job, were beginning to lose time on the heaviest trains, in spite of the most skilful handling, as soon as a patch of bad weather came along. On a dry day, even with a moderate cross-wind, time would normally be kept punctually though there was little or no margin for making up any time lost; but on a wet day with a cross-wind—and westerly winds blowing across the north-and-south line of the Great Northern main line were often bringers of rain—time was very frequently lost. The traffic department was continually pressing for double-heading to be permitted. It was a standard practice on the London & North Western and halfway to being a standard practice on the Midland, the two most important competitors of the Great Northern.

Stirling finally had to give way, in time for double-heading to be introduced simultaneously with the summer service timetable of 1894. He had done his best to postpone it until an enlarged design of 8-footer, which had been in hand since the beginning of 1894, could be built and put into service to tackle, single handed, the loads which were proving too much for the existing engines. The last of the 23 7 ft. 6 in. singles, No. 981, was completed at Doncaster on July 15, but the new and more powerful 8-footer which should be capable of handling single handed the fastest and heaviest expresses was not ready.

Stirling had, in conversation with Charles Rous-Marten, explained that although, as he put it, the 7 ft. 6 in. engines were 'fully more powerful than' the existing 8-footers, he felt that these latter engines were more suitable for development than the inside-cylinder engines. It is a curious point that, four years later, Ivatt reached an opposite conclusion and in his first single-wheeler, No. 266,

produced an enlarged version of the Stirling 7 ft. 6 in. singles. It is clear that Ivatt was influenced by being able to provide a larger diameter boiler, using 7 ft. 6 in. wheels, than could be done with 8 ft. wheels. Here again, Rous-Marten records that Ivatt told him that if only the 8-footers could be provided with a bigger diameter boiler, they would be able to cope with heavier trains, and expressed his regret that this was not feasible.

But Stirling felt that a larger firebox would give him the extra steam he needed, despite the small diameter boiler, and increased tractive effort and adhesion weight were to be his aim in his new design of express passenger engine. The drawings were actually made during the first half of 1894 and the first of the six engines of the enlarged class of 8-footers, No. 1003, was turned out of Doncaster works new on November 19, 1894. The general arrangement drawing, as was often the case, lagged behind a bit and when completed on December 3 still exhibited two minor features, important nevertheless from the point of view of the appearance of the engine, in which changes had been made during

No. 1003 as originally built, in early 1895, showing the cylinder covers which were shortly replaced by covers with a greater number of studs. Reproduced from an old print in the possession of the late F. H. Eggleshaw, Patrick Stirling's last pupil, afterwards works manager at Doncaster

actual construction. The drawing showed the standard cast-iron chimney and a rather deep version of the standard cab. When No. 1003 appeared, she was provided with a beautifully-proportioned built-up chimney and the side sheet of the cab had been cut away at waist level by 8 in., the roof remaining the original length proposed. But the shorter cast-iron chimneys were actually made, and fitted later to a number of the earlier 8-footers.

Of the essential dimensions, the cylinders were increased from 18 to 19½ in. in diameter and the distance between the centres of driving and trailing wheels was increased from 8 ft. 8 in. to 9 ft. The boiler barrel was shortened from 11 ft. 5 in. to 11 ft. 1 in. so that a firebox 6 ft. 10 in. long having a grate area of 20 sq. ft. could be accommodated; an appreciable increase in steam-raising capacity over the older engines with a firebox 6 ft. 2 in. long having a grate area of 17¾ sq. ft. The boiler pressure was also raised, fairly certainly, to 170 lb. per sq. in. from 160 lb. The figure of 175 lb. per sq. in., first given in *The Engineer,* was changed in a later article to 170 lb.

A wheel and screw reversing gear was provided in the cab similar to that used on Stirling's suburban tank engines, instead of the long lever previously used on all the single-wheelers. There had been, and were to be in the future, cases in which drivers injured themselves on the 7 ft. 6 in. engines in the ordinary course of 'notching up' with the reversing lever provided, long though this was. The reason for the stiff operation of the levers on this class of engine compared with the 8-footers was the combination of a higher boiler pressure than on the majority of the 8 ft. engines and a larger slide-valve, subjected of course to boiler pressure on its back and necessitating a correspondingly larger effort to move it. Since the boiler pressure of the No. 1003 class was yet higher and the slide-valve was the same size as that on the 7 ft. 6 in. engines, there was good reason for making the change to the more easily operated wheel and screw. It is a curious point that no actual locking-catch was provided to hold the gear fixed in its selected position; instead, an arrangement which had proved satisfactory on the suburban tank engines for the previous 14 years was also used on the No. 1003 class, a clamp with a small handle to tighten on the main screw spindle.

No. 1003's wheels were the same diameters, 3 ft. 11½ in. bogie wheels, 8 ft. 1½ in. driving wheels and 4 ft. 7½ in. trailing wheels, and had the same tyre thickness, 2¾ in., as on the final 18 in. cylinder engines. The trailing wheel spokes, however, were 14 in number as against 13 on the previous 8-footers with the same diameter wheel. The transverse distance between centres of cylinders was increased to 6 ft. 5 in. from 6 ft. 2 in. to give larger big-end and crosshead bearing surfaces and to maintain bogie wheel clearance on curves. As on all other 8-footers, the bogie wheel tyres were thinned to 5 in. width to help this clearance and the cylinder castings were arranged symmetrically between the bogie wheels.

The bogie itself had the same general design and the same 6 ft. 6 in. wheelbase, with the pivot 3 in. to the rear of the bogie centre line, as the earlier engines; but it was made rather heavier and stiffer in one or two places. The laminated bearing springs remained interchangeable with those on other 8-footers built since 1884, 2 ft. 4 in. between centres of spring shacklepins.

The pitch of the boiler was raised to 7 ft. 6 in. from 7 ft. 3½ in. No. 1003 remained unique in one small respect; her handrail stanchion positions along the boiler had been marked off in accordance with the position on the boilers of the earlier engines with lower pitched boilers so that there was a clearance of just over 2½ in. between the underside of the handrail and the top of the driving wheel splasher. The six engines of the class were built as a single batch, but all the other five engines had

No. 1005 about 1899, in original condition

No. 1006 at Nottingham, in her last days, about 1914, with secondhand chimney from 0-4-4 tank engine

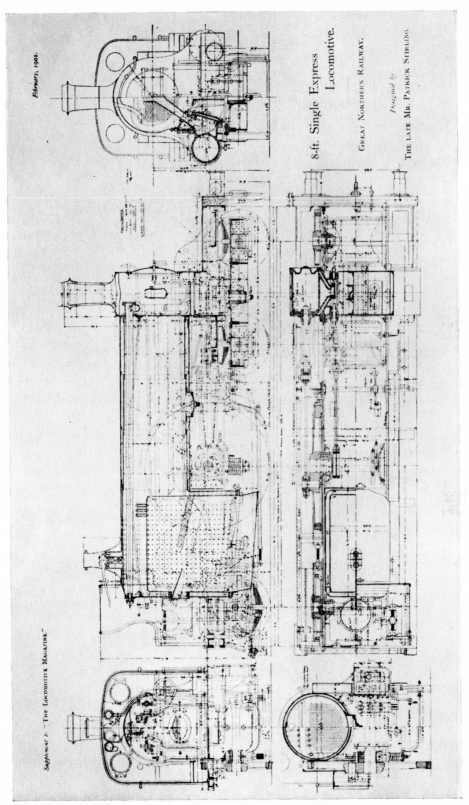

February, 1901.

8-ft. Single Express Locomotive.

GREAT NORTHERN RAILWAY.

Designed by

THE LATE MR. PATRICK STIRLING.

Supplement to "THE LOCOMOTIVE MAGAZINE."

General Arrangement Sectional Drawing of No. 1003

their handrails lowered so that they only just cleared the splasher.

The larger cylinders differed slightly in general design from the 18 in. diameter ones. The ports were increased to 16 in. in length, the same sizes, both for steam and exhaust ports, as the 7 ft. 6 in. singles of 1885 onward. The port face, instead of being vertical, was appreciably inclined downwards so that the slide-valve fell away from it when steam was shut off. This design helped also in the layout of the exhaust passages and blast-pipe arrangements.

These cylinders were at first provided with only 14 studs for their front covers, just one more than for the 18 in. cylinders. Whether this was the only defect in their design cannot now be stated with certainty because the relevant drawing has long since been destroyed; but all the cylinders of all six engines had to be replaced within two years, and the new cylinders had 18 studs in their front covers. The second engine of the class, No. 1004, was especially unlucky. Out of shops, new, on January 26, 1895, she was in again for a new right-hand cylinder on March 11. Out of shops again on March 30, she was in again, this time for *two* new cylinders, on April 8.

No. 1003's original cylinders were replaced after 11 months, No. 1005's after two months and No. 1007's after six months. No. 1006 managed to retain hers from March 1895 until November 1896, the longest lived of these highly unsatisfactory cylinders, No. 1008 being the 'runner-up' with a life of 17 months. The cylinders which replaced these defective ones were thoroughly satisfactory, however, and each pair lasted throughout the life of its engine; no new cylinders thereafter being required at all for the class.

Connecting rod and crosshead of No. 1004, Peterborough 1912. Driver Bellam with oilfeeder

No. 1008, the very last 8-footer to be built, was at first given 19 in. diameter cylinders experimentally, instead of $19\frac{1}{2}$. It is highly probable that the reason behind this experiment was a desperate hope that the cylinders thus reduced in diameter would not be subject to the troubles afflicting the earlier engines of the batch. There would be less total pressure for the studs to hold steam tight and the cylinder-cover gasket would be wider and therefore less likely to blow out.

It seems always to have been assumed that No. 1008 retained her original 19 in. cylinder diameter when new cylinders were fitted in 1896. There was a report in 1911, or thereabouts, that her cylinders had been rebored to $20\frac{7}{8}$ in. in diameter. In the 15 years since the cylinders had been installed this would have represented a very rapid wear from 19 in., thereby suggesting that the replacement cylinders were supplied $19\frac{1}{2}$ in. in diameter to correspond with the other five engines of the batch.

Connecting rods, crossheads and slidebars were strengthened to take the loads from the larger cylinders; and the slidebar brackets were made of cast-steel instead of wrought-iron as previously. Because of the increased dimensions of the crossheads the connecting rods were shortened by $1\frac{1}{4}$ in., from 6 ft. 11 in. centres to 6 ft. $9\frac{3}{4}$ in. Driving axles, crank pins, axleboxes and many other parts were increased generously in size.

The six engines were put on to top-link work as soon as possible, Nos. 1003, 1004 and 1005 at Peterborough, No. 1006 at Grantham and Nos. 1007 and 1008 at Kings Cross. They did excellent work during their first year and some notes of their performances are given later, though none of the six engines took any part in the 1895 Race to

No. 1007 starting out from Grantham about 1900

Aberdeen. Probably their cylinder troubles—it should be remembered that at the time of the Race five out of the six engines were still running with these suspect cylinders—would have been borne in mind when selecting engines for the racing trains; but an equally likely reason is that they had that summer been found far too useful on the heaviest fast trains to be released for a special and temporary duty which was well within the capacity of the smaller engines.

The adhesion weight was given officially as 19 tons 4 cwt., but, once more on Rous-Marten's authority, the actual weight is said to have been over 20 tons. The earliest official engine diagram, dated January 9, 1895 and referring to No. 1003 only, shows an axle loading, presumably intended to be taken as the actual adjusted weight, of 20 tons. The total engine weight is given as 48 tons 14 cwt., as against a later diagram total weight of 49 tons 11 cwt. The discrepancy in the figures for the total weights makes one more than a little suspicious of the nice round figure of 20 tons.

No. 1003 at Werrington Junction on up train from Boston to Peterborough, 1911. The exhaust steam from the chimney, not condensing until some feet from the chimney-top, indicates that the steam was nicely dry in the steam chest, and that the engine was being worked at a late cut-off with the regulator partially closed

Most unfortunately, both Nos. 1003 and 1006 were concerned in cases of the derailment of their trains due to defective permanent way. On November 10, 1895 No. 1006 broke a rail at St. Neots, though she herself did not become derailed. This rail had already been removed, due to wear, from the main line for lighter duty, but as a result of some culpable mistake it had been used again on the main line. On March 7, 1896 No. 1003 at full speed through Little Bytham came on to a section of line just relaid and not yet ballasted, but on which no speed restriction had been ordered. As a result the track became distorted to such an extent that, though the engine and the first coaches stayed on the rails, several of the rear coaches became derailed and three lives were lost.

Ivatt had just assumed power at this time and from his own personal observations had realised the generally poor state of the Great Northern permanent way. The adhesion weights of all the singles were reduced and the most drastic reduction of all, to a strict 18 tons, was suffered by the No. 1003 class. There is evidence, too, that by 1900 their boiler pressure had been reduced to 160 lb. per sq. in., and they were thereafter regarded as being just a minor variation of the older standard 8-footers.

During the summer of either 1906 or 1907 the three Peterborough engines were used in pairs on some of the Scotch expresses, which were then loading up to between 300 and 350 tons behind the tender. The present writer photographed them— uniformly unsatisfactorily, they were going too fast for his shutter—when they were on the up train due in at 4.10 p.m. and can vouch that they were always punctual when he was about.

The two Kings Cross engines were transferred to Hitchin, when the large Ivatt 'Atlantics' came out and began to be shedded at Kings Cross, and continued for some years to do good work, more especially on the Cambridge to London services. No. 1008 had the reputation of being by far the better engine of the two; No. 1007 certainly had begun to look rather a poor old thing by 1903, having had her built-up chimney replaced by a part-worn cast-iron one, even more shapeless than No. 1's present chimney. Moreover, No. 1007 always looked shabby; she never seemed to get a proper repainting after her general repairs, even when, in May 1907, she was given a domed boiler. This boiler was one of the batch of similar boilers which were originally intended as replacements for boilers on the older Stirling 8 ft. singles. They were to have been domeless, with three-ring barrels, but after the material had been ordered the decision was taken to provide the boilers with domes. All other domed boilers which Ivatt fitted to Stirling singles had two-ring barrels. The external difference was the altered position of the dome, which was 15 in. further forward on the three-ring barrel. No. 116, the Ivatt 0—8—2 suburban tank engine of 1903, received one of this batch of boilers when it was found that her original boiler made her too heavy. Three of these boilers also found their way on to the 7 ft. 6 in. singles. No. 1007 was 4 in. too long in the chassis for *her* sample, and the cab had to be set forward 4 in. to suit. Moreover, the hand-rail stanchions had been marked off for a 7 ft. 6 in. engine so that when No. 1007 emerged from Doncaster it was seen that the handrail was bent in an arc upwards to the curve of the driving-wheel splasher and downward again to the next stanchion and then on to the cab. The expansion brackets on this boiler were positioned to suit the 7 ft. 6 in. singles, too, and the curves of the firebox sides pre-vented their being re-positioned any higher, so that the greater height of the frame on No. 1007 in-volved raising the pitch of the boiler by $2\frac{3}{4}$ in., to 7 ft. $8\frac{3}{4}$ in.

No. 1007 is the only engine of the class for which any mileage figures are available. Her straightback boiler, when finally taken off in January 1907, had a mileage of 417,256.

The first of the class to be withdrawn was No. 1005 in October 1908. Her last appearance in the London area seems to have been on August Bank Holiday Monday that year when she worked an up special passenger train and appeared to be making very heavy weather of it when she was observed by

the present writer near Potters Bar. There was every indication that she was hard up for steam and the driver must have been very glad when he finally struggled past Potters Bar and had only the easy downhill road into Kings Cross to cover.

Nos. 1007 and 1008 were sent to Grantham in 1910 and the latter engine especially did some good main-line work from Peterborough north. No. 1007 was withdrawn on January 22, 1913 and No. 1008, after having again been transferred, this time to Louth, was condemned on June 6, 1914. The boiler from No. 1008 lasted a good deal longer as it was in use at Werrington from September 1917 to September 1931. It is perhaps of interest to note that No. 1008 in June 1898 was experimentally fitted with an 'Electrical Signal Appliance', presumably for trials with the early Raven cab-signalling devices tried out on the North Eastern Railway at about that time.

Nos. 1003 and 1004 remained at Peterborough throughout their existence. It was fortunate for them that when they were superseded for first-class main-line passenger work the level lines to Lincoln, Boston and Grimsby were available and highly suitable for their special characteristics. No. 1003 was regarded as the better engine of the two and lasted until May 1915. No. 1004 was withdrawn on August 27, 1914. She had been fitted with an experimental spark arrester in 1911 and since then had been barred from working the heaviest trains rostered for that link of engines.

No. 1006, which was shedded during all her existence at the Grantham shed, in her later days had a very easy job on the Nottingham and other minor branch lines from Grantham. From the out-break of war in August 1914 it is said that she remained in the shed at Grantham and was not used at all. The last of the 8-footers to survive, she was withdrawn on February 14, 1916.

The original fine built-up chimneys on these engines had all disappeared by 1908. No. 1005 for a short time had carried one of the very tall, skinny, Ivatt single-piece cast-iron chimneys, as did No. 1008 from 1903 to the end. Nos. 1003 and 1004 received shorter cast-iron chimneys, with mould-ings imitating the three-piece construction of the old built-up type of chimney, in 1907 and 1906 respectively and these chimneys also lasted out the engines. No. 1007 received a similar chimney with her domed boiler in 1907. No. 1006 having, like Nos. 1005 and 1008, mounted a tall, cast-iron chimney in 1905, received a third chimney in 1911, this time one of the much shorter chimneys origin-ally used on the Stirling 0—4—4 suburban tank engines, which certainly suited her appearance

No. 1007, rebuilt by Ivatt, at Hitchin, 1909. Driver Freestone, on the footplate, is referred to in Chapter 13. This photograph was taken after the photo-grapher, the late Cecil Laundy, had enjoyed an unofficial footplate trip on the engine

better than the previous one. It is likely that this was a second-hand chimney, possibly even from No. 776 which lost a similar chimney at a rather earlier date, but more probably from one of the tank engines which were then in the process of having their condensing gear and short chimneys removed, as they were transferred from London to country branches.

No. 1003 suffered a special indignity on one of her last workings into Kings Cross from Peterborough. She was checked outside the station on a wet morning and stalled when drawing her train across into the down side of the station. She had to be propelled into the platform road after having brought the terminus traffic to an unappreciated standstill. Even now it is little consolation to remember that some ten years after this incident with No. 1003 an exactly similar occurrence took place with an Ivatt large 'Atlantic'.

Looking back over 70 years to the circumstances of their design, it is indeed difficult to justify the construction of these last six 8-footers. The writing on the wall was clear and any younger man than Stirling would have rightly and properly looked ten years or more into the future and produced a new design of express passenger engine. Stirling himself had done so in 1870 in his original 8-footer design, which was not outclassed for over 20 years.

Nevertheless, the No. 1003 class were perhaps the most beautiful of all the 8-footers and succeeded in combining a grace and symmetry of outline with a hint of massive power, which the slighter outlines of the earlier engines did not quite achieve. The minor alteration to the standard Stirling cab side-elevation—which struck Doncaster works with horror at the time—certainly contributed that extra touch of graceful curvature which the severe line of the older cabs lacked.

The story has been told how Gresley adopted the blast-pipe and chimney proportions of the No. 1003 class on his high-pressure experimental engine No. 10000, in an attempt to make her steam better. His remark was: 'Those engines steamed all right, yet they had no boiler to speak of.' But though the Stirling proportions did effect an improvement, a Kylchap double-blast pipe and chimney were later provided, in 1935. This was while No. 10000 still carried her original high-pressure boiler.

For an example of the work of the No. 1003 class, one of them on the 2.20 p.m. from Kings Cross took a load of 290 tons tare to Grantham in the booked time of 122 min. in spite of having been stopped dead by signals at Holloway for 2 min. The actual time to passing Peterborough was 86 min. —probably a net time of between 80 and 81 min.

No. 1008, the last 8-footer to be built, at Cambridge about 1899

The following run from Grantham to York behind one of the class—almost certainly the Grantham engine No. 1006—shows how one of these engines could romp away with a medium-weight train. The log was compiled by Rous-Marten. He does not mention the weather, so it can be assumed as reasonably fine.

G.N.R. GRANTHAM—YORK
Load: 187 tons tare
Engine: 4-2-2 of No. 1003 class

Dist. Miles				Actual m. s.	Av. Sp. m.p.h.
0·0	GRANTHAM	.	.	0 00	—
4·2	Barkston	.	.	5 43	44·1
6·0	Hougham	.	.	7 14	71·3
9·9	Claypole	.	.	10 19	75·8
14·6	NEWARK	.	.	14 12	72·6
20·9	Carlton .	.	.	19 49	67·4
26·4	Tuxford	.	.	25 09	61·8
33·1	RETFORD .	.	.	31 38	61·8
50·5	DONCASTER	.	.	48 31	62·2
				sigs.	
68·9	SELBY	.	.	66 40	60·8
82·7	YORK	.	.	80 31	59·8

The 28·9 miles from Barkston to Retford were run in 25 min. 55 sec., an average speed of nearly 67 m.p.h.; Rous-Marten did not attempt to assess the cost in time of the three slacks he recorded, and in any case two of these were permanent restrictions at that period, so that it is hardly practicable to estimate a net time for the run. But it was a performance quite up to Racing quality.

Almost certainly the very last run actually timed with an 8-footer on a main-line express train was that recorded in 1910 by Mr. Cecil J. Allen. The engine was No. 1008, then stationed at Grantham, and the train was the 7.31 p.m., the continuation from Grantham to York of the 5.30 p.m. from Kings Cross. In 1910 this train was regularly worked by the Ivatt singles of the No. 266 class,

119

and No. 1008 seems to have taken turn-and-turn-about with them. The load on this occasion was 200 tons, and No. 1008 gained 1½ min. on the not very difficult 94 min. timing for the 82·7 miles, in spite of a very slow start out of Grantham.

ENGINE No. 1008
Load 200 tons

Dist. Miles		Actual m. s.	Av. Sp. m.p.h.
0·0	GRANTHAM . .	0 00	—
4·2	Barkston . . .	8 05	31·1
9·9	Claypole . . .	13 10	67·2
14·6	Newark . . .	17 15	69·0
20·9	Carlton . . .	23 15	63·0
26·4	Tuxford . . .	29 20	54·2
33·1	Retford . . .	36 25	56·8
38·4	Ranskill . . .	41 40	60·5
42·2	Bawtry . . .	45 05	66·7
	P.W. slack Rossington		
50·5	Doncaster . . .	54 50	51·1
57·5	Moss . . .	62 30	54·7
64·3	Templehirst . .	69 35	57·6
	P.W. slack Templehirst		
68·9	Selby . . .	74 30	56·2
75·6	Escrick . . .	83 55	42·7
82·7	YORK . . .	93 25	44·8

There were the usual service slacks at Selby and Chaloners Whin Junction. Mr. Allen allowed 1 min. for the Rossington slack, but no allowance seems to have been needed for the Templehirst slack. The maximum speed was 70·3 m.p.h., and 65 m.p.h. was held on the level before Bawtry. It is interesting to compare this run with No. 1's from Grantham to Doncaster with the same load, recorded in Chapter 12. The older engine had the better of it; but of course since No. 1008 was little by little gaining time on her schedule, there was no need to open up the engine any further.

Now that all the 8-footers have been passed under review, engine by engine, it may have been noted by the reader that a large proportion of them carried running numbers in which the same figure occurred twice and that the same two numbers were adjacent. Since numbers were allotted either by being taken at random from condemned Sturrock engines or by taking the next higher numbers not yet used, it can only have been pure chance; yet Nos. 22, 33, 221, 544, 550, 662-69, 771-78 and 1001-08 all carried these paired numbers—29 out of the 53 engines, a far higher proportion than could have been mathematically expected, and one which no other Stirling class approached.

No. 93, rebuilt by Ivatt, with especially large dome, at Kings Cross, 1896

No. 33 in 1900-1. With Ivatt chimney and smokebox door

CHAPTER 11

REBUILDS OF STURROCK ENGINES

DURING the early years of his superintendency Stirling rebuilt a large number of his predecessor's engines, and among them were several classes of single-wheelers. He also rebuilt as single-wheelers the six 2—4—0s with 7 ft. driving wheels which were Sturrock's last design, and also—with the exception of his special 'prestige' engine, No. 215—his largest express engines.

No. 215 was not rebuilt. If Sturrock had not thought fit to build any further similar engines, even though perhaps the only reason was the great cost per engine entailed, then Stirling can hardly be blamed for scrapping her when the need came to renew boiler, cylinders, and crank-axle.

Stirling undoubtedly went very carefully into the question of what was the best thing to do about every existing class of engine which he inherited.

The 'Little Sharps', Nos. 1 to 50 of 1847-50, had already been far outclassed by the needs of the traffic of 1867, and even earlier; and Sturrock had converted some of them, quite cheaply, into 2—2—2 well-tank engines, for use on country and local services where loads were light and timing easy. Stirling did in fact take in hand five of these engines and rebuilt them as 0—4—2 well-tanks, putting so much new work into four of them as to justify new Doncaster works numbers for them.

But the next series of single-wheelers, the 'Small Hawthorns' Nos. 51 to 70 of 1848-50, were still capable of coping with secondary traffic, and several of them were rebuilt by Stirling with straightback boilers and cabs, and new, rather larger cylinders. The new boilers in this instance had larger fireboxes than the originals, but this was the exception rather than the rule with Stirling's rebuilds of Sturrock engines. Usually not only were the fireboxes smaller and the working pressure of the new boilers lower, but the new cylinders, though in most cases larger than the originals, had smaller steam and exhaust ports. Sturrock provided very generous port areas, and the extra clearance volumes at the ends of the cylinders, which the large steam passages entailed,

must have adversely affected the economical use of the steam. It was not that very high speeds had to be attained in service. That would have probably justified the large ports, though the sharp internal corners used in the castings must have occasionally caused cracked portbars. But the smaller Stirling ports, round-ended to avoid casting stresses, were amply large for the conditions of those days. As usually was the case in Stirling's designs, the proportions were right.

In his later engines Sturrock had gone in for very large fireboxes, with big grates. No doubt he was influenced in doing this by his experience with Gooch's Broad Gauge engines at Swindon, but not only was the cost of large and elaborate fireboxes high, and their life not so long as that of a smaller and simpler design, but a greater amount of coal necessarily burned to waste when the engine was standing. Moreover, on engines with a water mid-feather in the firebox, no brick arch was used, and very great care in firing must have been necessary to avoid smoke and wasteful combustion. Here then also, Stirling's happy knack of balancing the capacity of the engine against the job it was intended to do, caused him to keep the size of his fireboxes, not only on his rebuilds, just big enough, but never very much more, to tackle the work called for, efficiently and economically.

Not all the 'Small Hawthorns' were rebuilt. Out of the 20 engines of the class, probably only seven were so dealt with, eleven being scrapped unrebuilt, and two, Nos. 67 and 70, rebuilt as 0—4—2s with 6 ft. coupled wheels. To rebuild a single-wheeler as a coupled engine was so completely out of character for Stirling, that an effort has been made to see if Sturrock might not have been responsible for the new wheel arrangement. But this is not so, and in 1870 Stirling took the two single-wheelers in hand and rebuilt them as front-coupled engines. The extra 6 ft. wheels needed were available, since several of the class had been superseded by new Stirling engines only a few months before.

It should be remembered that these two conversions took place three years before Stirling reversed the procedure, and began converting six Sturrock 2—4—0s to single-wheelers.

The next class to be considered are the 'Converted Cramptons', Nos. 91 to 99 and 200, which Sturrock had rebuilt from 4—2—0s to 2—2—2s. Stirling's rebuilding was not a very drastic one. Straightback boilers of almost the same dimensions as the originals, and, of course, cabs, were provided on the eight engines rebuilt.

Then came a pair of 'Jenny Linds', Nos. 201 and 202, which had inside bearings only to the driving wheels. They passed through an intermediate stage, retaining their early domed boilers, but being fitted with cabs and Stirling boiler mountings, before finally receiving straightback boilers.

None of the foregoing engines was of Sturrock's design, as built. But Nos. 203-14, of 1852-53, were his first type of single-wheeler, and all except Nos. 203 and 205 were rebuilt by Stirling, the majority of them surviving for many years.

Then came Nos. 229-40 of 1860-61, which were all rebuilt and, again, were doing useful work for many years thereafter.

Finally, the six 7 ft. 2—4—0s, Nos. 264 to 269, were taken in hand, not all at once, but two in 1873, two in 1875 and the remaining pair in 1878. It looks almost as if Stirling was reluctant to deal with them, and in each case waited until the engine became troublesome. These six engines were given Stirling straightback boilers, and remained in service long enough to wear out these boilers and be provided with new, larger diameter ones, and to wear these out also before finally succumbing.

That is the general picture of the single-wheeler rebuilds. The whole story of each type of engine, with all its details, cannot now be told; the records are no longer in existence. But so far as it can be pieced together, what follows gives as full an account as is possible of each of these six classes.

Photographs of the rebuilds are not available for all classes, but general arrangement drawings of the rebuilt engines are in existence covering five classes, and the original general arrangement drawing of 1859 of the remaining class. The line drawings showing four of the classes which have been made from the general arrangement drawings of the rebuilds are therefore accurate in the main outlines, but small details, such as lubricators and injectors, which are not shown on the sectional drawings, have been omitted.

Nos. 51-70

The earliest engines rebuilt were the survivors of the 'Small Hawthorns', Nos. 51 to 70. Exactly how many of these received Stirling boilers and cabs, and had their leading wheels placed further forward is not certain. Some idea of the various dates of scrapping of these engines can be gained by noting the dates of construction of the new Stirling engines which replaced them, but unfortunately this cannot be taken as conclusive evidence in all cases. From very early in his superintendency Stirling had started a 'Duplicate List', of engines inevitably doomed but respited for a more or less short time. Such engines were given the letter 'A' after their running numbers. At first there were only a few of them, and probably they did not last long. In later years, however, cases occurred in which the engine on the duplicate list survived a considerable time after the engine which had replaced it had been scrapped. From 1870 to the end of 1872 the numbers of the eight duplicate list engines are known, and none are between 51 and 70. But after this short period, track of specific engine numbers is lost, and the approximate scrapping dates of only nine out of the 20 engine can be given.

The following list gives the dates at which they were rebuilt, based on available information, and also the dates a new engine with the same number appeared.

Engine No.	Rebuilt	Date replaced on Capital List	Engine No.	Rebuilt	Date replaced on Capital List
51	—/1868*	1879	61	—	1869
52	—	1872	62	—/1867	1876
53	—/1868*	1875	63	—	1869
54	—	1870	64	—	1870
55	—	1869	65	—	1870
56	—	1870	66	—/1868*	1879
57	—/1868*	1878	67	11/1870†	not replaced
58	—	1870	68	—	1871
59	—	1870	69	—/1867	1877
60	—/1867	1878	70	5/1870†	not replaced

* these dates are not certain.
† rebuilt to 0-4-2.

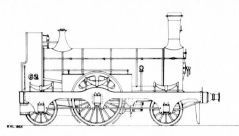

Small Hawthorn No. 62 as rebuilt by Stirling

It is quite certain that those engines replaced during 1869-72 were never rebuilt by Stirling, although the remaining seven engines, which lasted until 1875-79, were probably all rebuilt. Nos. 60, 62 and 69 were rebuilt in 1867 but unfortunately the dates of subsequent rebuilds are not now traceable. Nos. 67 and 70 were rebuilt to 0—4—2s in November and May respectively of 1870. They had much longer lives, No. 67 lasting until January 1900 and No. 70 until January 1901.

No photographs of these rebuilds, other than of Nos. 67 and 70, can be traced and the sole remaining source for the appearance of these single-wheelers is the general arrangement drawing of 1873. From this, the accompanying line drawing has been made. The 1873 drawing does not show any brake gear, since this was not fitted on passenger engines until 1876-78, and on goods engines from 1878 to 1881. It is probable that only Nos. 53 and 62 were withdrawn without brakes being fitted; but there is no real evidence one way or the other as to whether any of the class were fitted with brakes; or, if brakes were fitted, anything to indicate just how the brake gear was arranged. Almost certainly it would have been similar to that used on the other Sturrock singles rebuilt by Stirling.

It is a curious point about the boilers fitted to Stirling's rebuilds of all the six classes of Sturrock and pre-Sturrock singles, that each class had its own boiler, the dimensions of which were just a little different from each of the others, so that there was no interchangeability between the six classes. The width between frames was different on most of the different classes, so that either the fireboxes had to be made narrow enough to go between the narrowest frames, or—like the boilers of Stirling's 1886 7 ft. 6 in. singles—the boilers might have fireboxes and barrels the same length and yet only be suitable, by reason of the differences of firebox widths, each for its own class.

Nos. 91-99, 200

The next class of single-wheelers to be considered, which were taken in hand and rebuilt by Stirling, were the 'Converted Cramptons', Nos. 91-99 and 200 built in 1851-52 as 4—2—0 engines with the driving wheels behind the firebox, and thus, of course, having inadequate adhesion weight on those wheels. Sturrock had rebuilt the first nine of these engines as 2—2—2s, the tenth engine being converted to a 2—4—0. In this first rebuilt form, they had done useful work, though their dimensions were small. When taken in hand by Stirling they received new cylinders 16½ in. x 21 in. (according to the general arrangement drawing), the standard domeless boiler, with 4 ft. 10 in. firebox casing length, and the Stirling cab. The earliest drawing is dated July 23, 1867 and is for Stirling boilers to be fitted to the class, followed by a drawing a week later for the 6 ft. 6 in. diameter driving-wheels. New splashers for these wheels needed a fresh drawing in September 1867.

Nos. 91 and 96 were rebuilt in 1867, but the dates of later rebuilds are not recorded. No. 92 was withdrawn, unrebuilt, in 1870 and replaced by the new Stirling single-wheeler with that number. No. 200, which had passed through a brief transformation under Sturrock into a 2—4—0, and back again to a 2—2—2, was also replaced in 1870. A pencilled note on a Doncaster drawing seemed to indicate that No. 97 was also rebuilt as a 2—4—0 under Stirling, but there is no supporting evidence and the dimensions on the drawing seem to rule it out quite definitely, for they apply specifically to Sturrock's Nos. 223-28 which were always 2—4—0s.

Bird gives particulars of the engines as first rebuilt by Sturrock into 2—2—2s. A comparison of the leading dimensions with those on the drawing of the Stirling rebuilds shows that nothing at all drastic was carried out in the later rebuilding. The frames seem to have been unaltered, though new cylinders of Stirling design of the same stroke were provided. The Stirling boiler was almost identical with the one it replaced, the barrel being nominally the same diameter, but 1 in. shorter; this inch being added to the length of the firebox. The standard type of cab and sandboxes were fitted, and the Sturrock compensating beams between the leading

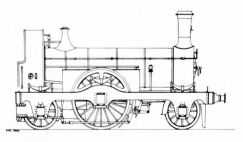

No. 91, 6 ft. 6 in. single as rebuilt by Stirling

and driving-wheel springs were removed. There may have been minor differences between engine and engine, as rebuilt; certainly, Bird's drawing of the rebuilt No. 99 differs in some minor respects from the general arrangement drawing.

The rebuilt engines survived for quite a long time, No. 95, at least, lasting long enough to carry the 'A' suffix, but the last of them had been withdrawn before Stirling died. The dates of rebuilding, taken from available information, are set out below, and also the dates the engines were replaced by new engines.

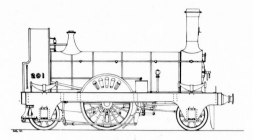

No. 201, 'Jenny Lind' single as rebuilt by Stirling

Engine No.	Rebuilt	Date replaced on Capital List	Engine No.	Rebuilt	Date replaced on Capital List
91	–/1867	1881	96	–/1867	1879
92	—	1870	97	–/1868*	1880
93	–/1868*	1879	98	–/1868*	1877
94	–/1868*	1876	99	–/1868*	1879
95	–/1868*	1880	200	—	1870

★ these dates are not certain

Nos. 201 and 202

The two 6 ft. 2—2—2 engines, Nos. 201 and 202, were not of course of Sturrock's design, but were supplied to the G.N.R. by the builders, Messrs E. B. Wilson, in January 1851. As built, they were, it has been stated, of David Joy's standard 'Jenny Lind' design, with the leading wheels placed well behind the smokebox. The very earliest locomotive diagrams, drawn out in about 1865, confirm this, but the drawing dated July 11, 1866 showing the engines as rebuilt by Stirling has the leading pair of wheels moved forward to a position immediately under the smokebox and in fact slightly ahead of the chimney centre line. The general arrangement drawing, rather sketchy like many of the other general arrangement drawings of that period, especially for rebuilds, shows both an earlier rebuilt state, with a domed boiler, possibly the original, but fitted with Stirling chimney and a straight-sided cab of his earlier design; and also a later rebuilding, with a standard Stirling domeless boiler and the later type of cab, these superimposed on the older parts of the drawing.

The cylinders at the earlier rebuild were shown as 16 in. x 22 in. Although there are several characteristic Stirling details on these cylinders, yet the slide-bar fixing lugs were of a type not used by Stirling (or Sturrock) elsewhere, and they were probably made thus to enable the existing slide-bars and motion to be used. The cylinder drawing was dated even earlier than the general arrangement, being drawn out on May 28, 1866.

The two engines were certainly thoroughly rebuilt, some 13 new detail drawings being needed in addition to the general arrangement, all prepared within a space of ten weeks. Apparently many of the features introduced by Stirling in the rebuilding of Nos. 201 and 202 set the standard for his future rebuilds. Very few new detail drawings were prepared for each succeeding class of singles rebuilt, usually only one or two being required.

The domeless boiler had a firebox only 4 ft. 10 in. long, compared with the 5 ft. 9 in. of the original firebox, and the height of the centre line from the rail level was raised by 2½ in. to 6 ft. 9 in.

No. 201 broke her crank axle, after eight years' service in which 198,317 miles had been covered, on April 12, 1872 at South Elmsall, whilst working an up fast passenger train from Leeds to Kings Cross. The engine had only left the works a few weeks before. At that time it was stated that crank axles were examined daily, but nevertheless the average number of breakages of crank axles was 82 per annum, though no accidents had occurred due to these breakages, between 1867 and 1872. This was an unfortunate comment, as soon afterwards another case of a broken axle occurred, this time on a rebuilt Sturrock 2—4—0, No. 224, at Wortley Jct. (Leeds) on November 14, 1872, whilst working the 12.10 passenger train Doncaster to Leeds; and the axle had had only 3½ years' service.

It is not known for certain when these two engines were withdrawn from service, but since new engines built by Stirling in June 1882 took over their running numbers, it is highly probable that the old singles were cut up about that time. They were pretty little engines and, for their time, were relatively modern in not having the old fashioned sandwich-type frames, of wood between two plates of iron, but true plate frames, all wrought-iron—except for wooden bufferbeams fore and aft—such as Stirling himself used for all his inside-cylinder singles.

Engine No.	Rebuilt	Date replaced on Capital List
201	–/1866	1882
202	–/1866	1882

Nos. 203-14

These were the survivors of Sturrock's earliest design of single-wheeler actually to have been constructed as new engines for the Great Northern. Nos. 91-99 and 200 were, of course, his rebuilds, and their appearance when he first rebuilt them was perhaps more truly 'Sturrock' than were Nos. 203-14. Almost certainly some of the details of the latter engines were to the existing standards of the makers, Messrs R. & W. Hawthorn. They were delivered to the railway company in 1852-53, and were always known as the 'Large Hawthorns'—as compared, of course, with the 'Small Hawthorns', Nos. 51-70. Stirling evidently considered that they would be useful engines for quite a long time, for he eventually rebuilt them very thoroughly. Some of the class, including No. 212, seem to have gone through an intermediate stage, in which a new flush-topped firebox was fitted to the old boiler barrel and smokebox, and Stirling cab, chimney and safety-valves were added, the frames and the rest of the engine remaining unaltered. In the final rebuilding, the total wheelbase was increased from 15 ft. to 16 ft. $3\frac{7}{8}$ in., all this extra length being

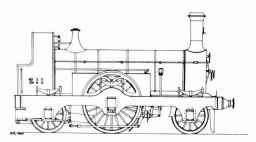

No. 211, Sturrock 6 ft. 6 in. single as later rebuilt by Stirling, with completely new boiler and with leading wheels set farther forward

obtained by setting the leading wheels forward 1 ft. $3\frac{3}{4}$ in. This leaves $\frac{1}{8}$ in. unaccounted for: Bird gives 7 ft. 3 in. for the trailing wheelbase; the general arrangement drawing of the Stirling rebuild gives 7 ft. $3\frac{1}{8}$ in. It is unbelievable that the frames were altered to the very small extent of $\frac{1}{8}$ in. when in fact there was no possible fouling point to justify it. It is more probable that Hawthorns were not fussy over things that didn't matter in the least, and that the Great Northern draughtsman, who took measurements from an existing engine, finding there was actually an odd $\frac{1}{8}$ in., showed it on the general arrangement drawing he was making.

The first rebuilds of the class were probably made from hand-sketches, for no new detail drawings seem to have been prepared, and even the general arrangement, showing the final rebuilding, was not drawn out until July 1874.

Sturrock always set the leading carrying wheels of his later engines right forward under the smokebox, and would not have disapproved of Stirling's following him in this. Certainly the rebuilt engines looked more dignified, and no doubt rode rather better for the change. It also enabled a rather heavier axle loading on the driving wheels to be obtained.

The work involved in altering the outside frames to set the leading wheels further forward was by no means an expensive or major operation. The frames were of wrought-iron, welding readily under the hammer, and there was nothing critical about the location of the leading wheels, so long as the two sides of the frame permitted the axle to lie truly square across the engine. In any case, Stirling had *carte blanche* to deal with his predecessor's engines, the cost of their maintenance and repairs coming into the current account and not being charged to the capital account. His concern with the economical side of his rebuilds really only began *after* he had rebuilt them to his own ideas and standards.

From the drawing it seems that Stirling supplied new cylinders of his own design, but of the same dimensions as the originals, 16 in. diameter by 22 in. stroke. The new boiler barrel was 10 ft. long with the usual dimension of 4 ft. $0\frac{1}{2}$ in. diameter outside the largest of the three rings of which it was constructed. The firebox casing was the usual 4 ft. 10 in. long, $3\frac{1}{4}$ in. shorter than the original.

Nos. 203 and 205 of the class were not rebuilt by Stirling, having been replaced in 1871 and 1869 respectively. Stirling rebuilt Nos. 207, 208, 211, 212 and 213 in 1867. No. 206 was given a heavy repair in 1867 so may just possibly have been rebuilt in fact, on this occasion. Nos. 204, 209, 210 and 214 very probably followed soon after.

THE STIRLING SINGLES

The following list shows the dates the engines were first rebuilt by Stirling and the dates they were replaced on the capital list by new Stirling engines. No. 214 is known to have been transferred to the 'A' list in September 1889, being finally withdrawn in November 1892. It is believed to have been the last survivor of the class.

maintenance—and he removed it from Sturrock engines soon after he took over.

Nos. 229-40, as built, had a large firebox, 7 ft. 4 in. long, with an elaborate water mid-feather, giving a total firebox heating surface of 180 sq. ft. (practically the same as a Gresley K3 'Mogul') and a grate area of about 20 sq. ft., to supply steam to

Engine No.	Rebuilt	Date replaced on Capital List	Engine No.	Rebuilt	Date replaced on Capital List
203	—	1871	209	–/1868*	1884
204	–/1868*	1888	210	–/1868*	1888
205	—	1869	211	–/1867	1886
206	–/1867*	1884	212	–/1867	1881
207	–/1867	1880	213	–/1867	1889
208	–/1867	1881	214	–/1868*	1889

* these dates are not certain

Nos. 229-40

There is no difficulty in agreeing with Bird who regards these 12 engines as 'Mr. Sturrock's masterpiece in designing', even though Bird does qualify his praise by saying that they might 'almost' be so regarded. His drawing of No. 229 as originally built omits the large compensating beam between leading and driving-wheel springs, which is a prominent feature of the general arrangement drawing made at Doncaster in November 1859, and revised in September 1862. Possibly Bird used a late photograph as the basis of his drawing; perhaps compensating beams were never actually incorporated in the engines, though this is unlikely. Sturrock's surviving general arrangement drawings invariably show compensating beams, an excellent device for smoothing out rough sections of permanent way for the driver, but one which can give a false sense of security to an inexperienced engineman on a dangerously rough patch of track, as the writer once discovered for himself, on a Baldwin 2—8—o in France in 1917. At any rate, Stirling seems to have had no use for compensating spring gear at all—it was costly and needed additional

17 in. diameter by 22 in. stroke cylinders driving 7 ft. diameter wheels. The steam ports were 17 in. long by $1\frac{1}{2}$ in. and the exhaust port 17 in. by 4 in., so that they should have been swift engines, within their power, and good steamers.

But their first cost was high, £35,000 for the 12, and their firebox maintenance must have been not only expensive, but troublesome also, so that when Stirling came to take them in hand for rebuilding, he provided fireboxes only 5 ft. 6 in. in length, and of his usual simple and straightforward pattern, the new boilers, however, not being interchangeable with those used on his own six-wheeled engines of the period. Some of the class—it is not known which engines—when their crank-axles needed renewing were given standard Stirling 17 in. x 24 in. cylinders and longer throw crank-axles to suit.

The dates of rebuilding are not known but it probably began in 1868, soon after the drawing for the straightback boiler fitted to these engines was prepared, in October 1867. The only details specially drawn out for the rebuilds were for new 7 ft. driving-wheels in October 1869 and for leading wheels and axles in August 1872. The latter drawing was no doubt the direct outcome of No. 234's breaking a tyre on one of her leading wheels whilst working the 4.25 down express from Kings Cross on April 29, 1872. Between October 1868 and the time of the throwing of this tyre No. 234 had run 98,920 miles.

On September 16, 1876 No. 236 broke her crank axle whilst working a newspaper train. In the $2\frac{1}{2}$ years since the axle had been fitted, in April 1874, No. 236 had run 109,000 miles. Stirling commented at the time that he had been experimenting with cast-steel cranks for some years, but with discouraging results.

No. 240, Sturrock 7ft. single, rebuilt by Stirling; about 1879 with built-up chimney, smaller boiler, spring balance safety valves and non-automatic vacuum brake

Their frames were not altered. Brakes were added —from 1876 on—and of course the usual Stirling cab and boiler mountings. The class proved thoroughly useful and efficient, and, though assigned to the duplicate list from 1885 onwards, the engines were found to be in too good condition to break up. The last survivor was No. 233A, condemned in January 1900; but Nos. 231A and 240A remained in service until May 1898 and October 1899 respectively. All the class survived to have their earlier built-up chimneys replaced by cast-iron ones. There must have been really good stuff in them to have continued to exist for over 30 years after their designer had retired. Compare also the life span of No. 231A, exactly 38 years old when withdrawn, with that of the Stirling 7 ft. 6 in. single No. 231 which replaced it on the capital list in 1888 and had a life span of slightly over 17 years.

As usual, there were minor differences between the engines, which had originally been supplied by three different manufacturers. One, affecting their outward appearance, was that on some the driving wheel splashers had radial slots, like the Stirling singles, on some the slots were in the form of kidney-shaped openings, similar to those on the Stirling four-coupled engines, and on some splashers there were no slots at all. In all probability these last were replacement splashers made after 1880. In all cases the slots were filled in with backing plates after that date.

The dates the engines were transferred to the duplicate list are shown below.

No. 267, 7 ft. single, rebuilt by Stirling from Sturrock 2-4-0, about 1895

permission to order six engines of an already proved and tested design, he allowed three months to elapse before suggesting to the Board that it would be preferable to alter the order from single-wheelers to coupled engines, from 2—2—2s to 2—4—0s, and at the same time increase the cylinder stroke from 22 in. to 24 in. It looks rather as if Sturrock was after 2—4—0s from the first, but felt it wiser to proceed in stages to avoid possible sales resistance from the Board. The general arrangement drawing date of the 2—4—0 design is recorded as March 1865, long before the initial order was placed. It must be admitted, however, that this date has to be taken on trust as the drawing itself is no longer in existence. The boilers of Nos. 264-69, as originally built, were apparently of the same dimensions as those of Nos. 229-40.

Engine No.	Date replaced on Capital List	Engine No.	Date replaced on Capital List	Engine No.	Date replaced on Capital List
229	1886	233	1888	237	1887
230	1887	234	1886	238	1885
231	1888	235	1888	239	1887
232	1885	236	1887	240	1889

Nos. 264-69

These engines were the last design of Sturrock for express work and delivery did not begin until it was almost time for Sturrock to leave the Doncaster scene. Their genesis is curious: the official archives record Sturrock as asking in November 1865 for 'six more 7 ft. express engines, as I have not enough of these powerful machines to enable me to do the description of work I am advised I shall be called on to perform'. This gives the impression that he was proposing to order another six engines similar to Nos. 229-40. Having thus obtained the Board's

Concerning the increase in cylinder size, it is interesting to recall that in five years' time Stirling was going to make the statement that the 17 in. by 24 in. cylinders on his own 7 ft. singles were proving too small for the heaviest trains. But Stirling's boiler pressure then was only 130 lb. per sq. in., and his statement was perhaps shaded by the need to explain the 18 in. by 28 in. cylinders on his 8-footers.

There is definite evidence that the coupling rods on Nos. 264-69 gave trouble. Certainly, at least one case of bent rods was recorded by a traveller in the train who was timing the running. The comment quoted by Bird, that they 'could not keep their side-rods on', seems to imply either the breaking of crank-pins or, less probably, the fracture of the coupling rods, perhaps at the relatively weak point where the cotter for adjusting the bearing-brasses passes through the enlarged eye end of the rod. The most likely reason for the trouble was defective balancing of the rotating and reciprocating masses of the moving parts, probably aggravated by an unsatisfactory and uneven permanent way.

Right up to 1914, and perhaps even later, cases of bent side-rods were by no means unknown, and the usual procedure was to remove the rods and continue the journey as a single-wheeler. Perhaps it did not pass unnoticed that as enforced single-wheelers Nos. 264-69 were quite able to cope with their trains. References, in some reports of brake trials carried out in March 1876, to a '7 ft. passenger engine, *uncoupled*', seem to suggest that at that time one or both of the engines not rebuilt until 1878 may have been running with coupling rods removed, but otherwise in Sturrock condition. At any rate Stirling did rebuild them as singles.

The Stirling boilers provided for these engines were similar to but not quite the same as used on Nos. 229-40. The frame plates were $\frac{1}{2}$ in. further apart on Nos. 264-69, and the fireboxes were made just that amount wider. The second Stirling boilers, fitted between 1885 and 1889, had 4 ft. 2 in. diameter barrels as used on all the Stirling singles from 1880 onwards, except for his own 7 ft. engines. It seems rather strange that Stirling should have to draw out a 4 ft. 2 in. diameter boiler around 1885 specially for these six engines, when he could possibly have utilised the existing 4 ft. 2$\frac{1}{2}$ in. design, which had been in use for some five years on his own 7 ft. singles, and simply fitted a different type of front tubeplate, to suit the Sturrock front-end.

Two of the class, Nos. 265 and 266, were for a time fitted with Westinghouse brakes, and were presumably used on trains made up of North Eastern Railway stock. No doubt they were also used in testing East Coast Joint Stock built at Doncaster, which was dual-fitted.

As with the No. 229 class, some of the engines had slotted splashers, while others had plain ones.

Nos. 264-69 lasted well, being scrapped between 1898 and 1902, Nos. 266 and 267 having been relegated to the duplicate list in 1898 and 1900 respectively. In the Ivatt 1900 engine classification the three survivors became class B6.

One cannot help wondering what were the first reactions of the enginemen to these rebuildings, especially as regards No. 229 and No. 264 classes, where the boiler pressure was so appreciably reduced and, due to the lower working pressure of the new boilers, the tractive effort also. No doubt some of the men must have resented this, at least for a start. But the first winter would probably have converted them to accept the cab gladly; and the increased reliability and freedom from minor troubles which came with the Stirling boilers, together with the realisation that the engines could still do their allotted work satisfactorily and on rather less coal than before, probably led in a relatively short time to the complete acceptance of the rebuilds as part of the Stirling picture.

It is curious that all Stirling's own inside-cylinder engines had the smokeboxes 'waisted', when viewed from the front, yet none of his rebuilds was shaped similarly. On all of them the sides of the smokebox were brought down vertically to the frames. Perhaps Stirling thought that this was more appropriate for outside-framed engines with the bearing springs in full view. There was no constructional reason, at any rate, for the demarcation between Stirling and rebuilt Sturrock engines; but the effect was to give the rebuilds a rather clumsy appearance compared with the elegance of the Stirling smokebox curves.

This concludes the detailed consideration of all the 'Stirling singles'. It would have been pleasant to have been able to find confirmation of the reason behind every act and practice which was embodied in them, but enough of the cloud surrounding their existence has been rolled away to enable a fairly thorough account to be given. It is unlikely that any alternative source of information about them is now available; the existing Doncaster records have been very thoroughly examined in the course of producing this account.

Engine No.	Rebuilt	Reboilered	Date replaced on Capital List	Withdrawn
264	10/1878	4/1886	—	2/1900
265	11/1875	3/1886	—	8/1901
266	12/1873	7/1885	10/1898	4/1899
267	2/1873	7/1886	6/1900	5/1902
268	3/1878	6/1888	—	6/1901
269	3/1875	6/1889	—	12/1898

CHAPTER 12

THE EIGHT - FOOTER REBUILDS

LATE in 1880 No. 1 went into the Doncaster shops for general repairs, and was thoroughly rebuilt; the work was completed on December 20 of that year. The rebuilding included a new boiler of slightly larger diameter, 4 ft. 2 in. as against 4 ft. 0½ in., working at a higher pressure; new frames; almost certainly new cylinders, though these are not referred to in the repairs book. But then the repairs book records no new cylinders at all for No. 1, or indeed for most of the early 8-footers. The modifications carried out on No. 1 set the standard for the next batch of new engines shortly to be built, of which No. 662, completed in February 1881, was the first. The slotted driving splashers of all classes were being filled in with backing plates, beginning at the end of 1880, and No. 1 was treated in the same way. She received 4 ft. 7 in. diameter trailing wheels and her rear suspension was altered from volute springs to laminated springs. The pitch of the new boiler, 7 ft. 3¼ in., was 2¼ in. higher than that of her original one.

No. 1 also became the prototype for the rebuilding of all 8-footers constructed prior to the end of 1880 and, as these fell due for heavy repairs, they also were taken in hand and brought up to date.

The existing records do not in all cases show clearly just what was covered by the expression 'rebuilt', and in a few instances the dates and details which are now given cannot be fully substantiated. There was, in the first few years after 1881, an attempt to economise on costs by replacing only the front portion of frames which required renewing. The exact location of the welded joint between the new front ends and the old rear portions is not now known. It would, of course, depend on whether the frames over the driving axleboxes were defective or sound. The joint might come in the one case in front of the driving axle, in the other case it would be to the rear of it.

Six of these older engines—Nos. 8, 60, 94, 548, 549 and 550—seem to have carried their original frames throughout their existence. This may well have been true for Nos. 60, 548, 549 and 550, which probably had their frames reinforced early at the weak points above the cylinders, but it seems more probable that No. 8's frames had been replaced before 1881 by new frames—to outward appearance just the same, but made, in fact, rather stronger behind the driving axle—even if No. 94 managed to carry her original frames throughout. In any case, it is practically certain that all these six frames were reinforced by fixing a ¾ in. plate inside each 1¼ in. thick main frame plate, to strengthen the weak part. Of course, this method would only be adopted in cases where the frames were still sound. It was where cracks had already begun to develop that the old frames, or the old front portions of frames, were replaced by deeper ones.

In those days the edges of frame plates, after being roughly cut to profile, were cleaned up by hammer and chisel, usually at the hands of apprentices, and were finally draw-file finished. Even as late as 1903 the curved footplate angle-irons of No. 116, the first 0—8—2 tank-engine, were forged rather too long and had to be reduced to length by hammer and chisel. One of the unlucky apprentices concerned later became the C.M.E. of the Southern Railway. He was Mr. O. V. S. Bulleid.

The new frames fitted to No. 1 and the other rebuilt engines were noticeably deeper and stronger over the cylinders than the original ones. The curves ahead of the smokebox on the engines receiving new frames up to about June 1883 differed slightly in profile from the later frames. The earlier ones had a 'plunging' effect, due to the concave profile, of 1 ft. 4 in. radius, where the frame came down to footplate level ahead of the smokebox, being incorrectly marked off. On the later frames a 'flowing' effect was produced by the profile merging smoothly into the footplate level, as the drawing clearly indicated that it was intended to do. This point was mentioned also in the chapters dealing with the Nos. 662-71 and the Nos. 771-78 batches of engines, where the same difference occurred.

The first four engines to receive new front-portion frames were Nos. 48, 69, 547 and 98. The date at which No. 98 received her new framing is not known; the dates for Nos. 48, 69 and 547 are June 1881, November 1882 and April 1883 respectively. The dates on which Nos. 48, 69, 547 and 98 were fitted with the larger boiler were June 1885, December 1886, October 1886 and September 1887 respectively.

Two engines, Nos. 47 and 546, received the later flowing form of front-portion frames, in September 1883 and November 1885 respectively. No. 47 received new cylinders as well as a new larger boiler on this occasion, and No. 546 also got her new boiler at this time.

All other rebuilt 8-footers which required new frames had them new complete. Why this was done is not clear: it might have been because cracks had been found at both cylinders and driving-wheels. But it appears to be a change of policy. The material of the frames has always been referred to as wrought-iron. Nevertheless, mild steel was rapidly ousting wrought-iron in constructional work, and it is highly probable that the newer frames were of mild steel, in line with the practice just then being made standard on new locomotives of other classes, and about to be introduced on the new 8-footers.

After the first three engines had received the new 'flowing' complete frames, there was a change in the design to the rear of the driving wheels, where the frame was made $4\frac{1}{2}$ in. higher, in line with the No. 771 class frames, involving a corresponding change in the position of the expansion bracket on the firebox. The three engines with the 'low frames' (as they were designated) were Nos. 5, 62 and 545; No. 5 received hers in May 1884, the other two both in November 1884. The dates on which these three engines were fitted with the larger boiler were September 1886, February 1886 and June 1887 respectively.

No. 62 is one of those somewhat uncertain cases referred to above and the circumstances show how careful one must be in accepting unchecked the official records. The boilers for the 'high-frame' 8-footers were not immediately interchangeable with boilers for low-frame engines, due to the difference in height of the expansion brackets. Because of this difference, all the 8-footers were segregated into high-frame or low-frame engines and their running numbers entered on the respective high-frame or low-frame general arrangement drawings. No. 62 is recorded as having low-frames and this is again confirmed on the January 1902 Boiler Diagram Sheet, which listed the survivors at this date. On the other hand, the remaining repairs books are, for their entries of early dating, condensed copies of a previous, more detailed series of books, now destroyed. There are occasional clerical errors, some obvious, some obscure; and one of the latter does certainly seem to be the date at which No. 62 received her new frames. This is given above as November 1884—but the entry in the book is on the next lower line, against the date February 1886, when No. 62 received her new larger boiler. The 1886 date seems unacceptable because, from November 1884 on, all new engines were being given high frames, and the rebuilt engines were, with this sole paper exception of No. 62, always in step with the new engines. There is just the faint chance that an odd set of low frames may have been made in 1884 and not used, or again there may have been an error on the general arrangement drawings by incorrectly listing No. 62 as having low-frames instead of high-frames.

All engines rebuilt from August 1886 onwards

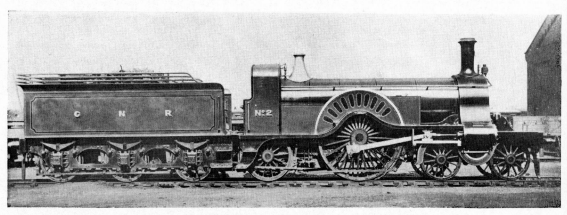

No. 2, probably at Grantham, about 1890

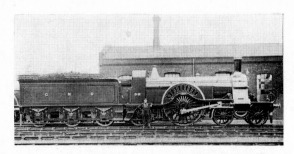

No. 98 at Peterborough, about 1896. The tall engineman figures in several photographs of the period

received the high frames complete. It was from these late rebuilds that Ivatt selected six out of the seven engines which he himself rebuilt between 1896 and 1899, this time with domed boilers; and the seventh engine (No. 776) was also a high-frame engine. The first four engines to receive these high frames were Nos. 33, 34, 22 and 221, in August 1886, October 1886, April 1887 and March 1888 respectively. The first three were reboilered at the same time, but No. 221 had had a new, larger boiler on her old frames in October 1882, and this lasted until May 1893.

Between May 1888 and June 1889, at a time when no new engines were being built, four sets of frames were marked off incorrectly for the horizontal location of the radii of the profile of the top edges of the frames ahead and to the rear of the smokebox. The effect was that the frame above the footplate projected some three inches further ahead of the smokebox than it should have, and the raised portion of the frame behind the smokebox did not extend so far back, by the same amount, as it should have done. These frames were used on No. 95 in May 1888, No. 53 in November 1888, No. 2 in December 1888 and No. 544 in June 1889. At the same time these engines were all reboilered.

A single set of replacement frames was cut in 1889, since by this time there seemed little prospect of using four sets on either rebuilds or new engines in the near future. These frames were used in rebuilding No. 93 in October 1889.

It was over two years before any occasion did arise for further frames for rebuilds. In November 1891, No. 7 came into Doncaster shops and a set of four pairs of frameplates was cut, of which she received the first pair, returning to work in May 1892 with a new boiler in addition. She had been rebuilt and had received her first larger boiler in December 1882, but had still retained her original frames at that date.

In September 1892, No. 3 came into Doncaster

for exactly the same treatment, new frames and new boiler, although—like No. 7—she had received her larger boiler while retaining her original frames, when rebuilt in June 1884. She was not out of works again until April 1893, and it may well have been her prolonged sojourn there which led Stirling to realise that there were still two sets of new frames in stock without much prospect of use in rebuilding engines, and gave him the idea of using them to erect two new 8-footers and charging them as renewals of old Sturrock engines. These were, of course, Nos. 264 and 265, soon to be renumbered 1001 and 1002.

Between July 1886 and August 1888 four consecutively built 8-footers, Nos. 548, 549, 60 and 550, were rebuilt with larger boilers, though they all retained their original frames. It has been said earlier that probably these had already been reinforced, perhaps only a year or two after the engines had been built.

There remained Nos. 8 and 94, both apparently retaining their original frames. No. 94 received her larger boiler in December 1887. No. 8 is quoted as having been rebuilt in February 1888, but did not receive a new boiler until May 1891. No. 8 was a Peterborough engine and it is quite likely that her first replacement boiler was fitted at Peterborough, since there is no record of one in the Doncaster repairs book. But whether this boiler, which was probably fitted sometime between 1879 and 1882, was a larger or an original size one, it is impossible to say. The earlier date and the smaller boiler seem more likely, since Nos. 8 and 33 had those almost certainly shortlived water midfeather boilers, but this is only a reasonable guess—the records are not merely silent; they no longer exist.

Apart from these relatively major rebuildings, it is perhaps worth mentioning that such things as the

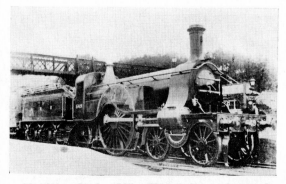

No. 549 at Sandy, 1895. The only known photograph of this engine, and the very first photograph taken by the late W. J. Reynolds as a boy. Beginner's luck indeed!

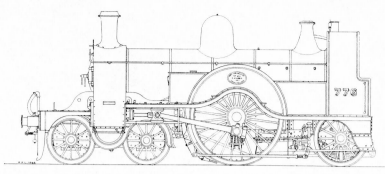

No. 776, rebuilt by Ivatt with domed boiler, as running in 1903 with chimney from a Stirling 0-4-4 suburban tank engine

original safety-valves and injectors had been re-placed by the corresponding up-to-date parts when-ever the older engines came in for general repairs. Here again, a change in the shape of the top of the brass safety-valve casings, introduced first on a new engine on No. 771, indicated whether the rebuilt engine had received its new casing before or after the beginning of 1884. The top ring of the funnel of the casing was made rather larger in diameter at that time, larger in fact than the neck below the rim.

There were two small items in the equipment of the engines which showed variations from engine to engine. One was the cylinder lubricator, mounted on the main frame adjacent to the smokebox, one lubricator for each cylinder. On some engines these lubricators were mounted ahead of the smokebox, outside the frames; on others they were between the frames. Some engines had them between the frames at the rear of the smokebox; and on a few engines their position was changed from one general repair to another. The other item was the experi-mental use of metallic packing in the piston-rod glands in place of the standard soft hemp packing, beginning about 1887 and gradually being applied to more and more engines. Eventually Nos. 5, 8, 33, 53, 62, 94, 666, 671, 772, 773, 774, 775, 1002, 1003, 1005 and 1006 were all so fitted, and also the seven engines rebuilt with domed boilers.

Many years ago an old fitter, long since dead, told the present writer how, in his apprentice days

at Kings Cross locomotive shed, the fitter with whom he was then working on No. 94 told him to go under No. 53, alongside on the next pit, and compare the hornblocks of the two engines. He said that the hornblocks on No. 53 were far heavier and more robust than No. 94's, and remarked that that was not the only point in which various engines of the class differed, although to outward appearance they were just the same, showing a continuous line of development through the experience of succeed-ing years. In this instance No. 53's heavier design of hornblock was due to her having received new frames and the latest design details, including helical springs to the driving-wheels, while No. 94's frames were of the old type. The fact that No. 53 was built in 1875 and No. 94 in 1876 was not the reason for the difference in their hornblocks.

At a later date, when, under Ivatt, the practice became standard, oilboxes with three feeds were mounted on the front of the leading sandboxes, to provide oil for the driving axleboxes and the horn-guides. No. 1003 at one time had such oilboxes on her bogie frames for her bogie wheels as well.

As the Stirling chimneys, both cast-iron and built-up, wore out, they were replaced in Ivatt days by somewhat similar cast-iron chimneys, on which the curves were not so graceful. It is fairly certain that the actual Stirling cast-iron chimneys differed slightly in shape from those shown on the drawings. It may well have been that Stirling did not like the appearance of the first chimney as made to drawing,

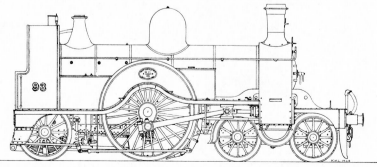

No. 93, the first 8 ft. single rebuilt by Ivatt with domed boiler. The dome was larger in diameter than on any other Ivatt engine

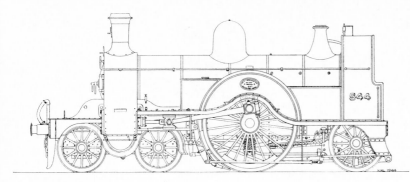

*No. 544, rebuilt by Ivatt
with domed boiler and steam
sanding gear, but retaining
the old Stirling cab*

and indicated to the foreman pattern-maker how he wanted the casting altered for the future; and that the alterations never were recorded on the drawing, or drawings. If so, it was not the first or last time that such a thing happened at Doncaster.

One of the very first things which Ivatt put in hand as soon as he took over at Doncaster was the design of a new boiler for the 8-footers, with a dome and a much larger grate than previously.

The first of these boilers, of which seven were constructed, carried a dome of larger diameter— 2 ft. 6 in. inside, as against 2 ft. 0 in.—than the other six. The water legs of the firebox were reduced to $1\frac{3}{4}$ in. from the previous dimension of 3 in. thus widening the grate, in spite of the 9/16 in. thick plates used as compared with $\frac{1}{2}$ in. thickness on the Stirling boilers, from 3 ft. $3\frac{1}{2}$ in. to 3 ft. $5\frac{3}{4}$ in. The length of the grate was extended from 5 ft. 6 in. to 6 ft. $8\frac{1}{4}$ in., by setting the throat plate forward at an angle instead of the usual design with the plates standing vertically. The grate area was increased very considerably, from 17·75 sq. ft. to 23·26 sq. ft.

At first, these boilers had 184 tubes, $1\frac{1}{4}$ in. diameter, but later the figures were quoted as follows:

tubes:	length	11ft. 7$\frac{9}{16}$in.
	no.	180
	diam.	1$\frac{3}{4}$in.
heating surface:	tubes	955·0 sq. ft.
	firebox	114·2 sq. ft.
	total	1069·2 sq. ft.

To accommodate this longer firebox, although the length of the boiler barrel had been reduced by 2 in. to 11 ft. 3 in., involved increasing the trailing wheelbase of the engines from 8 ft. 8 in. to 9 ft. —the same as on the No. 1003 class—by cutting the frameplates between the driving and trailing wheels and welding in a distance piece 4 in. long. The plate-stay between the frames just ahead of the

firebox had to be repositioned to lie at an angle similar to the angle of the firebox throat plate.

The new boilers, with their thicker plates and barrels in two rings instead of in three, worked at a higher pressure, 170 lb. per sq. in. for the first boiler, and 175 lb. per sq. in. at first on the other six. In the course of a year or two, all the seven engines were shown as working at 170 lb. per sq. in.

The first engine to be taken in hand was No. 93; she came into Doncaster works on March 19, 1896 for a new right-hand cylinder—she had had a new left-hand cylinder in December 1895—and was given the first of the new boilers, and fitted with a built-up chimney. She was dealt with reasonably quickly, and emerged from the works with her 'new look' on June 18, 1896. She did good work, but does not seem to have been entirely trouble-free, for she was in and out of Doncaster works three times in less than 18 months for so-called 'general repairs'. The domed boiler lasted until May 1906, when No. 93 was withdrawn and scrapped. For the last four years her built-up chimney had been replaced by a cast-iron one.

The next engine to be rebuilt was No. 776, the 'Exhibition engine', exactly similar to No. 93 except that her dome was smaller, 2 ft. diameter, and her boiler pressure 175 lb. per sq. in. She was out of works barely a month after No. 93, on July 15, 1896.

Six months later No. 544 entered the works and was rebuilt almost exactly as No. 776, except that her lever-reversing gear was changed to the screw type, though not exactly as on Nos. 1003 to 1008. Instead of a wheel there was a turn-handle, and the pivoted vertical lever was placed ahead of, instead of in, the cab. The three engines dealt with so far had all retained their original cabs, though No. 544's had had horizontal handrails added before she left the works again on May 26, 1897. All three were still fitted with the Stirling polished brass safety-valve casings and the Stirling smokebox doors.

But the remaining four rebuilds conformed much more thoroughly to Ivatt standards. They had cast-iron safety-valve casings, Ivatt smokebox doors and flat-topped cabs with extended roofs and larger windows in the spectacle-plates. They were fitted with the screw and turn-handle reversing gear as used on No. 544.

No. 95, the next to be rebuilt, was out of works on August 11, 1897, followed by No. 34 on December 31. But No. 34 had new cylinders as well as a new boiler, and these cylinders were fitted with balanced slide-valves—the first since No. 1's of 1870—exhausting through the back directly to the blast-pipe, exactly as on No. 990 and all the other Ivatt 'Atlantics' when new, apart from the last batch, Nos. 1452-61, which had piston valves. After withdrawal, No. 34's boiler was used for a while as a stationary boiler at Doncaster.

Then came the turn of No. 22. Externally exactly like Nos. 95 and 34, she had not needed new cylinders, so seems to have retained the old slide-valve design. She was out of works, rebuilt, on January 29, 1898.

After that there was a pause. It was very nearly a year later that the last engine to be rebuilt thus, No. 221, came into the shops, where she stayed for over six months, finally being out of works again on June 30, 1899. No. 221 also had new cylinders, like No. 34, with balanced slide-valves exhausting through the back, and the screw reverser, exhaust steam injectors and steam-sanding which the other rebuilds had had. But she was unique in one respect —she was fitted with a water-circulating pipe, 4 in. internal diameter, which, starting from a special seating on the underside of the boiler barrel 11 in. behind the smokebox tube plate, passed diagonally downwards at an inclination of 1 in 6, below the driving axle, to a special branch-casting on the fire-box throat-plate just above the foundation ring. This branch-casting led, through two holes $2\frac{7}{8}$ in. diameter and 1 ft. $9\frac{1}{8}$ in. apart, into the front water leg of the firebox, and was provided with washout plugs to the $2\frac{7}{8}$ in. diameter holes.

No. 95, rebuilt by Ivatt, at Grantham, 1909, with secondhand chimney from a suburban tank engine

It is clear that Ivatt was not satisfied with the water circulation in his fireboxes with $1\frac{1}{4}$ in. water legs, and this was an attempt to improve it. It is not certain how long the device was retained, probably for the whole life of the boiler; not a very long life, for it was replaced in June 1907 by a second-hand boiler from the scrapped No. 773. At any rate, Ivatt in the next year or so became satisfied that the $1\frac{1}{4}$ in. water legs were too narrow, and for all new boilers they were increased to the old Stirling figure of 3 in. It is quite feasible that a shorter life, due to more rapid burning of the fire-box plates on Stirling rebuilds, was a price Ivatt was prepared to pay in order to increase the steaming capacities of the boilers without major structural changes to the chassis. As soon as his own designs of larger engines began to appear in numbers, the $1\frac{1}{4}$ in. water legs were abandoned. No. 990, for instance, was the only 'Atlantic' on which the water legs were $1\frac{1}{4}$ in.; all the others, large and small, had 3 in. ones.

No. 221 was the last of the older 8-footers rebuilt by Ivatt, and she was the best. With her high boiler pressure and very free exhaust, she could run just that little bit faster in everyday service than the other 8-footers, except perhaps No. 34, similarly equipped. But No. 34 seemed to spend rather more of her time in shops for repairs than No. 221 did, 18 months as against 12 months, up to 1907. Perhaps, however, this may have been due to No.

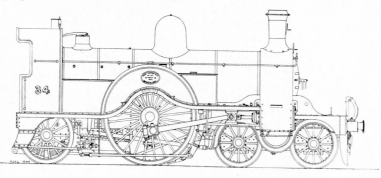

No. 34 rebuilt with domed boiler, new cab, and all the standard Ivatt boiler mountings. This engine and No. 221 were given new cylinders with balanced slide valves exhausting directly to the blast pipe through the backs of the valves

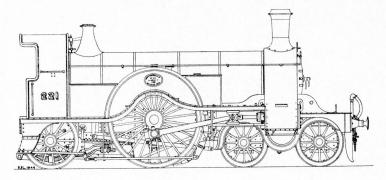

No. 221 as running in her last days with boiler from the scrapped No. 773. The firebox was shorter than that of the Ivatt domed boiler previously carried, so that the Ivatt type cab had to be set forward 4 inches

34's being a Doncaster engine, nice and handy for the works, whereas No. 221 was a Peterborough engine, where they were accustomed to fend for themselves as far as possible.

All the rebuilds except No. 776 had been 'slotted splasher' engines. These received new plain splashers with the oval brass date plates, and new, longer, rear dummy sandboxes. No. 93's date plates stated, incorrectly, that the G.N.R. at Doncaster Works were the 'Makers' in 1896; and the original date plates on the footplate angle-iron, at the top of the curve over the driving-wheel centre, were removed; but the other five ex-'slotted-splasher' engines retained their original date plates and the new oval plates announced, correctly, 'Rebuilt' followed by the year of rebuilding.

With the exception of No. 221, all the rebuilds were scrapped as their domed boilers became due for replacement. No. 22 went in November 1909, but she had done no work for several months immediately previously. No. 34 had gone in November 1907, and No. 93 even earlier, in May 1906. No. 95 lasted until May 1911, though her case was similar to No. 22's; both were Grantham engines. No. 544 was broken up in October 1906. No. 221, however, when her domed boiler required replacement in June 1907, received a secondhand straightback one from the scrapped No. 773. She retained her Ivatt cab, which had to be set forward 4 in. to suit the shorter firebox of the straightback Stirling boiler. She was last stationed at Hitchin, and was finally withdrawn in August 1909.

No. 776 remained in full work at Peterborough until she was called in to Doncaster for scrapping in November 1911. This was a quite unexpected tragedy for the 8-footer enthusiasts of those days. No. 776 in her last few years had been regularly employed to work inspection saloons when required. It was thought, not without some reason, that she might well last some years longer, as a 'court favourite', even though perhaps restricted to light duties. No. 776 had lost her built-up chimney as

early as 1903, when she was given a chimney, almost certainly secondhand, of the shorter and more compact type used on the Stirling 0—4—4 tank-engines fitted with condensing apparatus and used on the restricted profile 'widened lines' in the London area. This seemed to enhance her size, and suited her very well. It did not last long, however, being replaced by a rather longer cast-iron chimney, while the lower portion of the chimney ran smoothly into the base. This chimney lasted till the end.

During their first rebuilt years these seven engines were given the hardest and fastest work of any 8-footers, with the exception of Nos. 1003 to 1008, which took turn-and-turn-about with the rebuilds. Only when the large Ivatt 'Atlantics' began to appear in numbers in 1904 were they all relegated to secondary work.

In 1901 Ivatt began a series of tests with two different forms of spark arrester on engine No. 548. The first tests were carried out between April and November 1901 with a so-called 'G.W.R. pattern' of arrester consisting of a corrugated plate or 'diaphragm', lying horizontally in the smokebox above the top row of tubes. This was dished at the blast-pipe, so that the orifice was above the plate.

No. 548, with extended smokebox, at Doncaster, 1901. The tall youth by the front buffer is the late J. R. Bazin, afterwards chief mechanical engineer, Great Southern & Western Railway, Ireland

Since this plate extended well forward of the blast-pipe, an extension of the smokebox was fitted in front, to give as unrestricted a flow of gases past the front edge of the plate as possible.

This circular extension was made 4 in. less in diameter than the original smokebox, because of the difficulty of cutting the top edges of the frames away to clear this extension without weakening too severely the already rather meagre cross-section above the cut-away for the cylinders. The appearance of the engine in this state was unfortunate, to say the least, when she came out of shops thus, at the end of March 1901. It is possible that Ivatt was not pleased with the effect, for in July 1901 he noted on the drawing that a smokebox extension was to be made, of the full diameter and rather longer. No evidence exists that this was ever done; the most likely reason for inaction may well have been the very serious frame weakness which would have been inevitable unless the pitch of the whole boiler had been raised by some 3 in. The report on the G.W.R. arrester was that there was little reduction in spark throwing, and that the engine steamed about the same. In November 1901, the G.W.R. arrester was removed, and a Drummond patent arrester fitted, similar to those which Drummond used on his L.S.W.R. engines. This consisted of wing-shaped plates at each side of the blast-pipe, which could be folded up (if not rusted up solid) to give access to tubes and washout plugs. The blast-pipe itself wore a sort of 'pair of blinkers' in the shape of two nearly vertical plates, one each side of the blast-pipe, extending fore and aft inside the smokebox. In a month it was removed because the engine steamed badly.

A few weeks later an altered version was fitted. This also lasted a month and was then removed for the same reason as before.

For a year, No. 548 was not subjected to any further victimisation, but in February 1903 the G.W.R. arrester was once again fitted. In spite of the test report, that the engine threw fire as badly as before and also steamed badly, the unfortunate No. 548 was suffered to carry this arrester for a further 19 months, until in fact she was withdrawn from service and scrapped.

No. 548 also ran for a time with Brierley's fog-signalling device; this was put on in November 1901 and remained *in situ* until the engine was withdrawn from service in September 1904. It was the subject of enquiry on what had happened to it as late as March 1905 and it does seem possible that the equipment was later refitted to 7 ft. 6 in. single No. 240, as this engine is recorded as having had 'fog signal gear refitted May 1906'.

The last engine to receive a domed boiler was No. 1007, in May 1907. Since this was a special case, more by accident than by serious design, and the boiler was never intended for one of the class and did not fit the engine, it has seemed best to deal with it in the chapter assigned to the batch of 8-footers Nos. 1003 to 1008.

As the Stirling smokebox doors wore out, they were replaced even on straightback engines by the Ivatt type of door. Nos. 33, 221, 545, 664 and 771 were among those so fitted.

In 1907, slide-valves of a new design were drawn out, for both the older 8-footers and the No. 1003 class, and also for the 7 ft. 6 in. engines. At the locomotive running sheds these were known as the 'heavy' slide-valves, the walls being thicker and the exhaust cavity smaller than on the original valves; and engines fitted with them were invariably described by the enginemen as 'spoilt'. It could certainly have been predicted that the reduction in cross-sectional area of the exhaust cavity—over 30 per cent for the older 8-footers—would adversely affect the free running of the engines. But, in addition to this, some valves were made with steam laps increased by $\frac{1}{8}$ in., for both classes of 8-footer.

Considerable alteration to the existing valve-gear would have been needed, including an extra $\frac{1}{4}$ in. travel on the slide-valves, to use this extra lap to advantage, and there is no record of anything of this sort being done. A fairly early photograph of No. 1007, taken in 1899 or 1900, shows, by the legend on the bufferbeam, that she was even at that time one of the engines with 'long lap' valves—only $\frac{1}{8}$ in. longer, it is true, but, used with the original valve-gear, this would very seriously reduce the steam lead and port openings, the latter especially in expansive working of the steam.

In Stirling's day the standard valve travel of the No. 1 class 8-footers was $4\frac{1}{2}$ in. in full gear, with $1\frac{1}{8}$ in. steam lap, no exhaust lap; the valve travel of the No. 1003 class was $4\frac{3}{4}$ in., with $1\frac{1}{4}$ in. steam lap, no exhaust lap.

For the 7 ft. 6 in. engines there was only one size of 'heavy' valve, with the steam laps increased by 3/32 in.; the exhaust cavity, already restricted by the cylinder design, was reduced in cross-sectional area by over 20 per cent.

It really is a mystery why these 'heavy' valves were ever made. Metaphorically, they might even be called 'nails in the coffin' of the Stirling singles. An old driver once remarked, on the attitude of the Doncaster authorities towards the 8-footers in their last days: 'They hate the sight of them; but they're too good to break up.'

The Ivatt domed rebuilds certainly did very good

work, on trains usually heavier than in earlier years. No. 34, with direct exhaust slide-valves, ran from Kings Cross to the stop at Peterborough, 76·4 miles, in 86½ min. with a load of 246 tons. There was a strong side-wind. Two runs behind No. 776, then rebuilt with the domed boiler, were recorded by the Rev. W. J. Scott and the logs are given below. In the first case, from Kings Cross to Peterborough with a train perhaps not unduly heavy, the remarkable feature is the very fast start from Kings Cross, the time to passing Finsbury Park being considerably quicker than was normally the case in Ivatt, and even in Gresley days, except, of course, on such light high-speed trains as the *Silver Jubilee*.

No. 776 was fitted with a special design of chimney liner in September 1896, which was made and fitted at the New England running shed. This liner, which seems to have been entirely a Peterborough idea, conformed very closely with the proportions found at Swindon in 1950 to be the optimum. It is probable that No. 776 as turned out from Doncaster in July 1896 did not steam as well as she ought to have done and that this liner fulfilled expectations in improving her steaming, thus rendering possible such runs as these.

Scott notes that the engine was eased after Abbots Ripton, but that in spite of this the arrival was nearly 4½ min. early.

G.N.R. 1.30 p.m. KINGS CROSS—PETERBOROUGH
Load: 189 tons tare
Engine: 4-2-2 No. 776 rebuilt with Ivatt domed boiler

Dist. Miles				Actual m. s.	Av. Sp. m.p.h.
0·0	KINGS CROSS	.	.	0 00	—
2·6	Finsbury Park	.	.	4 49	32·4
4·1	Hornsey	.	.	6 48	46·5
5·0	Wood Green .	.	.	7 40	62·2
6·5	New Southgate	.	.	9 23	52·6
9·2	New Barnet .	.	.	12 45	48·2
12·7	Potters Bar .	.	.	17 18	46·2
17·7	HATFIELD .	.	.	22 40	56·0
22·0	Welwyn	.	.	26 55	60·7
25·0	Knebworth .	.	.	30 23	52·0
28·6	Stevenage	.	.	33 49	62·9
				p.w.s.	
31·9	HITCHIN .	.	.	37 00	62·2
37·0	Arlesey .	.	.	41 49	63·5
41·1	Biggleswade .	.	.	45 31	66·5
44·1	Sandy .	.	.	48 13	66·7
47·5	Tempsford .	.	.	51 27	63·2
51·7	St. Neots .	.	.	55 59	55·7
56·0	Offord .	.	.	60 34	56·3
58·9	HUNTINGDON .	.	.	63 45	54·6
63·5	Abbots Ripton	.	.	69 36	47·2
69·4	Holme .	.	.	74 49	67·9
72·6	Yaxley .	.	.	77 49	64·0
76·4	PETERBOROUGH	.	.	81 58	—

The other run with No. 776 was from Doncaster to Peterborough with a considerably heavier train. The stop at Newark involved the engine in relatively hard 'collarwork' all the way up to Stoke summit. In view of the load, the speed attained and held on this section was definitely good, but the driver evidently felt that to keep time it would be necessary to run really fast once over the top and on the succeeding favourable grades. Scott does not give the maximum speed reached, but to average 76·2 m.p.h. between Little Bytham and Essendine, with lower speeds before and after, must almost certainly have involved at least an 80 m.p.h. maximum.

G.N.R. DONCASTER—PETERBOROUGH
Load: 247 tons tare
Engine: 4-2-2 No. 776 rebuilt with Ivatt domed boiler

Dist. Miles				Actual m. s.	Av. Sp. m.p.h.
0·0	DONCASTER	.	.	0 00	—
8·3	Bawtry	.	.	11 35	42·9
12·1	Ranskill	.	.	15 10	63·6
17·4	RETFORD	.	.	21 05	53·8
24·1	Tuxford	.	.	29 36	47·3
29·6	Carlton .	.	.	34 35	66·0
35·9	NEWARK .	.	.	41 18	
4·7	Claypole	.	.	7 00	40·3
10·4	Barkston	.	.	14 17	46·9
14·6	GRANTHAM	.	.	19 51	45·3
20·0	*Stoke Box*	.	.	26 50	46·3
23·0	Corby .	.	.	30 10	54·1
27·9	Little Bytham	.	.	34 44	64·5
31·5	Essendine .	.	.	37 34	76·3
35·2	Tallington .	.	.	40 49	68·3
43·7	PETERBOROUGH	.	.	49 59	—

It is perhaps worth noting that in all the records of runs quoted in this book, as well as in all the numerous other records of Stirling single performances which the present writer has succeeded in unearthing, there is no instance of any failure or trouble with the engine, other than lack of adhesion. Nothing mechanical is perfect and failures must have occurred. Brick arches do not always give notice of their collapse and tubes can develop leaks or become choked or 'birdsnested' with caked ash quite rapidly in certain conditions. But, day in, day out, Stirling's engines always had the reputation of being free steaming, even at the cost of throwing a lot of fire. They were well designed and robust: but the excellent standard of maintenance which was the invariable rule under Stirling must have an equal share of the credit for their reputation and reliability in the days of their supremacy.

CHAPTER 13

SOME PERSONAL REMINISCENCES

By KENNETH H. LEECH

I WAS conditioned into a love of locomotives, and, in particular, of the G.N.R. 8 ft. singles, at a very early age, for on my first birthday anniversary my father had the large steel engraving of No. 773, issued just before by *The Engineer,* framed and hung in our hall. Moreover, not only my father, but also my cousin Cecil Laundy, 12 years older than I, was a devoted enthusiast for Stirling singles and spent his holidays for a number of years staying at Peterborough in order to photograph the engines then surviving, the majority of which were shedded at New England.

My parents removed from an inner London suburb to New Barnet in May 1898, on the very day on which Ivatt's first 'Atlantic', No. 990, was completed at Doncaster works; a portent indeed of great changes in the locomotive stock of the Great Northern Railway, but changes which only began to develop markedly nearly five years later.

In 1898 New Barnet was not the crowded dormitory it has since become. Across the fields the main line from Kings Cross was clearly in view, and my memory is of seeing hardly any engines but 8-footers on the expresses. An occasional 7 ft. 6 in. single was seen—always there was one of these on the 7.15 a.m. down Leeds express—but the prevailing nostalgic memories are of the flash in the sunlight of the highly-polished safety-valve casing, and the striding-out effect of the equally highly-polished steel connecting-rod of the 8-footers.

But it was not until I started to attend day-school at Holloway in January 1903 that my lasting passion for steam locomotives really developed. The two train trips daily, going and returning, were the most exciting part of my day and, as it was usually necessary to change trains at Finsbury Park, I enjoyed a wide variety of engines to travel behind and to observe.

In May 1898 there were about 900 Stirling 'straightback' engines in service, against fewer than 100 Ivatt engines with domes. In January 1903 the proportion had dropped to about 700 Stirling engines to some 400 Ivatt, but the odds were still in favour of a Stirling engine appearing at the head of all but the heaviest and most important trains.

Thus, from the year 1903, I remember seeing the 8 ft. singles on all sorts of trains, from No. 53 on the 8 a.m. 'stopper' from Kings Cross—quite a regular turn for her—to No. 1003 on the 4.15 p.m. down express, which stopped at Finsbury Park, and once gave me a thrill when the whole left side of the engine lifted what seemed well over an inch as the regulator was opened—a sensation I have often since enjoyed from the footplate on many classes of locomotive.

The 7 ft. 6 in. Stirling singles were newer engines than most of the 8-footers, and lasted rather longer in the London district. In 1903-05 the 5.0 p.m. down express from Kings Cross seemed to be invariably headed by one of this class, and here my memory is of the sound of the exhaust beats as this train came through Finsbury Park at about 40 m.p.h., with the engine working surprisingly hard, as it sounded from the beats of the exhaust.

No. 60 at Kings Cross, probably about 1893

No. 544 as built, in 1877

Turning to runs behind particular engines, I recall a rather slow trip with No. 671 on the 3.48 p.m. semi-fast from Kings Cross some time about June 1903. The 8 ft. singles—and practically all express engines—were allowed to work their passage to Doncaster for repairs, and even their last trip of all from which they did not return. No. 671 was broken up in October 1903 and it is just possible that on my trip she was making her very last journey, but my memory is insistent that my date was not later than July 1903.

A few years later, when the remaining Kings Cross singles had been transferred to another London District shed, Hitchin, I frequently travelled behind Nos. 1007 (domed) and 1008, 8-footers, and No. 879, a straightback 7 ft. 6 in. engine, as well as the two Ivatt singles Nos. 263 and 264, and occasionally behind the rebuilt Stirling singles Nos. 872, 873 and 877. The train was usually the 5.5 p.m. from Kings Cross, and the start from Finsbury Park was a most awkward one, taking place, not from the main-line platform, but from the adjacent suburban platform, from which

No. 1005 on her last visit to London, August 1908, approaching Potters Bar.

the line first started up the steep ascent to the High Barnet branch and then, over facing points, turned abruptly right-handed, downhill and left-handed to finish up parallel to the main line.

On this wicked start for a single-wheeler hauling the 11-coach set suburban train, weighing with passengers about 150 tons, No. 1008 seemed always to give the best start, though No. 1007 was nearly as good. Nos. 879, 263 and 264 were poor starters, so that they had to make up for their very slow getaways by running at higher speeds through Wood Green, still on the suburban relief line, with a layout on leaving Wood Green just like the Finsbury Park one, the uphill portion here being instead the climb to the Enfield branch overbridge.

On one occasion I timed No. 879 at 60 seconds exactly between the fourth and fifth mileposts, the latter situated in Wood Green station. Our speed was rising between these points, due to the first part of this mile being downhill, and through Wood Green station we must have been doing nearer 65 miles an hour than 60. The G.N.R. four-wheel suburban stock was stiffly sprung and rode pretty hard, so that I was thrown about the carriage quite violently over the points and curves—and of course so were the other passengers. As a result a 40 mp.h. speed limit was put on very shortly afterwards and was thereafter most strictly enforced.

On the up line there were in those days several semi-fast trains (9.11, 9.49 a.m., 12.48, 2.9, 3.43, 6.30 and 7.10 p.m. from New Barnet), which ran non-stop from New Barnet to Finsbury Park, just under seven miles, downhill most of the way, some of which trains were worked by the Hitchin singles. If these were routed on the main line all was well and usually the speed between mileposts five and four was about 70 to 72 m.p.h., the engine being worked very lightly. On one occasion No. 221, the last of the seven 8-footers rebuilt by Ivatt between 1896 and 1899, achieved 76 m.p.h. over this mile;

the sharp curve at Hornsey was most noticeable as the side of the carriage pushed one firmly westwards. No. 221 at that time was fitted with a secondhand straightback boiler, having worn out her Ivatt domed boiler. Her driving-wheel tyres were worn 'hollow', so that she was extremely prone to slipping. But she still had the Ivatt cylinders, with balanced slide-valves exhausting through the back, and was universally known as the swiftest 8-footer—once she could get up to speed.

But not all these New Barnet up trains ran on the fast line and those which used the relief line had to thread a series of curves at each suburban station, including an especially severe reverse curve through New Southgate station, where I believe the speed limit was 30 m.p.h. In those remote days of 60 years ago, when speedometers were unheard of, a very elastic view of these particular limits was often taken by enginemen. I always had the notion that the slow revolutions of the large driving-wheels of the single-wheelers upset the speed judgment of the drivers, who were by then far more accustomed to coupled engines with smaller diameter driving-wheels.

My only run behind any of the earlier 7 ft. 6 in. Stirling singles was in fact marred by this running on the up relief line. The engine was No. 229 and the run was smart enough but most tantalising as the driver checked the engine and reduced speed appreciably through each station. I remember vividly the clean state of No. 229, and the connecting rods and big-ends tucked away almost out of sight behind the sandboxes and the big driving-wheels. The late W. J. Reynolds used to say about No. 229 that she was 'the most vexatiously ubiquitous engine on the Great Northern'. Whenever he went to the lineside and hoped for an 8-footer on any particular express, No. 229 would be sure to turn up instead.

There used to be a late Sunday afternoon 'Parliamentary' train from Kings Cross to Don-

No. 229 at Cambridge, about 1900

caster which stopped at almost all stations. On one occasion when I happened, very exceptionally, to be travelling by this train to New Barnet the engine was No. 1, then a most dignified old warrior with a graceful, deep-lipped chimney and all the latest Stirling characteristics. This must have been in 1904, for at the end of that year that chimney was either replaced by a worn out, secondhand one, or else the top had begun to erode away and had been ground down to its present shallow proportions.

Although I travelled behind only a few of the Stirling singles, I was fortunate enough to see very many more of both the 8 ft. and the 7 ft. 6 in. classes. But I never saw No. 92, and saw only three of the 7 ft. singles and these, Nos. 21, 41 and 61, after they had been rebuilt by Ivatt with high-pitched domed boilers. With the exception of No. 21 they had disappeared from the London district before I began to take notice of individual engines.

No. 668, the famous engine of the 1895 Race to the North, was a Peterborough engine and therefore might be expected to have been a frequent visitor to Kings Cross. This was not so, at any rate during the hours of daylight. In those remote days there were no lists published of engines withdrawn or transferred and, since the other engines of the '662-71' batch had long since disappeared, it was assumed that No. 668 had also been condemned. I had just alighted onto the up platform at Holloway one morning in 1908 on my way to my engineering school, when I heard the measured beat of an engine on a down train ascending the 1 in 105 gradient which continues from Kings Cross to Holloway. As the engine came into sight I saw it was an 8-footer with a built-up chimney and, as always, with the paintwork and polished brass gleaming. I could hardly believe my eyes as I read the actual number 668 on the bufferbeam and realised that this most celebrated 8-footer was still in existence: I had certainly never set eyes on her before. The driver was leaning over the side of the cab, his left shoulder pressed against the vertical wall of the cabside, a dignified and severe-looking

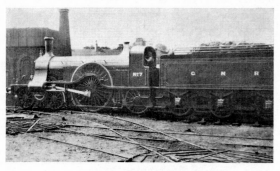

No. 7 at Peterborough, about 1896

oldish man, with a long, greying beard. I waved to him but only got an unresponsive glare, which damped my excitement for a moment. I found out afterwards that this was Jim Falkinder himself, the actual driver on that night of August 21 1895 when No. 668 made her fastest run from Kings Cross to Grantham. He had the reputation of being a surly individual, and my cousin Cecil Laundy was advised at New England that it would be useless to attempt to get into conversation with him or to seek to hear his account of that night's run; a great pity.

My last opportunities of seeing 8-footers working trains on the main line from Kings Cross were between 1908 and 1914 when Peterborough singles, including the 8-footers Nos. 668, 776, 1001, 1003 and 1004, and the Ivatt singles Nos. 265, 269 and 270, were used on up night 'vacuum goods'—fish trains from Grimsby—to London and returned normally on the 5.20 a.m. from Kings Cross. I was then living at New Barnet in a house which possessed in those days an uninterrupted view of the line—except for a few trees and one building—from the exit from Oakleigh Park tunnel, through Oakleigh Park station right to New Barnet station. I would regularly be at an upstairs window at 5.35 a.m., with field glasses, and could pick out the polished brass of the safety-valve casing as the engine came out of the tunnel, and then follow it in the glasses all the way to New Barnet station, a truly lovely sight.

Those mornings were very quiet and, if the wind was right, I could hear the beat of the engine almost from New Southgate station—certainly long before she entered the Oakleigh Park tunnel—and could usually decide which class of engine was on the train. My cousin Cecil Laundy did better than I; he was up and out every fine morning with his camera and, with his loving care in processing,

No. 48, about 1898. Her original crosshead has been replaced by one of the later pattern

obtained many beautiful pictures. The regular working of the 5.20 a.m. by single-wheelers was terminated at the end of July 1912, but even after this, up to the end of 1914, No. 1003 and one or other of the Peterborough Ivatt singles occasionally worked the 7.45 a.m. or the 8.45 a.m. from Kings Cross as a return working for a night special fish train. My very last sight of any Stirling single on other than a special train was on July 4, 1914 when No. 1003 worked the 8.45 a.m. from Kings Cross. Having noted her at the head of her train as my up suburban train arrived at Kings Cross, I went over to pay my respects and noted that her working pressure was reduced to 160 lb. per sq. in. and that the regulator handle on the driver's side had a copper pipe extension, presumably to give more sensitive control.

In 1938 No. 1 was brought out of York Railway Museum and worked special trains over many of the L.N.E.R. lines. With the help of my Rover car, in which I covered over 1,500 miles for the purpose, I was able to obtain a number of ciné films, mostly in colour, of No. 1 in action, taken with a telephoto lens, and covering in each shot some half-mile of her running. On most of these occasions I was able to photograph her at two points on the same trip, by dint of driving my car, after the first shot had been exposed, fast enough to overtake No. 1 and set up my camera a second time for her approach. This was not really as difficult as it may sound: because of her small and inappropriate tender there was usually a stop for water on the part of No. 1 between my first and second shots; but it earned me a mildly scoffing editorial paragraph in the *Railway Gazette* at the time.

Between 1919 and 1939 I was happy in getting to know two enthusiasts who became my good friends, the late Messrs J. F. Vickery and W. J. Reynolds. Vickery was born in 1872 and had been

No. 668 on 5.20 a.m. from Kings Cross, 1910. Photograph by the late Cecil Laundy, at New Barnet.

devoted to Stirling singles all his life. Some of the logs of his trips behind them appear in another chapter. He had seen and been familiar with the sight of all the 8-footers with one exception, No. 662, which never seems to have worked into Kings Cross and was one of the first engines withdrawn.

Reynolds, born in 1883, is still well remembered as a railway photographer and to him are owed most of the later photographs of Stirling singles, taken most frequently at Kings Cross, Cambridge and Hatfield. 'Josh', as he was affectionately called, had known several of the top-link Kings Cross enginemen, including Sam Watson the regular driver of No. 774 from her first arrival at Kings Cross at the end of 1885 until the arrival towards the end of 1901 of the Ivatt single No. 264, when he was given this latter engine. Watson was once asked by Mr. Ivatt himself what he thought of No. 264 and his reply was that 'she had the makings of a good engine in her'. This was not exactly the opinion of a later driver of No. 264, Walker, of Hitchin, who on one occasion said to my cousin Cecil Laundy: 'There is one thing about 8-footers, when you have done a trip you seldom have to do more than put a few drops of oil here and there, and you are all ready to go back again. But with 263 and 264 there is always something wants doing; you've got to be for ever tinkering with spanner and hammer. I can assure you that every time I go underneath, I can find something wrong and, really, you never know whether you are all right or not, until you get going.'

George Wilson, who lived to be over ninety, was a senior driver at Hitchin and had No. 1008 when she was used regularly on the Cambridge expresses. He also gave his views on this engine, and on the 8-footers in general, to my cousin on February 12, 1909: 'I've been driving eighteen years and it is the comfortablest eighteen months I've had, since I've had this engine. Never any trouble with 'em, they'll run from London to Grantham and finish up

No. 1003 just north of New Barnet, on the 8.45 a.m. from Kings Cross on July 4, 1914.

in just as good condition as they started. There is not a better engine in the London district for her class of work than 1008.'

Another Hitchin driver, W. Freestone, also contributed his views on the Stirling singles thus: 'One night last week with 1007 I had 52 pairs of wheels coming back from Grantham, and we passed Stoke, $5\frac{1}{2}$ miles, in eleven minutes. The expresses often take twelve minutes. 1007 is the best engine uphill I ever had. On Friday I had 879 with 48 pairs of wheels, and we took fourteen minutes to Stoke. There is one thing about 879. Although she is no class uphill, she can wake 'em up downhill. The 879 class are certainly the fastest engines the Great Northern ever had. One of them holds the record, 874 or 875, I forget which. She had a heavy train and took a long while getting to Potters Bar, but she had a record run from there to Peterborough, 58 minutes I think it was. Well, soon after that Mr. Ivatt sent for the engine for examination, and when she came back she was no good at all; the driver couldn't knock her along.' And again: 'I was standing pilot with 221 and our time was nearly up, so we hadn't got her quite up to the mark as we should have done if we'd known. Well, the engine of a down express broke down at New Barnet and a

No. 774 at Hatfield, 1900. The driver is Sam Watson, who had 774 new

"Long Tom" (Ivatt 0—8—0 goods engine) brought it on to Hitchin, and we took it on from there. We had eight cars (probably just about 300 tons with passengers) and we got to Peterborough in 51 minutes for the 44 miles. Another time with 221 I had to take on the train of North Eastern cars due at Kings Cross at 3.58 p.m. We had seven cars. We were a little bit slow getting to Knebworth, but down she went over the other side, then up again without seeming to notice it. Then I tell you we *did* just go through those tunnels; then up to Potters Bar; then down again—and you would have had to be very sharp to have got a snap of us at Wood Green. And we stopped at "the Cross" in 39 minutes'—for 32 miles. 'There is not a doubt that a single engine is the best for our class of work and, for my part, I don't care if I never have another coupled engine.'

Finally, Driver Simpson, yet another Hitchin driver in the same link: 'When 1008 came out, she passed Peterborough from Grantham in 26 minutes (29 miles) with a heavy train. Mr. Ivatt was on the footplate and he said, "I think you had better ease up a bit, driver". 1008 went into the shops and was never the same engine again.'

These views and stories could be multiplied in the same strain. There is really not much doubt that the practically universal feeling that Ivatt ruined the performance of the Stirling singles was due to his reducing the adhesion weight, after the broken rails at St. Neots and Little Bytham in 1895-96. It made all the difference between the success and failure of the engines to handle the heavier trains: at all events during their latter years.

For myself, on looking back, there can be no doubt that the disappearance of the last 8-footer in early 1916 had a deeper effect on me than I realised at the time or for long afterwards. It was not until No. 1 reappeared for her 'Hundred Days' in 1938 that my locomotive enthusiasm began to revive to any degree. The 8-footers have passed into history now. I have been fortunate, not only in having seen them at work, but also in having had the opportunity of going into the old records and studying the old Doncaster drawings, not only of the 8-footers but of all the other Great Northern Railway locomotives of that most delightful and fascinating era.

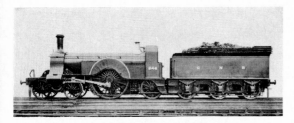

No. 546, about 1895–6, probably at Doncaster since it is an official photograph

No. 776 at Peterborough, 1909, in her last days. The chimney (intended for a Stirling goods engine) was her third

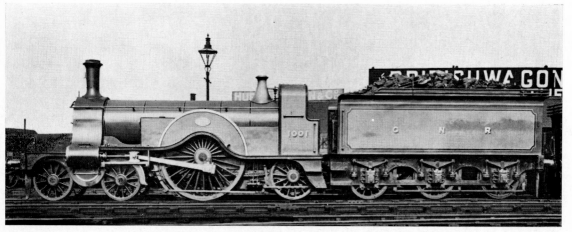

No. 1001 at Peterborough, 1909. The last survivor of the 18 in. cylindered 8-footers

CHAPTER 14

MISCELLANY

COMPARATIVE DIMENSIONS OF STIRLING 7 FT. AND 7 FT. 6 IN. SINGLES

First of batch	No. 6	No. 6	domed 21	92	92	238	234	871	876	domed 873
Date introduced	1868	1880	1897	1870	c1883	1885	1886	1892	1894	1898
Cylinders:										
diam. in.	17	17	17½	17½	17½	18½	18½	18	18½	18½
stroke in.	24	24	24	24	24	26	26	26	26	26
Leading wheels:										
diam. ft. in.	4 1	4 1	4 1½	4 1	4 1½	4 1½	4 1½	4 1½	4 1½	4 1½
Driving wheels:										
diam. ft. in.	7 1	7 1	7 1½	7 7	7 7½	7 7½	7 7½	7 7½	7 7½	7 7½
Trailing Wheels:										
diam. ft. in.	4 1	4 1	4 1½	4 1	4 1½	4 1½	4 1½	4 1½	4 1½	4 1½
Wheelbase:										
leading ft. in.	9 6	9 6	9 6	9 9	9 9	9 9	10 8	10 8	10 8	10 8
trailing ft. in.	7 6	7 6	7 6	7 9	7 9	8 1	8 5	8 5	8 5	8 5
Boiler barrel:										
max. diam ft. in.	4 0½	4 2½	4 5	4 0½	4 2	4 2	4 2	4 2	4 2	4 2
length ft. in.	10 2	10 2	10 1	10 6	10 6	10 6	11 5	11 5	11 5	11 5
Firebox casing:										
length ft. in.	5 6	5 6	5 6	5 6	5 6	5 10	6 2	6 2	6 2	6 2
width ft. in.	4 0½	4 0½	4 0½	4 0½	4 0½	4 0½	4 0½	4 0½	4 0½	4 0½
Boiler:										
tubes no.	206	186	215	192	—	186	186	174	174	180
outs. diam. in.	1¾	1⅝	1¾	1¾	—	1⅝	1¾	1¾	1¾	1¾
length between tubeplates ft. in.	10 6	10 6	10 5	10 10	10 10	10 10	11 9	11 9	11 9	11 9
Heating surface:										
tubes sq. ft.	922·25	777·2	1020·7	953.3	—	861	1001	936	936	970
firebox sq. ft.	89·5	92·47	103·1	—	—	106·8	114	114	114	114
Grate Area sq. ft.	16·4	16·4	17·8	16.4	16·4	17·29	18·4	18·4	18·4	20·3
Boiler pitch ft. in.	7 2	7 3	7 11	7 4	7 5	7 6	7 6	7 6	7 6	7 6

COMPARATIVE DIMENSIONS OF STIRLING 8 FT. SINGLES

First of batch	No. 1	No. 8	34	221	662	771	775	1003	1008	domed 93	boilers 1007
Date introduced	1870	1870	1875	1876	1880	1884	1887	1894	1895	1896	1907
Cylinders:											
diam. in.	18	18	18	18	18	18	18	19½	19	18	19½ (nom.)
stroke in.	28	28	28	28	28	28	28	28	28	28	28
Bogie wheels:											
diam. ft. in.	3 11	3 11	3 11	3 11	3 11	3 11	3 11½	3 11½	3 11½	3 11½	3 11½
Driving wheels:											
diam. ft. in.	8 1	8 1	8 1	8 1	8 1	8 1	8 1½	8 1½	8 1½	8 1½	8 1½

COMPARATIVE DIMENSIONS OF STIRLING 8 FT. SINGLES—(continued)

First of batch .	No. 1	No. 8	34	221	662	771	775	1103	1008	domed 93	boilers 1007
Trailing wheels:											
diam. ft. in. .	4 1	4 1	4 1	4 7	4 7	4 7	4 7½	4 7½	4 7½	4 7½	4 7½
Wheelbase:											
bogie ft. in. .	6 6	6 6	6 6	6 6	6 6	6 6	6 6	6 6	6 6	6 6	6 6
leading ft. in. .	7 9	7 9	7 9	7 9	7 9	7 9	7 9	7 9	7 9	7 9	7 9
trailing ft. in. .	8 0	8 8	8 8	8 8	8 8	8 8	8 8	9 0	9 0	9 0	9 0
Boiler barrel:											
max. diam. ft. in.	4 0½	4 0½	4 0½	4 0½	4 2	4 2	4 2	4 2	4 2	4 2	4 2
length ft. in. .	11 5	11 5	11 5	11 5	11 5	11 5	11 5	11 1	11 1	11 3	11 5
Firebox casing:											
length ft. in. .	5 6	6 2	6 2	6 2	6 2	6 2	6 2	6 10	6 10	6 8	6 2
width ft. in. .	3 11½	3 11½	3 11½	3 11½	3 11½	3 11½	3 11½	3 11½	3 11½	3 11½	3 11½
Boiler:											
tubes no. .	175	217	183	183	194	186	174	174	174	184	174
outs. diam. in. .	1⅝	1 9/16	1¾	1¾	1¾	1¾	1¾	1¾	1¾	1¾	1¾
length between tubeplates ft. in.	11 9	11 9	11 9	11 9	11 9	11 9	11 9	11 5	11 5	11 7 9/16	11 9
Heating surface:											
tubes sq. ft.	875·5	1043	984	984	1044	1001	936	909·98	909·98	980	936
firebox sq. ft. .	92·5	122	109	109	109	109	109	121·72	121·72	114·2	107·7
Grate area sq. ft. .	15·8	17·75	17·75	17·75	17·75	17·75	17·75	20	20	23·26	17·75
Boiler pitch ft. in. .	7 1	7 2	7 2½	7 2½	7 3¼	7 3¼	7 3½	7 6	7 6	7 3½	7 8¾

COMPARATIVE DIMENSIONS OF STURROCK ENGINES REBUILT BY STIRLING

(all 2-2-2s)

Class	51	91	201	203	229	264	264
Date introduced . .	1867	1867	1866	1867	1868	1873	1885
Cylinders:							
diam. in. . . .	16	16½	16	16	17	17	17½
stroke in. . . .	21	21	22	22	22	24	24
Leading wheels:							
diam. ft. in. . . .	3 10	4 1	3 6	4 1	4 3	4 3½	4 3½
Driving wheels:							
diam. ft. in. . . .	6 1	6 7	6 1	6 7	7 0	7 0	7 0
Trailing wheels:							
diam. ft. in. . . .	3 10	4 1	3 6	4 1	4 3	4 3½	4 3½
Wheelbase:							
leading ft. in. . .	8 6	9 6	9 10	9 0¾	9 6	9 7	9 7
trailing ft. in. . . .	6 10	7 0	7 3½	7 3⅛	8 6	7 9	7 9
Boiler barrel:							
max. diam. ft. in. . .	4 0½	4 0½	4 0½	4 0½	4 0½	4 0½	4 2
length ft. in. . . .	10 0	10 0	10 2	10 0	10 0	10 2	10 2
Firebox casing:							
length ft. in. . . .	4 9	4 10	4 10	4 10	5 6	5 6	5 6
width ft. in. . . .	4 0	4 0½	3 11½	4 0½	4 0	4 0½	4 0½
Boiler:							
tubes no. . . .	—	172	187	187	—	—	—
outs. diam. in. . .	—	2	—	1¾	—	—	—
length between tubeplates ft. in. . .	10 4	10 4	10 6	10 3⅞	—	10 6	10 6
Heating surface:							
tubes sq. ft. . . .	—	875	—	884	—	—	—
firebox sq. ft. . . .	—	97	—	—	—	—	—
Grate area sq. ft. . .	14	14	14	14	16	16·25	16·25
Pitch	6 9½	6 10½	6 7	6 11	—	7 2	7 2

K

THE STIRLING SINGLES

TABULATED HISTORY OF THE ENGINES

7-ft. singles built 1868-70

No.	Works No.	Date built	Reboilered 4ft. 2½in. diam.	Reboilered 4ft. 5in. diam.	Withdrawn	Remarks
No. 6	4	3/1868	5/1880		5/1904	
222	5	4/1868	5/1893		1/1906	
41	6	5/1868	9/1882	3/1898	4/1907	
No. 4	8	6/1868	3/1882		6/1906	
21	9	7/1868	6/1883	10/1897	11/1906	
14	11	8/1868	4/1882		7/1904	
55	26	5/1869	12/1883	9/1903	7/1906	
61	27	6/1869	3/1883	4/1898	11/1907	
63	32	8/1869	6/1884		10/1907	
215	34	10/1869	3/1884		10/1907	
37	48	6/1870	4/1888		7/1905	
39	51	6/1870	12/1884		6/1906	

7ft. 6in. single No. 92 built 1870

No.	Works No.	Date built	Reboilered 4ft. 2in. diam	Transferred to duplicate list	Withdrawn	Remarks
92	49	6/1870	c. /1883	6/1901	10/1902	

7ft. 6in. singles Nos. 238, 232 built 1885

No.	Works No.	Date built	Withdrawn	Remarks
238	389	6/1885	11/1908	
232	390	8/1885	6/1906	

7ft. 6in. singles built 1886-94

No.	Works No.	Date built	Rebuilt Ivatt domed boiler	Withdrawn	Remarks
234	409	6/1886		11/1912	
229	410	7/1886		1/1908	
237	428	3/1887	9/1910	12/1913	
230	434	4/1887		1/1907	
236	445	9/1887	3/1903	4/1907	
239	446	11/1887		8/1909	
231	455	2/1888		4/1905	
233	456	4/1888	9/1899	4/1913	
235	469	11/1888	8/1902	12/1913	
240	470	1/1889	7/1898	8/1913	
871	562	1/1892	8/1899	5/1913	
872	566	2/1892	5/1901	12/1913	
873	571	3/1892	4/1898	9/1911	
874	573	5/1892		3/1912	
875	576	6/1892		4/1911	
876	651	4/1894	3/1899	10/1911	
877	652	5/1894	11/1901	6/1913	
878	653	6/1894		9/1909	
879	654	6/1894		1/1911	
880	655	6/1894	5/1903	8/1911	
981	656	7/1894		12/1909	

8ft. singles built 1870-80

No.	Works No.	Date built	Rebuilt by Stirling	Reboilered 4ft. 2in. diam.	Rebuilt by Ivatt	Withdrawn	Remarks
No. 1	50	4/1870*	12/1880	12/1880		9/1907	Preserved at York
No. 8	61	12/1870*	2/1888	5/1891		8/1907	
33	66	3/1871	8/1886	8/1886		7/1904	
No. 2	77	12/1871*	12/1888	12/1888		11/1902	
No. 3	82	3/1872*	6/1884	6/1884		1/1903	
No. 5	105	8/1873*	5/1884	9/1886		1/1904	
No. 7	107	9/1873*	12/1882	12/1882		2/1905	
22	120	3/1874*	4/1887	4/1887	1/1898	11/1909	
48	150	10/1874	6/1881	6/1885		11/1902	
34	165	4/1875*	10/1886	10/1886	12/1897	11/1907	
47	170	6/1875	9/1883	9/1883		3/1903	
53	185	11/1875	11/1888	11/1888		4/1906	
62	195	2/1876	2/1886	2/1886		3/1903	
221	212	7/1876	3/1888	10/1882	6/1899	8/1909	Reverted to straight-back boiler 6/1907
94	215	10/1876	12/1887	12/1887		12/1904	
69	219	2/1877	12/1886	12/1886		6/1901	
98	220	3/1877*	9/1887	9/1887		5/1900	
544	230	8/1877	6/1889	6/1889	5/1897	10/1906	
545	231	9/1877	6/1887	6/1887		11/1903	
546	232	11/1877	11/1885	11/1885		11/1902	
547	233	1/1878	4/1883	10/1886		3/1903	
548	240	5/1878	2/1887	2/1887		9/1904	
549	245	6/1878	8/1888	8/1888		11/1902	
60	247	9/1878*	7/1886	7/1886		9/1899	
550	248	10/1878*	5/1887	5/1887		8/1901	
93	281	12/1879*	10/1889	10/1889	6/1896	5/1906	
95	285	4/1880	5/1888	5/1888	8/1897	5/1911	

* These dates are approximate.

8ft. singles built 1881–93

No.	Works No.	Date built	Rebuilt by Ivatt	Withdrawn	Remarks
662	303	2/1881		6/1901	
663	312	4/1881		1/1906	
664	320	6/1881		12/1903	
665	321	9/1881		4/1904	
666	323	11/1881		10/1906	
667	324	2/1882		10/1903	
668	341	5/1882		6/1912	
669	342	8/1882		12/1903	
670	349	12/1882		10/1903	
671	350	3/1883		10/1903	
771	379	11/1884		3/1903	
772	380	3/1885		5/1903	
773	393	8/1885		12/1903	
774	394	12/1885		1/1905	
775	427	1/1887		11/1905	
776	433	3/1887	7/1896	11/1911	
777	441	9/1887		5/1903	
778	442	11/1887		6/1904	
1001	631	8/1893		7/1912	Originally numbered 264
1002	632	12/1893		7/1908	„ „ 265

8ft. singles built 1894-95

No.	Works No.	Date built	Rebuilt by Ivatt	Withdrawn	Remarks
1003	671	11/1894		5/1915	
1004	672	1/1895		8/1914	
1005	673	2/1895		10/1908	
1006	674	3/1895		2/1916	
1007	675	3/1895	5/1907	1/1913	
1008	676	4/1895		6/1914	

ALLOCATION OF ENGINES TO RUNNING SHEDS

7ft. singles
> Peterborough: 4, 21, 39, 63, 222, 41★ (at first).
> Grantham: 14, 37, 61, 215.
> Retford: 6, 41★ (transferred from Peterborough).
> Doncaster: 55.

7ft. 6in. singles
> Kings Cross: 229, 230, 872, 873, 877, 879.
> Peterborough: 233, 234, 237, 874, 875; 92.
> Grantham: 231, 871, 878, 880.
> Doncaster: 232, 238; 235, 236, 239, 240, 876.
> York: 981.

8ft. singles
> Kings Cross: 53, 94, 544, 547★ (at first), 666, 671, 774, 1007, 1008.
> Peterborough: 7, 8, 22, 48, 69, 98, 221, 545, 549, 663, 668, 772, 776, 1001, 1003, 1004, 1005.
> Grantham: 2, 3, 5, 60, 62, 93, 95, 665, 771, 773, 775, 777, 778, 1002, 1006.
> Doncaster: 1, 33, 34, 47, 546, 547★ (transferred from Kings Cross before 1885), 548, 550, 662, 664, 667, 669, 670.

Nos. 33 and 47 were stationed at Leeds for a year or two in the 1870s. The above lists show the original allocations, but from 1895 on, and perhaps a year or two earlier, there were a fair number of changes in the allocations of the 7ft. and 8ft. singles.

COMPARATIVE COSTS OF GREAT NORTHERN SINGLES
excluding tenders

Wheel arrangement	Nos.	Year	Cost each	Remarks
4-2-2	No. 1	1870	£2,033	
	544–50	1877–78	£2,163	
	662–71	1881–83	£2,125	
	771–72	1884–85	£2,148	
	773–74	1885	£1,877	Mild steel frames and boilers
	775–78	1887	£1,969	
2-2-2	871–75	1892	£1,871	
4-2-2	1001–02	1893	£1,926	estimated (because originally charged to Current Account).
2-2-2	876–80, 981	1894	£1,756	
4-2-2	1003–08	1894–95	£2,240	

REBOILERED BY IVATT

Domed boilers fitted (1896–99) to seven 8ft. singles, involving lengthening of frames (Ivatt class A3).

Barrel:
max. diam.   4ft. 2in.
length   11ft. 3in.★

Firebox casing:
length   6ft. 8in.★
width   3ft. 11½in.

Safety valve casing	Boiler pressure	Fitments	
brass	170 lb. per sq. in.	93	6/96– 5/06
,,	175 ,, ,, ,, ,,	776	7/96–11/11
,,	,, ,, ,, ,, ,,	544	5/97–10/06
cast iron	,, ,, ,, ,, ,,	95	8/97– 5/11
,, ,,	,, ,, ,, ,, ,,	34	12/97–11/07
		later used as a stationary boiler	
,, ,,	,, ,, ,, ,, ,,	22	1/98–11/09
,, ,,	,, ,, ,, ,, ,,	221	6/99– 6/07

★On boiler drawing

Ivatt standard 4ft. 5in. diameter domed boilers fitted new to 7ft. 0in. singles rebuilt 1897–1903 (Ivatt class B7).

Barrel:
max. diam.   4ft. 5in.
length   10ft. 1in.

Firebox casing: length   5ft. 6in.
width   4ft. 0½in.

After removal from the 7ft. singles, these boilers were fitted to other engines.

Doncaster Order No.	Water-legs	First fitments	
500/21	1¾in.	21	10/97–11/06.
500/26	,,	41	3/98– 4/07.
500/27	,,	61	4/98–11/07.
543/ 1	3 in.	55	9/03– 7/06.

Boilers built after 1898 for fitting to 8ft. singles (Ivatt class A2, domed and straightback) and 7ft. 6in. singles (Ivatt class B3 straightback, class B4 domed) without alterations to frame length.

Barrel: max. diam. 4ft. 2in.
         length   11ft. 5in.

Firebox casing: length 6ft. 2in.
                 width   3ft. 11½in. or
                         4ft. 0½in.

Doncaster Order No.	Dome or straightback	Firebox casing width	Water legs	Fitments
204/1	dome	4ft. 0½in.	1¾in.	876 3/99–10/11
„ /2	„	„	„	240 7/98–12/08
„ /3	„	„	„	873 4/98– 9/11
„ /4	„	„	„	871 8/99– 6/06; 240 12/08– 8/13
„ /5	„	„	„	233 9/99– 5/10
507/1	straightback	3ft. 11½in.	„	771 7/98– 3/03; 234 8/04–11/12
„ /2	„	„	„	69 6/98– 6/01; 53 2/02– 4/06
„ /3	„	„	„	94 5/98– 8/03
514/1	„	„	„	548 3/99– 3/03
„ /2	„	„	„	7 6/99– 2/05; (a)
„ /3	„	„	„	670 7/99–11/03
„ /4	„	„	„	2 12/00–11/02; 1002 1/03– 7/08
„ /5	„	„	„	778 8/00– 6/04; 668 7/10– 6/12; (a); 1 5/25– still carried
„ /6	„	„	„	664 9/00–12/03; (a)
522/1	dome	4ft. 0½in.	„	877 11/01– 7/06; 233 5/10– 4/13
„ /2	„	„	„	872 5/01– 6/07 (b); (c); (d)
„ /3	„	„	„	236 5/03– 4/07; 872 6/07– 5/10; 237 9/10–12/13
„ /4	„	„	„	880 7/03– 8/11
„ /5	„	„	„	235 8/02–12/13
537/1	„	3ft. 11½in.	3in.	872 5/10–12/13
„ /2	„	„	„	1007 6/07– 1/13
„ /3	„	„	„	first used on Ivatt 0-8-2T No. 116; (d)
„ /4	„	„	„	871 6/06– 5/13
„ /5	„	„	„	877 7/06– 6/13
„ /6	„	„	„	first used on Ivatt 0-8-2T No. 128; (d)

(a) These boilers were later used as stationary boilers at Doncaster.
(b) This boiler was fitted to No. 872 at Kings Cross, where she was rebuilt.
(c) This boiler was later fitted to an Ivatt 0-8-2 tank engine.
(d) These boilers later had their barrels shortened by 11in. and were then fitted to Gresley 0-6-0 tank engines.

Note: It was a remarkable chain of circumstances that led to a boiler of a batch designed for use on old 8-footers being used first on a new 0-8-2 tank engine, and later transferred to a new 0-6-0 shunting tank engine. And it is curious that none of these boilers was used on the engines for which they had been designed, three going on 7ft. 6in. singles and one on an 8-footer of the larger class, for which it was not intended or suited.

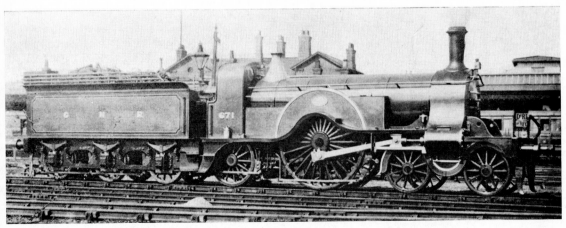

No. 671 at Hatfield, after working Lord Salisbury's daily 'special' in 1900

G.N.R. ENGINE CLASSIFICATION: JUNE 1900

In June 1900 Ivatt introduced a system of classifying engines, using as its basis the wheel arrangement of the engine types. Thus the 4-2-2s were all under letter A, the 2-2-2s under letter B, and so on. Each letter was followed by a number to segregate the different types with the same wheel arrangement. The numerical order employed put to the fore the classes with the largest diameter driving-wheels, and gradually worked downwards to the classes with the smallest driving-wheels. Thus for example the 8-footers came before the 7ft. 6in. singles. The drawback with such a classification was that it left no provision for new construction, which had to be tagged on to the end regardless of wheel diameter. The classification as it affected the Great Northern singles running in June 1900, including the Ivatt singles, is as follows:

Class	Wheel Arrangement	Description
A1	4-2-2	Stirling 8-footers, No. 1003 class
A2	,,	Remaining straightback Stirling 8-footers
A3	,,	8-footers rebuilt by Ivatt with domed boilers
A4	,,	Ivatt 7ft. 6in. single, No. 266
A5	,,	Ivatt 7ft. 6in. singles, No. 267 class
B1	2-2-2	Stirling 7ft. 6in. single, No. 92
B2	,,	Stirling 7ft. 6in. singles, Nos. 238, 232
B3	,,	Remaining straightback Stirling 7ft. 6in. singles
B4	,,	7ft. 6in. singles rebuilt by Ivatt with domed boilers
B5	,,	Stirling 7ft. singles, straightback
B6	,,	Rebuilt Sturrock 7ft. singles, Nos. 265, 267A, 268
B7	,,	Stirling 7ft. singles rebuilt by Ivatt with domed boilers

Note: The fitting of a domed boiler to No. 1007 in June 1907 did not introduce a new classification. The engine remained class A1.

For loading purposes a power classification was introduced in 1906. Under this classification, all the single-wheelers were grouped under P. The letter was indicated on the engine in the form of a metal plate bearing this letter and affixed to the vacuum brake standpipe at the front end of the engine. It was by this loading classification letter that engine types were referred to by the enginemen in the latter days of the Great Northern, the classification by wheel arrangement not coming into prominence until after the formation of the L.N.E.R., when an up-to-date version was produced.

TENDERS

THERE were three distinct types of tenders during Stirling's lifetime. The oldest ones, which he had inherited from Sturrock, had 'sandwich frames' and were mainly kept to Sturrock engines. Occasionally they were noted in later days attached to engines of several Stirling classes, but never his own single-wheelers. The diameter of the wheels varied from 3 ft. 6 in. to 4 ft. 6 in. and frequently, in the case of passenger tenders, the diameter was the same as that of the carrying wheels of the engines, thus making them interchangeable. For example, the diameter of the tender wheels of Sturrock's No. 229 class 2—2—2s was 4 ft. 3 in. like the engine carrying wheels.

The outside frames of these 'sandwich frame' tenders were timber beams, usually 10 in. deep and 3 to 5 in. wide, strengthened on either side by wrought-iron plates of around $\frac{1}{2}$ in. thickness, to give a sandwich effect. The springs were positioned above the running plate and on the middle and rear axleboxes were often connected by compensating beams. Sometimes there were additional inside frames, though on well-tenders this was not necessary; the wells themselves being arranged to give added strength, transverse stays being used to connect the sides of the well with the outside frames.

Quite a number of the old Sturrock sandwich frame tenders were later modernised by Stirling— and Ivatt too—and after alterations usually resembled Stirling's wood frame tenders. The tender now attached to No. 1 in York Museum is an example of one of these old Sturrock tenders after being modernised by Stirling. The tender now has wood frames, of Stirling's first type, and on close inspection it can be seen where the tender originally had outside springs and has had these re-positioned below the footplate level at a later date.

In October 1866 Stirling drew out a new tender design which had a modified frame arrangement. The outside frames were made of $\frac{7}{8}$ in. iron plate placed 6 ft. 7$\frac{1}{2}$ in. apart transversely; this figure was shortly afterwards altered to 6 ft. 8 in. Next to the inner faces of the plate frames were timber beams, 11 in. deep and $4\frac{1}{2}$ in. wide. Inside frames were used and these were timber beams too, 11 in. deep and 4 in. wide. The inner and outer timber frames were $10\frac{1}{4}$ in. apart. For additional strength, transverse timber beams 11 in. deep and 4 in. wide separated the inner frames at two places. At the ends of the frames, two 16 in. deep by 6 in. wide timbers provided the bufferbeams. The whole wooden framework was 'well morticed and tenoned and put together with white lead'. For his timbers, Stirling specified 'well seasoned Quebec white oak or pitch pine'.

The springs were now positioned out of sight behind the outside frames, immediately above each axle box, and no doubt were awkward to examine for broken plates, and even more awkward to change.

These tenders were intended for goods engines and so had flat bottom tanks, holding only 1,500 gallons of water, though an alteration was made to the drawing in March 1867 increasing the capacity by a further 500 gallons by extending upwards the tank side sheets by 9 in. to a height of 3 ft. 8 in. above footplate level. To support the extra weight the slots in the frames were made slightly smaller.

In February 1876 a larger capacity version was drawn out with the side sheets now 4 ft. 10 in. above footplate level, thereby increasing the water capacity to 2,500 gallons. The timber framework was basically the same, but whereas the earlier design had employed 3 ft. 6 in. diameter wheels, this new design had 4 ft. 0 in. wheels. Both designs, having flat bottom tanks, were essentially for use attached to goods engines and Stirling probably soon found that with the slower speeds at which these tenders ran, there was no marked superiority of the larger wheel over the smaller one. Thereafter he used only 3 ft. 6 in. wheels, which were cheaper to manufacture, on his goods tenders. On the other hand, he found that with passenger tenders larger wheels were less liable to run hot at the higher speeds, this advantage outweighing the higher cost. Henceforward all his passenger tenders had 4 ft. 0 in. wheels, and also wells—again adding to the cost; but high capacity tenders were more essential for passenger engines than goods.

The well version followed in 1867, outwardly similar to the flat bottom type just referred to, apart from slightly shallower side sheets. The water capacity was 2,470 gallons, the shallower top tank being balanced by the well between the inside frames. The transverse timbers had to be dispensed with, the well being in the way. It is difficult to see what advantage this design had over the previous one, also with 4 ft. 0 in. wheels, but having a flat bottom tank, which actually held more water. Perhaps lowering the centre of gravity was thought advisable when contemplating high speeds on a rough track, with the curves not canted as they are today. Still, the well left scope for increasing the capacity in the future, and in fact the height of the side sheets was later varied a little. A higher version, holding 2,700 gallons of water, is reported to have been fitted to 8-footers Nos. 8, 33, 34, 47, 48, 53 and 62.

A slight change in the shape of the front frame slot (near the step) appeared in 1872, with the leading edge now vertical instead of slanting. The same arrangement drawing shows the large wooden brake blocks replaced by the cast-iron pattern, similar to those used today. The outside-frame plates are now noted as being 6 ft. 9 in. apart.

Further slight changes appeared from time to time, and the final wood frame tender design, drawn out in October 1881, had $6\frac{1}{2}$ in. wide outside timber beams, and 4 in. wide inside ones. These beams were now only $8\frac{3}{4}$ in. apart, whilst the outside frames were still of $\frac{7}{8}$ in. wrought-iron. (The timber was now of 'well seasoned Quebec white oak' only, pitch pine evidently having fallen out of favour.) Three coal guards were now added to the top of the coping plate, another Stirling feature come to stay, except for a variation in the number of rails at a later date.

The first 'iron frame' tender drawing is dated May 1883. The use of timber was discarded except for the oak bufferbeam. An inner iron frame was introduced, 13 in. deep and $\frac{3}{4}$ in. thick. The inner and outer frames were 7 9/16 in. apart now, the outside frame plates having been brought inwards, nearer to the wheels, by dispensing with the timber beams. The outside frames were now only 5 ft. $6\frac{3}{4}$ in. apart and this enabled the axlebox guides to be bolted now to the outer faces of the outside frames. Thus the axleboxes themselves were positioned outside the frames and consequently the springs too—in a more accessible position.

The last Stirling 8 ft. singles, Nos. 1003 to 1008, received 3,850-gallon tenders, the highest capacity Stirling tenders. These differed from earlier Stirling tenders in having only two coal guards instead of three. These tenders long outlived the engines and the last one, tender No. 1005, was not condemned until June 1954, after finishing its time behind one of the Ivatt goods engines.

This was the final Stirling tender design, and Ivatt made only slight alterations, chiefly dispensing with the inner frames, and substitution of a steel bufferplate in place of the bufferbeam. Also whereas

Stirling had standardised very quickly on well-tanks and 4 ft. 0 in. wheels for his passenger tenders, and flat bottom tanks and 3 ft. 6 in. wheels for his goods tenders, Ivatt almost straightaway standardised on 4 ft. 0 in. wheels for all new tender construction, to give a greater interchangeability of tenders amongst all classes of engines. From 1907 only well-tank tenders were constructed at Doncaster.

Ivatt introduced the tender classification, using the letters A to G, grouping all tenders broadly speaking into seven basic groups as follows:

Class	Frames	Tank	Wheel Diameter	Origin	Year
A	iron	flat bottom	4ft. 0in.	Ivatt	1896 on
B	”	well	”	”	”
C	”	flat bottom	3ft. 6in.	Stirling	1883–96
D	”	well	4ft. 0in.	”	”
E	wood	flat bottom	3ft. 6in.	”	1867–83
F	”	well	4ft. 0in.	”	”
G	sandwich	both	various	Sturrock	pre-1867

The 'sandwich frame' tenders became extinct during Gresley's superintendency at Doncaster, and the letter 'G' was re-used for his eight-wheel Pacific tenders, introduced in 1922.

BRAKE TRIALS

The Newark brake trials of 1875, though carried out actually on the Midland line and not on the Great Northern, have a bearing on the subject of this book, in that the 7 ft. single No. 55 was the Great Northern engine selected to demonstrate the Smith's vacuum brake. All the trains equipped with the rival brakes were of the same make-up, two guards' vans and 13 coaches, but the total weights of the competing trains varied quite a lot. The Great Northern was the heaviest, weighing nearly 196 tons empty, and consisting mainly of six-wheeled stock; the only exceptions were two four-wheeled coaches.

Surprising as it may seem, the engine was un-braked and the tender had only a handbrake operating on wooden blocks. These, and the wooden brake-blocks with which the guards' vans were equipped, showed up very badly in the wet weather in which some of the tests were run, especially when comparative distances for the then normal braking, by tender and guards' van hand-braking only, were obtained.

A series of varied tests was made with each of the competing forms of brake. The general spirit of the tests was intended to be strictly practical and not at all scientific, and, to an old Westinghouse engineer such as the present writer, it is very gratifying to be able to say that the Westinghouse automatic air-brake simply wiped the floor with all the other forms of brake, an undoubted fact well rubbed in at the time by *Engineering* and *The Engineer*. If only George Westinghouse had been able to command the tact necessary to conceal his opinion of one of the Locomotive Superintendents! As it was, in spite of the obvious defects of the simple vacuum-brake, exhibited in a glaring manner during one of the tests, when the train was deliberately parted in halves at speed and the front half with the engine had to put on steam to avoid being hit by the handbraked rear portion, it was this so-called simple vacuum-brake which was standardised on the Great Northern for the next ten years.

It was not really so simple, because it involved two brake-pipes, with their hose couplings, running the length of the train, the pipes being cross-connected at the rear of the last coach. The idea was to apply the brake as nearly as possible simultaneously at the front and rear of the train. The engine had a duplex ejector, which necessarily consumed a great deal of steam, and in addition each brake van had a small exhauster, or 'air-pump', which was triggered into action by the first movement of the collapsible rubber sack which, when partially evacuated, served as the brake cylinder. This tensioned a belt drive from one of the axles of the van to the exhauster.

Some of the results were as follows. The engine and tender, running alone, stopped, without any brake application at all, in 6,772 feet from a speed of 42 m.p.h. Again, for engine and tender only, with handbrake fully applied and engine reversed with full steam, the stopping distance from 47½ m.p.h. was 828 feet. No doubt the engine driving-wheels were 'picked up' and skidding throughout this test! At any rate, with the tender handbrake only applied, the stopping distance from 40 m.p.h. was 700 feet, for the engine and tender only. The whole train, with engine and tender, rolled to a stop in 5,063 *yards* from 42 m.p.h., no brakes at all being applied.

With the use of brakes, in different ways, the results are tabulated below.

Initial speed, m.p.h.	Stopping distance, ft.	Method of braking
49·5	3,591	Applying handbrakes only, on tender and guards vans
47·5	1,200	Vacuum brake applied by guard, and also all hand brakes
49·5	1,448	Using all means except sand
43·0	860	Using all means including sand
45·0	920	Using all means including sand
42·75	1,670	By guard's signal and communication cord NOTE: Cord did not work!
43·5	1,038	By guard's signal and communication cord NOTE: Cord specially adjusted!
43·0	1,088	By guard only, driver not applying the brake and not signalled NOTE: The brake in this case seems to have been applied by cutting in the small exhauster on the brakevan, which would gradually, as the degree of vacuum was increased, cut in the other small exhauster to assist

Less than a year later, in March 1876, the Great Northern held a series of vacuum-brake trials on its own. By this time both engines and tenders had been equipped with vacuum braking, and were fitted with iron brake-blocks. Twelve runs were made, the first five with a 15-coach train, weighing $217\frac{1}{2}$ tons, this weight including the engine and tender. The remaining seven runs were with a lighter train, 10 coaches only, with a total weight of 162 tons. The type of engine used is not mentioned.

Run No.	Gradient	Speed, m.p.h.	Stopping distance, ft.	Method of braking
1	1:198 dn.	56	800	All means
2	1:1100 up	40	345	All means
3	1:400 dn.	50	580	All means
4	1:1100 dn.	45	610	All means
5	1:198 dn.	60	780	All means
6	Level	47	560	All means
7	Level	62	790	All means
8	1:400 up	55	555	All means
9	Level	56	2,290	Hand brakes only
10	Level	47	875	Pipe open at tail end
11	1:400 dn.	45	570	All means
12	1:660 up	56	780	Air pumps not used

The above figures were a good deal better than the figures of similar trials furnished by the G.N.R. to the Board of Trade, and published in 1877.

Trials made with Smith's Vacuum Brake on G.N.R. in 1876-77, on the Lincolnshire Loop, between Doncaster and Lincoln. Brakes were applied on engine and tender as well as on train.

Date	Description of train	Total weight of train, including engine and tender T C	Speed m.p.h.	Gradient		Stopping distance feet
March 1876	7ft. passenger engine uncoupled, with 6-wheel tender, 13 carriages, 2 luggage vans	217 10	56	1:198	dn	1,068
			60	1:198	dn	1,038
			50	1-400	dn	771
			45	1:1100	dn	813
			40	1:1100	up	459
March 1876	7ft. single passenger engine and tender, 8 carriages, 2 luggage vans	162 5	47	Level		741
			47	Level		1,164*
			60	Level		1,056
			45	1:400	dn	759
			55	1:400	up	738
			56	1:660	up	1,038
May 1876	7ft. single passenger engine and tender, 10 carriages, 2 luggage vans	190 12	50	Level		930
			56	1:176	dn	960
			56	1:400	dn	882
			60	1:200	dn	1,230
March 1877	7ft. single passenger engine and tender, 10 carriages, 2 luggage vans	165 5	53	Level		933
			54	1:400	dn	1,017
			62	1:400	dn	1,143
			60	1:200	dn	1,236

*Connecting pipes open at tail ends.
Note: The actual engines used are not known.

These Board of Trade figures include other, further tests and are tabulated on page 153. There is no mention of the brake being applied by 'all means', which may have meant sanding. The brake was 'put on by the engine-driver opening a steam tap'.

It must have been felt that either something was not quite right or that there was something more to be learned, for in July 1877, and again in September of that year, still further runs were made. The engine on both trials was a '6 ft. 6 in. four-coupled passenger engine'—probably Stirling 2—4—0, No. 541.

The total loads were 13 and 12 coaches, with an overall weight of 195 and 165 tons respectively.

Run No.	Gradient	Speed m.p.h.	Stopping distance ft.
1	Level	47	730
2	Level	56	835
3	Level	42	645
4	1:198 dn.	60	960
5	1:1100 dn.	60	1,140
6	1:440 dn.	62	1,080
7	1:198 dn.	64	1,200

Here there is no mention of any particular method of applying the brake, and from the figures obtained it looks as if no sand was used—this on the assumption that 'all means' in the 1876 trials included sanding.

Although nothing is stated, it seems possible that these last trials were made without the extra exhausters in the brake vans. The 'Heath Robinson' character of the gear for engaging them and the wire-rope drive must inevitably have been troublesome and it looks as if these trials were made in the hope that adequate stops would be recorded without the use of the auxiliary exhausters. No doubt this was the conclusion arrived at, even if it was not due to the results of these trials. The discrepancy in stopping distance in Run No. 5 may have been due to a slightly leaky brake-pipe, or to a slightly slower response by the driver in applying the brake.

But the overall indication of these and the Newark trials is that the results of even non-automatic braking were so much superior to those of the totally inadequate handbraking hitherto employed that there was no immediate call for any further perfecting of the vacuum-brake, or any need for any 'laboratory' type testing.

PAINTING

The bright but mellow shade of light green used on the Great Northern from about 1880 onwards is still remembered from its continuance in London & North Eastern days, right up to nationalisation; though the details of the lining-out were not the same in the two cases. So that it comes as somewhat of a surprise to realise that during nearly half of his superintendency Stirling seems to have continued the Brunswick Green of his predecessor, a much darker colour approximating to Great Western green, and almost certainly surviving vestigially throughout Great Northern days in the dark green surrounds of tender and tank panels.

The exact date of the change to the well-known light green is not known, but it was at some time between 1876 and 1881. At the same time the brown of the frames was apparently also altered, to lake. But the only grounds we have to go on are the painting specifications of engines built by outside contractors: there are no clues to the exact shades of the colours used, because in later years 'green to pattern' was the official description; and, anyway,

no singles were built in Stirling's day by outside contractors. Nevertheless, it seems clear that nearly half the 8-footers first appeared in a much darker livery than they wore in later days.

The description of the post-1880 colour as 'a bright, almost grass green' does seem to be as true as any description of colour can be. The boiler, splashers, cab and wheels were all of this green. Boiler bands were black with a white line at both edges. Cabs and splashers had a black border edged with a white line. Frames were painted vermilion on the inside: on the outside they were lake with a black border edged with a vermilion line. Buffer-beams were vermilion, with a black border edged with a white line. Tender frames and bufferbeams were similar to the engines. Tender tanks were light green, inside a black band forming a panel, the black band edged with a white line on either side. Outside the panel was a surround of darker green, probably either a Brunswick or a Holly Green.

The details of the painting and lining are shown in the illustration.

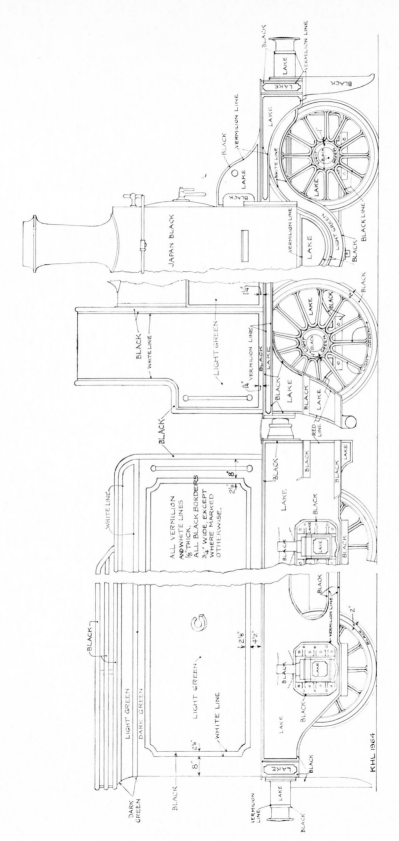

Diagram of painting and lining, Great Northern Railway locomotives

PHOTOGRAPHS

All the Stirling singles were photographed, and copies exist today of at least one photograph of each engine. Possibly also all the Sturrock rebuilds may have been photographed, but in this instance there do not seem to be any photographs still in existence of quite a large proportion of the engines, and there are gaps in even those classes which were the last to survive.

There were few cameras about in the seventies of last century, and it was not until the nineties that photography became a popular pastime; but the two main reasons for the paucity of early photographs were the slow speed of the emulsions then available, which practically ruled out photography of moving trains, and, most of all, the extremely strict privacy of all railway precincts. Photography from stations or lineside was forbidden and access to running sheds was almost impossible in the early days of Stirling. A few favoured individuals, almost always professional photographers, were permitted to take posed photographs of engines, and at Doncaster there were professionals who were called in from time to time to take official photographs, a few of which are still in existence.

No doubt numbers of surreptitious photographs were taken, but none of those remaining shows any high standard of photography, and probably most of such photographs were poor, or very poor. In the nineties, however, things became easier, and most of the photographs surviving today were taken after 1890.

It is surprising by how narrow a chance photographs of certain engines came to be taken. W. J. Reynolds, as a boy of 11, was given his first camera on the day in 1895 on which his parents took him to the Agricultural Show at Sandy. His first exposure was on 8-footer No. 549. By great good fortune it came out well. It remains the only known photograph of this engine and is reproduced in this book. Of the same batch of engines, there seem to be only two photographs of No. 545, the better one of which is reproduced in this book. This is not a 'portrait' of the engine, which in fact is heading a

down express train just south of Hitchin.

Many photographs of the 8-footer No. 95 were taken after she had been rebuilt by Ivatt with a domed boiler, but only one seems to be known of this engine when 'straightback'. Even this is not a satisfactory one, for it shows her slung from a traversing crane in the Doncaster works where she had just arrived for repairs, on November 21, 1892.

And although two photographs were taken of the 8-footer No. 3 in her first year, only one, and that a head-on view, seems now to survive from her last thirty years of existence.

Perhaps the most curious instance of all, as far as this book is concerned, is that of the 7 ft. single No. 215. For many years it had been generally accepted that her only known photograph was, like No. 95's (and indeed taken almost at the same time), one showing her slung from a crane in the works. Moreover, No. 215 was partially masked by the vertical boiler of the steam-driven crane. It really seemed that this highly unsatisfactory photograph would have to appear in this book; but at the very last moment Mr. J. E. Kite, who had been looking out for nearly thirty years for another photograph of No. 215, was fortunate enough to come across the portrait of the engine reproduced, by his kind permission, on page 47.

Most of the photographs reproduced in the book are from Kenneth Leech's collection, built up over some sixty years. They include photographs known to have been taken by the late W. J. Reynolds, Cecil Laundy, Dr. T. F. Budden, H. G. Tidey, R. E. Bleasdale, and P. W. Pilcher; there are a few 'official' ones, and a number by photographers whose names are no longer known.

Apart from those of the preserved No. 1, the newest photograph was taken at least fifty years ago and the oldest just on one hundred years ago; we can only be thankful that such a surprisingly good pictorial record has in fact been made. It will be appreciated that some of the older photographs have needed much careful treatment in copying to bring them up to reproduction standard.

Acknowledgements

The authors and publishers wish to express their thanks to the following for permission to use illustrations:

Real Photographs Co. Ltd.: p.18, 60, 89 top.

Messrs Higginbottom and Oubridge: 55, 56 top, 57, 59.

Messrs Ian Allan Ltd.: 115.

Props. of *Engineering*: 42, 43.

Props. of *The Engineer*: 65, 79.

Props. of *The Railway Gazette*: 90.

F. H. Gillford Esq.: 114 bottom.

F. C. Hambleton Esq.: 58, 66 to 68, 72, 76, 78, 98.

J. E. Kite Esq.: 47, 63.

K. H. Leech Esq.: 54, 75, 123 to 125, 132 to 135.

The late K. A. C. R. Nunn Esq.: 97 right, 140.

STIRLING SINGLES CHRONOLOGY

March	1866	Stirling resigned as Locomotive Engineer, G. & S.W.R.
July	1866	Stirling's first rebuild of old single-wheelers: Nos. 201 and 202
October	1866	Stirling formally appointed Locomotive Engineer, Great Northern Railway
March	1868	The first 7 ft. single completed, No. 6
April	1870	The first 8-footer completed, No. 1
June	1870	The first 7 ft. 6 in. single completed, No. 92
July	1876	The first 8-footer with vacuum brakes, No. 221
June	1881	The first 8-footer with plain splashers, No. 664. Exhibited at Newcastle
June	1885	The first of the intermediate 7 ft. 6 in. singles completed, No. 238
June	1886	The first of the enlarged 7 ft. 6 in. singles completed, No. 234
March	1887	The last 'exhibition' 8-footer completed, No. 776. Exhibited at Newcastle 1887 and Edinburgh 1890
July—August	1888	The Race to Edinburgh
December	1893	The last of the original design of 8-footer completed, No. 1002
July	1894	The last of the 7 ft. 6 in. singles completed, No. 981
November	1894	The first of the enlarged 8-footers completed, No. 1003
April	1895	The last 8-footer completed, No. 1008
July—August	1895	The Race to Aberdeen
November	1895	Patrick Stirling dies and is succeeded by Henry Alfred Ivatt
June	1896	The first 8-footer rebuilt with domed boiler, No. 93
September	1899	The first 8-footer scrapped, No. 60
May	1902	The last rebuilt Sturrock single scrapped, No. 267A
May	1904	The first 7 ft. single scrapped, No. 6
April	1905	The first 7 ft. 6 in. single scrapped, No. 231
November	1907	The last 7 ft. single scrapped, No. 61
December	1913	The last 7 ft. 6 in. singles scrapped, Nos. 235, 237, 872
February	1916	The last 8-footer scrapped, No. 1006

NOTE ADDED IN PROOF

On page 41 it was stated that the boiler mileages for only seven of the twelve boilers first fitted to the 7-foot singles were known. Since going to press, one additional mileage figure has been discovered: No. 222's first boiler was in use for 428,368 miles.

No. 62 at Peterborough, about 1900. Her original wrought iron driving wheels have been replaced by cast steel ones

No. 547 at Kings Cross, about 1894–5.   She is about to leave the 'loco yard' and back down on to her train

No. 221 at Hitchin, 1908.   With boiler ex No. 773, Ivatt cab and tender.   She has cylinders with the exhaust passing to the blastpipe through the backs of the balanced slidevalves

INDEX

Illustrations are denoted in italic type

Chronology, 157
Cockshott, F. P., 111

Drawings
    Boiler, No. 1, *34*
    Boiler, Nos. 771–774, *35*
    Connecting rod, etc., No. 1 class, *54*
    Cross-section, No. 6, *42*
    Cylinder, No. 1, *83*
    Cylinders, No. 234 class, *92*
    Elevation, No. 6, *43*
    Firebox, Nos. 8, 33, *30*
    General arrangement, No. 1, *51*
    General arrangement, No. 1003 class, *115*
    General arrangement, No. 33, *65*
    General arrangement, No. 776, *79*
    General arrangement, No. 234 class, *90*
    Line drawings of engines, *58, 63, 66 et seq., 72, 76, 78, 98, 123 et seq., 132 et seq.*
    Main frames, 8 ft. singles, *75*
    Painting diagram, *155*
    Simple vacuum brake, *69*

Engineers
    Bulleid, O. V. S., 129
    Churchward, G. J., 14, 15, 56
    Gresley, Sir Nigel, 61, 119
    Ivatt, H. A., 15 *et seq.*, 29, 117, 142, 157
    Joy, David, 77
    Park, J. C., 62, 63
    Stanier, Sir William, 27
    Stirling, Patrick, 12 *et seq.*, 29, 77, 88 103, 105 *et seq.*, 113, 157, *12*
    Sturrock, A., 13 *et seq.*
    Worsdell, T. W., 106, 107
    Worsdell, Wilson, 106
Enginemen
    Bellam, *116*
    Cornthwaite, J., 105
    Edis, William, *26*
    Falkinder, Jim, 24, 141
    Freestone, W., 142, *118*
    Jones, J., 104, 106
    Peary, 49
    Shipley, E., 105
    Simpson, 143
    Tappenden, Harry, 25
    Walker, 142
    Watson, Sam, 25, 86, 106, 142
    Wilson, George, 142
Exhibitions
    Darlington (1925), 59, 61, (1875), 68
    Edinburgh (1890), 81, 157
    Newcastle (1881), 76, 157, (1887), 81, 157
    White City (1909), 60

Great Northern Railway
    Brake trials, 41, 68, 152 *et seq.*
    Coal consumption, 11, 103 *et seq.*, 111
    Doubleheading, 22, 95, 113
    Duplicate stock, 17 *et seq.*

Locomotive construction (1866–95), 19 *et seq.*
    Steam tenders, 13
Gripper, H. T., 105, 106

Locomotives, other than singles
    Glasgow & South Western, 13
    Great Northern
        0-4-2 No. **112A,** 60
        0-4-2 Nos. **67, 70,** 121, 123
        0-8-2T No. **116,** 118, 129
        2-6-0 No. **1000,** 60
        Gresley 'Pacifics', 27, 60 *et seq.*, *60*
        Ivatt 'Atlantics', 11, 27, 59, 60, 72, 117, 119, 134, 135, 138
        Proposed 4-4-0, 62, *63*
        Sturrock '264' class, 63, 127
    Great Western, 50, 56
    L.N.E.R., 4-6-4 No. 10000, 119
Logs of runs
    Doncaster – Peterborough (776), 137
    Grantham – Doncaster (No. 1), 59
    Grantham – Kings Cross ('234' class), 101
    Grantham – Peterborough (47, 664), 86
    Grantham – Retford (55), 45
    Grantham – York ('1003' class), 119
    Grantham – York (1008), 120
    Hatfield – Finsbury Park (21), 45
    Kings Cross – Doncaster (876), 99
    Kings Cross – Grantham (872), 99
    Kings Cross – Peterborough (22), 84
    Kings Cross – Peterborough (776), 137
    Kings Cross – Peterborough (877), 99
    Kings Cross – Potters Bar (22, 48), 84
    Kings Cross – Stevenage (No. 1), 62
    Miscellaneous, 85, 97
    Peterborough – Kings Cross (231), 98
    Peterborough – Kings Cross (774), 86
    Race to Aberdeen, 1895, 112
    Race to Edinburgh, 1888, 109

Moon, Sir Richard, 14

Oakley, Sir Henry, 111

Race to Aberdeen (1895), 24, 27, 77, 110 *et seq.*, 116, 117, 140, 157
Race to Edinburgh (1888), 61, 180 *et seq.*, 157
Rous-Marten, Charles, 24, 32, 84, 85, 88, 98, 100 *et seq.*

Singles, Sturrock
    4-2-2 No. 215, 46, 49, 50, 121, *14*
Singles, rebuilt by Stirling
    '51' class, 121 *et seq.*
    '91' class, 122 *et seq.*
    '201' class, 38, 96, 122, 124, 125
    '203' class, 122, 125, 126
    '229' class, 122, 126 *et seq.*, *126*
    '264' class, 122, 127, 128, *127*
Singles, Stirling
    Reference to types,
    7 ft. singles, 20, 38 *et seq*

7ft. 6in. singles, 21, 31, 32, 46 *et seq.*, 87 *et seq.*, 101
8 ft. singles, 20, 21, 30, 32, 48, 50 *et seq.*, 96, 113 *et seq.*, 129 *et seq.*
Rebuilt by Ivatt,
7 ft. singles, 44
7 ft. 6in. singles, 95 *et seq.*
8 ft. singles, 133 *et seq.*
Individual engines,
Engine **No. 1,** 20, 29, 31, 32, 36, 41, 47, 50, *et seq.*, 64 *et seq.*, 71, 72, 75, 76, 81, 105, 106, 129, 134, 140, 141, 143, 150, *52 et seq.*, *59 et seq.*; **No. 2,** 66, 67, 75, 131, *130*; **No. 3,** 66, 75, 85, 109, 131, *65*; **No. 4,** *39*; **No. 5,** 29, 30, 67, 68, 75, 130, 132, *31;* **No. 6,** 39, 44, *39*; **No. 7,** 67, 75, 109, 131, *29, 102, 140*; **No. 8,** 8, 29, 31, 41, 60, 64 *et seq.*, 75, 110, 129, 131, 132, 151, *19*; **No. 14,** *38*; No. **21,** 44, 45, 60, 140, *40, 106*; **No. 22,** 27, 67, 75, 82, 83, 109, 111, 112, 131, 134, 135, *108*; **No. 33,** 64, 66, 67, 75, 86, 131, 132, 136, 151, *120*; **No. 34,** 67, 68, 75, 82, 102 *et seq.*, 106, 131, 134, 135, 137, 151, *68, 107*; **No. 37,** *41*; **No. 39,** 87, *20, 44*; **No. 41,** 44, 140, *45*; **No. 47,** 68, 75, 76, 130, 151, *32*; **No. 48,** 67, 68, 75, 84, 109, 110, 130, 151, *22, 120*; **No. 53,** 25, 68, 75, 131, 132, 138, 151, *16, 29, 68*; **No. 55,** 39, 41, 44, 152, *46*; **No. 60,** 72, 75, 129, 131, *138*; **No. 61,** 44, 60, 140, *46*; **No. 62,** 68, 75, 130, 132, 151, *157*; **No. 63,** 44, *13*; **No. 69,** 55, 71, 72, 75, 109, 110, 130, *70, 110*; **No. 92,** 21, 29, 46 *et seq.*, 50, 87 *et seq.*, 93, 94, 140, *15, 48*; **No. 93,** 72, 75, 97, 131, 133, 135, *71, 120*; **No. 94,** 69 *et seq.*, 75, 76, 129, 131, 132, 138, *33, 69*; **No. 95,** 72, 75, 82, 108, 109, 131, 134, 135, *134*; **No. 98,** 71, 75, 109, 130, *131*; **No. 215,** 44, *47*; **No. 221,** 57, 69 *et seq.*, 75, 76, 81, 82, 102, 110, 131, 134 *et seq.*, 139, 140, 142, *17, 158*; **No. 222,** 31, 41, *28*; **No. 229,** 94, 140, *140*; **No. 230,** 95, *88, 103*; **No. 231,** 21, 95, 97, *104*; **No. 232,** 21, 31, 87 *et seq.*, 96, *88*; **No. 233,** 84, 85, 95, 108 *et seq.*, *88*; **No. 234,** 21, 94, 97, 103, 109, *89*; **No. 235,** 95 *et seq.*, *89*; **No. 236,** 95, *17*; **No. 237,** 95 *et seq.*, 101, 109, *91, 99*; **No. 238,** 21, 31, 87 *et seq.*, 94, 96, *87*; **No. 239,** 94, 95, *93*; **No. 240,**

95, 104, 106, 136, *93*; **No. 544,** 72, 75, 82, 131, 133 *et seq.*, *139*; **No. 545,** 72, 75, 110, 112, 130, 136, *103*; **No. 546,** 72, 75, 130, *143*; **No. 547,** 72, 75, 130, *159*; **No. 548,** 72, 75, 129, 131, 135, 136, *21, 135*; **No. 549,** 72, 75, 129, 131, *131*; **No. 550,** 72, 75, 129, 131, *105*; **No. 662,** 76, 129, 142, *36, 73*; **No. 663,** 76, *24*; **No. 664,** 59, 76, 77, 136, *73, 106*; **No. 665,** 77, 84, 100, *73*; **No. 666,** 77, 132, *26, 100*; **No. 667,** 85, *74*; **No. 668,** 24, 77, 81, 82, 111, 112, 140, 141, *74, 111, 141*; **No. 669,** *76, 102*; **No. 670,** *102*; **No. 671,** 109, 132, 139, *149*; **No. 771,** 80, 103, 132, 136, *76, 106*; **No. 772,** 80, 132, 77; **No. 773,** 80, 81, 87, 132, 134, 135, 138, *27, 104*; **No. 774,** 25, 80, 81, 132, 142, *104, 142*; **No. 775,** 74, 80, 81, 95, 108, 109, 111, 112, 132, *110*; **No. 776,** 11, 77, 81, 109, 119, 131, 133, 135, 137, 141, *78, 104, 143*; **No. 777,** 59, 81, 108, 109, *80*; **No. 778,** 81, *81*; **No. 871,** 95, *94*; **No. 872,** 95, 97, 139, *94, 104*; **No. 873,** 95, 97, 139, *95*; **No. 874,** 94, 95, 112, 142, *36*; **No. 875,** 84, 85, 95, 142, *95*; **No. 876,** 94, 95, 97, *96, 106*; **No. 877,** 95 *et seq.*, 139, *97*; **No. 878,** 95, *25*; **No. 879,** 95, 139, 142, *99, 100*; **No. 880,** 95, 96, *98*; **No. 981,** 95, 113, *97*; **No. 1001,** 82, 85, 100, 131, 141, *143*; **No. 1002,** 82, 100, 112, 131, 132, *82*; **No. 1003,** 26, 32, 113 *et seq.*, 132, 135, 138, 141, *107, 113, 117, 142, 160*; **No. 1004,** 116 *et seq.*, 141, *18, 37, 116*; **No. 1005,** 116 *et seq.*, 132, *114, 139*; **No. 1006,** 116 *et seq.*, 132, *27, 114*; **No. 1007,** 116 *et seq.*, 136, 139, 142, *116, 118*; **No. 1008,** 116 *et seq.*, 139, 142, 143, *119*

Singles, Ivatt, 97, 113, 119, 139, 141, 142, *106*
Singles, other than Great Northern
  G. & S.W.R., 13, 50
  Great Eastern 2-2-2 No. 293, 50
  Great Western, 27, 50, 58, 84
  L.N.W.R., *Cornwall*, 61
  Midland, 61
  North Eastern, No. 1519, 104 *et seq.*
Stirling, Rev. Robert, 12

Westinghouse, George, 152

'The setting sun, and music at the close'—the music of a mellow exhaust note. The last duties: No. 1003 in a pastoral setting north of Peterborough about 1913

Date Due

DE 7-78			
AG 19			

Demco 38-297